G000149505

Handbook

The
Actor's

Contents

Introduction

The aim of this book is to provide practical information, and sensible advice for actors and others involved in the theatre. It will be a useful source of reference for hard-bitten veterans as well as fresh-faced beginners. Even experienced and successful actors may be total strangers to particular areas of the profession. Although aimed principally at actors, attention is given to directors, lighting designers, wardrobe assistants and others. Some of the advice is little more than common-sense; for example, the repeated plea to respect any 'no phone calls please' injunction. Experience suggests that many beginners can believe that their personal charm permits them to ignore such requests with impunity.

Acting is powerfully attractive to a vast number of people. Admiration and envy of conspicuously successful screen-heroes and theatre-idols persuades many to consider work in a profession which can lead so quickly – and some might think, so effortlessly – to worldwide fame, vast wealth, and a life of luxury and ease.

For the majority of actors life turns out to be rather less glamorous, although not without reward. Many make a decent living from their talent, and if not worldwide fame, then they do achieve widespread recognition and sincere acclaim. Even for those who live in chronic uncertainty, struggling for a living, with frequent and lengthy bouts of unemployment, there is an excitement, variety and satisfaction about their work which is genuinely envied by many in secure employment, who really ought to know better.

Acting calls upon so many resources in an individual; intellect, emotion, instinct, vocal agility, physical expression, self-knowledge, self-discipline, team-work and concentration. It presents great personal challenges (and achievements) for the practitioner. A number of theatre companies are of interest to specific acting groups: black actors, Asian actors, disabled actors, Welsh actors, feminist actors, Christian actors, gay actors, and actors with particular political views, for example. The pleasure derived from these is sufficient for many, to whom fame and fortune proves elusive. Even for the vastly famous performing is rarely without effort. Making it look easy is one of the most difficult tricks to master – and never ceases to require courage: 'Acting is standing up naked and turning around very slowly' (Rosalind Russell). It has been said that the shock to an actor's nervous system every time they walk on stage or stand before a camera, feels the same as being in a car-crash. It is clearly not an occupation for the faint-hearted.

British theatre and British acting are widely held to be the best in the world. However, times are hard for the actor. Actors wages, never particularly generous, are now very low. Necessary expenses are not. Irregular, unpredictable work can be borne as long as there is enough of it in the long term to sustain a living. It is no longer clear that there will be enough in the long term: opportunities for work seem to be shrinking, and in some areas drying up altogether.

Recent assaults by the Inland Revenue on the tax-status of actors have introduced PAYE to theatre-work, and removed previously-accepted tax-deductable allowances. This has hit relative newcomers to the profession with particular severity. Many actors are finding it impossible to accept work if it means paying for temporary accommodation as well as a permanent home. The complications of Poll Tax legislation for those who might leave a permanent home empty while working in another region, are prohibitive. They remain unaltered at the time of writing.

That the British film industry is constantly struggling for survival (despite its numerous successes), is not new. That the current uncertainty in television production – a result of deregulation and the impending renewal of franchises, can be expected to improve, is reasonable to hope for. That the collapse of subsidized theatre is to be avoided, is now to be prayed for.

According to the National Campaign for the Arts, thirty out of thirty-two major theatres are in deficit. Companies large and small are closing. Theatres now hire actors for individual plays, where only a few years ago they hired a company for a season. A cast of eight is far beyond the resources of many yet most classic plays require more. It is increasingly difficult to commission new writing, and authors find themselves constrained to write for three or even two performers.

In short, there are less jobs to go round, and if you get one, you may not be able to survive on the wages. Times are hard for the actor. The only certainty is that competition will become yet more intense. This book will help you to compete more effectively, whether you seek to further an idealistic dedication to the craft, or pursue wealth, luxury and worldwide fame.

Black actors in Britain have a professional experience quite distinct from their white counterparts. Although they may find opportunities for employment with many theatre companies, they are likely to find the range of roles open to them quite limited. They may well have their self-confidence undermined by the suspicion that they have been employed principally to fulfil some kind of ethnic minority quota. Integrated casting, which ignores the ethnic identity and/or sex of individual actors, is not particularly new. The most conspicuous example of its successful application over many years is in Peter Brook's Paris-based International Centre for Theatre Research. Audiences appear to have very little resistance to the idea, as long as it is applied with confidence. Unfortunately it remains relatively rare in Britain.

Television production has to date shown little interest in integrated casting, and still tends to cast black actors within relatively narrow social boundaries. Having several regional accents at your command can improve your chances of casting within these boundaries. British black actors find themselves portraying Americans, Africans, and 'neutral' characters more frequently than specifically black British parts. In the most prestigious theatres black actors can play major roles, but so far not with noticeable regularity. On television such casting is much more infrequent, and, in general, shows are not built around black personalities in the way that they frequently are with white actors. If a black 'star' is required, very often managements look to America.

In the specifically black theatre companies, in community theatre and T.I.E., there are many opportunities for good work, but there is a marked tendency towards social-issue plays, and some actors feel that the pressures to be a part-time politician shift the focus away from the quality of their performance. However, black theatre enjoys a function within the black community which other companies can only envy.

The smooth operation of a professional theatre relies on many people besides the actors: directors, designers, wardrobe staff, lighting designers, stage-managers and make-up artists are all essential to a production's success. Some are more conspicuous than others: directors, stage-managers and designers tend to be trained in the same institutions as actors; others remain largely unknown and in many cases undervalued.

Wardrobe staff find, make, alter, and repair costumes. Theirs is a highly responsible job and they often receive little recognition or gratitude. They are generally poorly paid. Wardrobe staff are normally involved from an early stage in the production process. They arrange hires and loans, and decide what can be bought and what must be made. They will take overall instructions from the designer, and realise these in practical terms after checking with the script and with the performers. Problems arising from quick changes must be accounted for, as well as specific details such as extra pockets, special fastenings, and the practicality and flexibility of each costume. Wardrobe supervisors are responsible for the time-management of their department, and for the allocation of their share of the production budget. Their duties involve not only arranging for the making of costumes, but for regular cleaning; and for obtaining necessary fabrics. They need an eye for historical detail which is theatrically significant, and for the effects of stage-lighting – which can be startling, and discovered only late in the day. Particularly in film and television, they require an understanding of different clothing tastes in differing character-types, relating to class and style.

Training is available within design courses at some drama schools and colleges, and there is a cutting course offered by the London College of Fashion. Work opportunities range from those offered by small-scale theatres which require a combination of initiative and versatility, through repertory theatres where specific cutting experience is desired, to major opera companies which employ a permanent staff of experienced makers. A considerable number of Wardrobe Assistants and Supervisors work freelance. It is very difficult to get a 'start' in Wardrobe as vacancies often become known by word-of-mouth rather than advertising, and wages can be appalling. There is little point in writing to Wardrobe departments in large theatres: only dressers are likely to be taken on in this fashion.

Almost all lighting designers are originally trained as electricians and learn about design 'on the job'. Formal training can be obtained at some drama schools, generally as part of a stage-management course. Such courses tend to concentrate on the technical aspects of lighting rather than aesthetic considerations. In the USA there are three-year university courses available, and there is a particularly fine education in the art offered at Hong Kong Arts Centre.

The real concern of the lighting designer is not simply how a lantern works, but what effect it has; how to make the most effective use of the available resources; how to build a degree of flexibility into a design to take account of changes of direction and blocking; and how to enhance the stage-picture without inhibiting other performances.

Lighting design is quite a large field, encompassing drama, opera, dance, television and film (a specialism with a different union from the theatre), rock shows, architectural lighting and trade shows. There is a lot of travel involved, and, in general, the larger the employer, the larger the fee. As always, the first steps are the most difficult: directors have to be impressed by technical capability, imagination and professionalism. Organisational ability is a very important aspect of the job. Expect low fees and negligible equipment in fringe and small-scale companies.

The London College of Fashion offers specialized courses in make-up and hair-styling; these require qualifications in History, Art, and Biology. Further training may be acquired by those who work for the BBC, although much time will be spent dealing with thousands of extras and promotion will be slow. More money can be earned with ITV companies, but no training is available. Some people involved with television companies accept promotion into the more bureaucratic areas of production: most prefer to remain in the practical areas, even if this means going freelance.

There is quite a lot of work available in the 'beauty' side of the business, with photographers and models, beauty editors, model agencies, and art directors. In order to establish a reputation, you may have to do lot of work for no money.

With television, in the studio or on location, the make-up artist will have to be able to transform actors for the camera (sometimes in frighteningly large numbers), and maintain a constant check on the condition of the make-up. Diplomacy is vital in a situation where every check and delay may cost vast sums, and where many actors have strong views about appropriate make-up, and many others are constitutionally incapable of keeping their hands away from their wigs, moustaches, and delicately balanced facial effects. Very long working hours are the norm, during which concentration cannot flag. A make-up artist should expect to rise the earliest, and retire the latest, long after the last extra has been extracted from their false beard.

Part 1 *Getting Started*

1 *The Basics*

In order to get a job as an actor, you have to persuade someone that you are worth an audition or an interview. In order to persuade them, you require two basic tools: a *Curriculum Vitae*, or CV; and a photograph.

Your CV should be clearly set out and easy to understand. It is best to confine yourself to a single sheet of A4 paper, typed or printed; starting with your name, address and phone number (or that of your agent if you prefer); followed by a list of parts you have played, starting with the most recent and working backwards. You should give the name of the director of each production, and which theatre company it was with. It is generally useful to include also your height, hair and eye-colour, and – if you think it helpful – your physical build.

You may also wish to include accents, musical and other skills. You should identify which is your native accent and RP (*Received Pronunciation*) if you are confident performing in it, and other accents you can perform in. But don't exaggerate your abilities: a poor impersonation of a Glaswegian to an audience in Glasgow is unlikely to pass unnoticed. Fluency in a foreign language should certainly be noted. Musical ability is in great demand: don't be afraid to offer it in detail, with your standard or grade. Above all, be honest. It is quite reasonable to play to 'busking' standard as many jobs require no more. However, you will most assuredly be caught out if you exaggerate. Skills to note include the ability to drive, but long lists of sporting activities are not very helpful. Confine sports to those in which you have a recognised grade which reflects above-average ability. Unusual hobbies, interests, and expertise can help, if only by raising a smile, but the golden rule is to 'keep it brief': anything which detracts from clarity and ease of understanding, is to be avoided. You can always elaborate particular features in a letter.

Your photograph is your major selling-point. The accepted standard is the black-and-white 10″ × 8″, although some people favour the smaller 7″ × 5″. While a flattering photograph is a natural choice, be aware that it must actually look like you, and that it should help to obtain work. (Glamour and glitz may place you in a very restricted pigeon-hole; everyday reality may be interpreted into many differing roles.) It is sound advice to obtain your photograph professionally, preferably from someone who has some experience of theatrical photography. These are unlikely to be cheap, though some established photographers offer a discount to drama students. Friends or amateur enthusiasts rarely if ever come up to the standard of a good professional, and a lot of time and money can be spent for a result that is of no help to you at all. In any event, try to select a print in which your face and head fill the frame, and in which the eyes look alive. Multiple copies of your photograph, for distribution to potential employers, can be obtained through a number of specialist companies who advertise regularly in *The Stage*. The quality of these varies in direct relation to their cost. If you choose expensive high-quality reproductions, make sure you send them out with a stamped addressed envelope.

Most actors also ensure that they have a photograph in *The Spotlight*, which remains the standard casting aid throughout the profession. Many think it best that this should be a different photograph from the one they circulate with their CV.

When sending out your CV and photograph, take account of who you are writing to and what their interests are likely to be. A theatre director will prefer an application for a specific part, and a letter which contains some personality rather than blank formality. Do not allow informality to turn into familiarity or casual cajoling. Jocular appeals of the 'gi's a job' variety are unlikely to create an impression of professionalism. If there is a reason you think you are well-suited to a role, say so; but beware of sounding fixated as directors generally prefer to work with actors, rather than obsessives.

Casting directors will prefer high-quality photographs and a note of where they might see you performing, than a lengthy letter. A few conduct general interviews, but most see actors only when casting for something specific.

In general you should seek to present as professional an image as possible. Young actors should not worry too much about the brevity of their CV; no-one will expect a lot of credits. Older newcomers need only make it plain how recently they joined the profession, and their experience in other walks of life may well be of great interest.

If you are offered an interview or audition, make sure you are prepared. Wherever possible, read the play. Try to gather some idea of the part (or parts) for which you are being considered, not only what sort of personality and style, but also what function they provide within the story. Don't become dogmatic with such ideas: directors like actors who are open to suggestion. It is only sensible to dress appropriately, without resorting to fancy dress. (If it helps a director to visualize you in a role, it can't do any harm.) But remember, outside a casting-session for commercials, anything too specific may be judged comic, and may conflict with the director's preconceptions of character.

Don't be late. This may seem blatantly obvious, but it needs to be said. Many auditions are held in London, where distances are considerable, traffic-jams unpredictable and frequent, parking virtually impossible, and the public transport system subject to frequent delay and cancellation. Always aim to be early. However relaxed the interview turns out to be, if you are a smoker, refrain. Similarly, turn down offers of tea or coffee to be sipped during the interview. Apart from the dangers of nervous hands spilling a hot drink, you may suddenly be asked to perform, at which point the cigarette or coffee-cup may create a serious obstruction.

A word of caution. The days are over when young actors could get their foot on the lowest rung of the ladder by accepting a so-called 'spear-carrier' contract at one of the major national companies. 'Spear-carrier' contracts still exist, but the ladder has vanished. These days such jobs do not lead to a progression of steadily improving roles. They lead to more spear-carrying. The same is true in television and film, in which there is a real danger of being pigeon-holed for the rest of your career as an extra or walk-on, and never considered for even the humblest role.

Training

Training for actors is available in many forms and varies enormously in intensity and quality. Britain boasts some of the finest drama schools in the world, justly famous for their nurturing of major talents who have graced stage and cinema for generations. These schools admit only a limited number of new students each year, and aspiring actors should be aware that there are other training opportunities open to them.

It is possible to start training for the stage when barely more than a toddler. Children's theatre schools exist throughout the country. Most offer part-time evening and weekend courses. A small number provide an intensive structured education. Of the latter, the best known are the Anna Scher theatre school, and the Italia Conti Academy (both of which are based in London). Some of these schools are associated with agencies for child and teenage actors.

The major drama schools offer full-time courses of up to three years duration, combining theory with hard practice. They are unrivalled in their provision of the technical skills of acting and maintain rigorously high standards. Each has a distinct doctrine and a different emphasis. Most put great store by their training in the classics, particularly Shakespeare. They are sometimes criticized for being less attentive to film and television skills which modern actors may have to depend on. Nevertheless British acting is particularly admired for the ability to combine stage and screen work with confidence.

Applications for the major drama schools far outnumber the number of vacancies they have on offer. Less well-known schools are not necessarily less worthy, but graduates of the major schools will certainly find their qualifications taken much more seriously at the start of their careers. The Accreditation scheme, established to maintain high standards in drama training, is a useful standard by which to judge schools – but some of the finest schools do not subscribe to it.

If you are fortunate enough to secure a place in a drama school, you must surmount another difficulty – paying the tuition fees. For a three-year course these may well be in excess of £10,000. Grants for such schools are discretionary, and local education authorities are notoriously unsympathetic to aspiring drama students. Some refuse to consider funding them at all. Worth remembering are the numerous charities and trusts which came into being before state-funded education was generally available. Some of these may operate within eccentric restrictions, but they may be more receptive to drama training than your education authority. It may also be possible to combine financial support from more than one charity.

Drama may also be studied within the state education system at a number of higher education colleges, polytechnics and universities. These will almost inevitably place greater emphasis on academic study than on purely practical skill, but their more broadly-based courses may offer a wider choice of career after graduation. Grants for such institutions are mandatory, not discretionary.

It is only common sense that aspiring drama students should investigate the character of different schools and the philosophy behind their training. It is all too easy to be overwhelmed by an acceptance in the teeth of tremendous competition, and find yourself on a course which does not suit your interests or temperament. It is also easy to be overwhelmed by a sense of gratitude for acceptance, a feeling which can result in a very uncritical response to a school's teaching, and in extreme cases dog an entire career in acting.

For those who cannot consider full-time training, there are other institutions. The Poor School (in London), where the fees are relatively inexpensive, conducts full-time courses scheduled for evenings and weekends for the truly determined.

In addition there are specialist schools (mime and related physical skills are increasingly popular), short-course and occasional classes available for established professionals in a wide variety of skills, notably at the regional Actors' Centres in Birmingham, London, and Manchester; and at the Actors' Institute in London. Learning new skills and refreshing old ones can be a very effective way of revitalising your enthusiasm. A new skill may enhance your employability, and renewed enthusiasm readily communicates itself to potential employers.

2 *Drama Schools*

Drama school acting/stage management courses accredited by the National Council for Drama Training

Academy of Live & Recorded Arts	3-year acting course
Arts Educational Schools	3-year acting course
Birmingham School of Speech Training & Dramatic Art	3-year acting course
Bristol Old Vic Theatre School	2- and 3-year acting courses 2-year stage management course
Rose Bruford College	3-year degree courses in theatre arts & community arts 3-year stage management course
Central School of Speech & Drama	3-year acting course 2-year stage management course
Drama Centre London	3-year acting course
Drama Studio	1-year post-graduate course
Guildford School of Acting	3-year acting/musical theatre course 1-year post-graduate course 2-year stage management course
Guildhall School of Music & Drama	3-year acting course 2-year stage management course
London Academy of Music & Dramatic Art (LAMDA)	3-year acting course 2-year stage management course

Manchester Polytechnic	3-year acting course
Mountview Theatre School	3-year acting course
	1-year post-graduate course
	2-year stage management course
Royal Academy of Dramatic Art (RADA)	3-year acting course
	2-year stage management course
Royal Scottish Academy of Music & Drama	3-year acting course
	2-year stage management course
Webber Douglas Academy	2- and 3-year acting courses
	1-year post-graduate course
Welsh College of Music & Drama	2 3-year acting courses
	1-year Advanced Certificate course
	3-year stage management course

Academy of Live & Recorded Arts (ALRA)

Royal Victoria Building, Trinity Road, London SW18 3SX
Tel (081) 870 6475
Principal Sorrel Carson
Contact Gillian Davison (administrator)

Founded 1979 by Sorrel Carson, ALRA grew rapidly in size and reputation. Total training in the Performing Arts – embraces Classical Theatre, Musical Theatre, Modern Recorded Media.

Courses on offer:
- Actors' course: 3-year full time, NCDT accredited. Min. age 18. Designed for students who wish to pursue a career in classical and modern theatre and the recorded media.
- Performing arts dance course: 2-or 3-year full time. Min. age 16.

- Stage management course: 4 terms, full time.
- Post-graduate course: four terms, full time, designed for graduates and other advanced or mature students with experience.
- Summer courses.

Places available:
No fixed numbers policy. Intake flexible according to demand and development of courses. Currently 180 students in the whole Academy on different courses. Eligible for student grants. Prospectus available.

Audition requirements:
First audition: classes in voice, dance, improvisation; no pieces. Second audition: screen test and rehearsal of scenes from plays. Audition fee: £28.75 inc. VAT.

'. . . We believe that no art form can survive unless it relates to its own age and fully embraces its challenges. The Royal Victoria Building symbolizes our philosophy – for it has been transformed from a Victorian asylum into a centre of creative endeavour with its feet firmly planted in the 21st century.' Graduates at the Royal Shakespeare Company, National Theatre, in the West End and on Television.

Ackerley Studios of Speech and Drama

Crane Building (5th floor), Hanover Street, Liverpool 1
Tel (051) 709 5995
Principal Margaret Parsons

Founded 1919 by Mrs Harold Ackerley.

Courses available:
Private tuition for ALAM Dip and LLAM Dip, LGSM and LRAM examinations. Telephone to make an appointment for interview. Prospectus on request.

Actors' Residential Theatre & Television Skillcentre International (ARTTS International)

Highfield Grange, Bubwith, Selby, N. Yorks. YO8 7DP
Tel (0757) 288088
Principal John P. Sichel
(artistic director)
Contact Norman Y. Smith
(administrator)

1-year multi-media courses offering skills based training in Theatre, Film, Television and Radio for actors, directors and production operations staff.

Prospectus from: ARTTS International, 251 Friern Barnet Lane, London N20 0ND.

Ads Agency & Stage School

Reform Road, Maidenhead, Berks. SL6 8BT
Tel (0628) 29346
Contact Betty Curtis

A part-time school for children, with classes on Wednesday evenings and on Saturdays. Drama, movement and singing. Ages 5–17, with one class available for adults. Classes are also held in Watford.

Arts Educational Schools Drama Department

14 Bath Road, London W4 1LY
Tel (081) 994 9366
Contact Mr D. Robson (head of drama department)

Courses on offer:
3-year, NCDT-accredited, full-time acting course; and 1-year, full-time course for post-graduates, mature students and actors seeking a renewed focus in their work. Discretionary grants available. Ask for prospectus.

Audition requirements:
3-year course: full day's audition consisting of classes in movement, voice and improvisation, followed by two short contrasting pieces of the candidate's own choice; there may also be an interview. 1-year course: two contrasting pieces, one classical and one

modern, and an extensive interview; university degree and/or evidence of appropriate experience and talent is required. Audition fee: £30.00.

'The Drama Department offers a three-year acting course that is Stanislavsky based. The work is concentrated and demanding. Training places considerable emphasis on the education of the individual so that he/she may be sensitive to the requirements of any kind of text. Our aim is to produce actors who have a respect for the theatre, for acting and for themselves.'

Birmingham School of Speech & Drama

45 Church Road, Edgbaston, Birmingham B15 3SW
Tel (021) 454 3424
Principal Patricia A. Yardley

Founded 1936.

Course on offer:
3-year full-time acting course; 30–35 places available; NCDT accredited; students eligible for grants.

Audition requirements:
Speech from Shakespeare, speech from a modern play, a lyrical poem, a song – each of which must be no more than 2 minutes in duration. Sight reading, improvisation and movement will also be required. Audition fee: £20.00.

'Education is no longer limited to the mere absorption of knowledge; it is concerned with the development of the whole being – body, mind and spirit. Because of the special value of speech and drama in assisting in the development of the personality, the teaching at the Birmingham School of Speech and Drama is based on the realization that these arts have an ever-increasing part to play.'

Boden Studio

13 Essex Road, Enfield, Middx
EN2 6TZ
Tel (081) 367 1836/2692
Principal Maureen Boden/Tony Boden

Founded 1979.

Courses on offer:
Part-time classes in speech, acting, singing and dance. Ages 3–20. All students work towards examination standard, and full-scale productions (25 in the last ten years) are frequently mounted. Summer courses are also held.

Braithwaite's School of Acrobatics And Dance

8 Brookshill Avenue, Harrow Weald, Middx HA3 6RZ
Tel (081) 954 5638
Principal Valerie Braithwaite

Founded 1968.

Courses on offer:
Classes in acrobatics, singing, dance, drama for ages 6–20+. After normal school hours. Also operates as an agency.

Brighton Academy of Performing Arts

See Shandy Stage School.

Brighton School of Music & Drama

12 Buxton Road, Brighton, E. Sussex
BN1 5DE
Tel (0273) 553187
Principal Carole Nina Best, LGSM,
ANEA Gold Medallist
Contact The Secretary

Founded 1883. For many years, a music school in central Brighton, then a full-time speech and drama school. For the last 20 years has been a part-time school for drama and singing. Private lessons are offered for all ages, and class lessons for those under 18. About 100 students per term; prospectus available. Class and general drama involve mime, improvisation, play production and festivals. Private drama lessons include Guildhall teaching work, performing for examinations and festivals and preparation of auditions for London colleges, drama schools and theatres.

Audition requirements:
Interview with the singing staff and trial lesson, one song, interview with the principal. No charge for audition.

Bristol Old Vic Theatre School

2 Downside Road, Clifton, Bristol
BS8 2XF
Tel (0272) 733535
Principal Christopher Denys
Contact Erika Neumann (secretary)

Founded 1946 by Laurence Olivier; moved to its present premises in 1956.

Courses on offer:
● 3-year full-time acting course.
● 2-year full-time acting course: more suited to mature students, post-graduates and/or those with some theatre experience.
● 1-year post-graduate course: should only be undertaken by those with exceptional application, determination and stamina.
● 2-year stage management and technical course.
● 1-year design course.
● 1-year wardrobe course.
The acting and technical courses are NCDT accredited; grants available. Ask for a prospectus.

Audition requirements:
Preliminary audition: excerpts from one classical verse play (preferably Shakespeare) and one modern prose play, the two pieces together not exceeding 4 minutes. A short unaccompanied song is also required. Following the preliminary audition, candidates may be invited to attend a weekend school where they work with members of staff, who will then short-list or offer them a place. Audition fee: £18.00.

The school aims to train and prepare actors for a career in theatre, radio, TV and films, with a particular emphasis on preparation for work in the classical repertoire. All courses are essentially practical. No one 'philosophy' of teaching, acting, design or production is adhered to. The aim is to offer students the best possible training and preparation for a successful career in a profession that makes increasingly varied demands upon the individuals it employs.

The school has close links with the Bristol Old Vic Company, Bristol City Council and Avon Education Authority. As a result, there are opportunities to perform in a wide variety of venues: theatres, art centres and schools throughout the city and region. Links are also maintained with the BBC and HTV. Every effort is made to enable students to obtain as much professional work experience as possible.

British Ballet Organization

Woolborough House, 39 Lonsdale Road, London SW13 9JP
Tel (081) 748 1241
Fax (081) 748 1301
Principal John Field, CBE (director)
Contact Mrs Pepper (manager)

Founded 1930. An examining body conducting ballet and tap/jazz dance examinations in its new syllabus at venues throughout the country. Courses are open to all.

Rose Bruford College of Speech & Drama

Lamorbey Park, Sidcup, Kent
DA15 9DF
Tel (081) 300 3024
Principal Phil Robins
Contact Admissions officer

Founded 1950, by Rose E. Bruford. Established a fine reputation for its training of actors and teachers. Developed and began the first degree courses in 1976, becoming the first and only institution of its kind to offer professional training to degree and honours degree level.

Courses on offer:
- BA (Hons) Theatre Degree (60 places).
- Diploma in technical theatre arts: 3-year full time (20 places).

Courses are accredited by the National Council for Drama Training. Grants for degree courses are mandatory, and discretionary for the diploma course. A prospectus is available. Application

to the college should be made in September, and interviews/auditions are held from December to July.

Audition requirements:
Candidates are informed of requirements when they are told of the date and time of the interview. Audition fee: £15.00.

'Our courses are all advanced courses of higher education, but at the same time are courses of vocational, professional training. The teaching on the courses is of the highest standard in both respects, and makes considerable academic, intellectual, physical and artistic demands upon the student. The staff expect, equally, that demands will be made on them.'

Advice to aspiring actors: 'Apart from a trained body and voice, you will require a trained mind in order to make critical choices and to fully engage in the process of making theatre. The Courses are designed to enable you to become resourceful and socially aware actors and technicians with a real understanding of the theatre and the community it serves.

Central School of Speech and Drama

Embassy Theatre, Eton Avenue, London NW3 3HY
Tel (071) 722 8183/4/5/6
Principal Robert S. Fowler, MA (Oxon) LGSM, FRSA
Contact Linda Cookson

Founded 1906 at the Albert Hall by Elsie Fogerty, moving to its present premises in 1956.

Courses on offer:
- Diploma in acting: 3-year full-time, NCDT accredited.
- Higher National Diploma in stage management (BTEC): 2-year full-time, NCDT accredited.

- BEd (Hons) in drama and spoken language: 4-year full time.
- BA (Hons) in drama and a language: 3-year full-time.
- BSc (Hons) speech and language pathology: 4-year full-time.
- MA in Stage Design: 1-year full-time, 2-year part-time.
- MA in Arts Education (Drama): 1-year full-time, 2-year part-time.
- Central School Sesame Joint Certificate in the use of drama and movement in therapy: 1-year full-time.
- Advanced Certificate in speech and drama.
- Advanced Diploma in voice studies.
- Advanced Diploma in Stage design: 1-year full-time.
- Advanced Diploma in Costume Design: 1-year full-time.
- Diploma in Scenic Art: 1-year full-time.
- Advanced Diploma in Fine Art (Painting): 1-year part-time.
- Advanced Diploma in Creative Writing: 1-year full-time.
- Diploma in Stage Carpentry: 1-year full-time.
- Diploma in Prop Making: 1-year full-time.

Applicants for acting course should normally be aged between 17 and 25 on starting the course. Grants available for first degree courses, and discretionary grants for NCDT-accredited courses and others. Limited number of bursaries available for shorter courses. Ask for prospectus.

Auditions:
Held throughout the year for entrance in the autumn. Audition fee: £20.00.

'The Central School of Speech and Drama is much older than many universities and polytechnics; and its traditions, confirmed by experience, constitute the basis of its reputation. At the same time, the school is alive to contemporary developments and offers its students the best possible preparation for a successful career in their chosen field.'

As is clear from the variety of its courses, the school's training has evolved into three main areas: acting and stage management; speech therapy; and teaching. It has contact with other institutions such as the Polytechnic of Central London, Thames Polytechnic and Queen Mary and Westfield College (University of London). It has a student population of around 450, but it is still possible for staff to know all the students, and the school cherishes its family approach and friendly working environment, which is conducive to effective learning.

Constructive Teaching Centre

18 Lansdowne Road, London
W11 3LL
Tel (071) 727 7222
Contact The Secretary

The training course for teachers of the F.M. Alexander Technique run by Walter Carrington has been at 18 Lansdowne Road since 1960. Private lessons are available also, between 8 a.m. and 7.30 p.m.

Cygnet Training Theatre

Friars Gate, Exeter EX2 4AZ
Tel (0392) 77189
Principal Monica D. Shallis, LRAM, LGSM
Contact Mary G. Evans (administrator)

Founded 1980, the company grew out of an association between Monica

Shallis, Mary Evans and the Northcott Theatre Company. It is now a full-time training company, with Peter Brook as patron. Formal training in voice, movement, music, dance etc. are all part of the daily work of the company, but rehearsal and performance remain the strongest features of the experience-based training. Takes open-minded young actors who are expected to work with a fully professional attitude from their first day. High standards of technique and flexibility are aimed for, and among others, the disciplines of Stanislavsky and Michel Saint-Denis are in constant use. Has a good professional standing as a touring company, and aims to provide maximum contacts and opportunities of further work for actors.

A maximum of sixteen new members taken on each September. While members' needs and developments may vary, it is usual for trainees to spend 3 years in the company. Receive about 200 applicants each year. Grant eligibility*. Prospective students should write with a large SAE for prospectus and application form. No academic qualifications are required. Professional actors may join company for three or six months, to refresh skills or to study and tour specific role.

Audition requirements:
2 contrasting pieces of own choice, plus interview and workshop session with other prospective candidates and company members. Audition fee: £20.00. A further fee of £8.00 is payable if an assessment of the audition is required.

*Because Cygnet is unique and different from most conventional drama schools, some local education authorities use this as a reason for refusing grants. However, the DES has stated that Cygnet is eligible for discretionary grants on the same footing as any drama school, and both Devon and Dorset LEA are giving grants. Cygnet's fees are considerably lower than those of most schools, and Cygnet actors have an exceptionally high success rate in obtaining professional work as a result of appearances and contacts made during touring. This should encourage local education authorities to give financial help to applicants who obtain places.

Drama Centre London

176 Prince of Wales Road, Chalk Farm, London NW5 3PT
Tel (071)267 1177
Principal Christopher Fettes
Contact Mark Pemberton
(Administrator)

Founded 1963 when a group of directors and teachers – John Blatchley, Yat Malmgren and Christopher Fettes – broke away from the Central School of Speech and Drama and founded the Drama Centre London based on the teachings of Stanislavsky and the American Method.

Courses on offer:
• Diploma acting course: 3-year full time; 30 places.
• Diploma professional instructors course: 2-year full time; 10 places.
• Masters Degree in Directing: 3-year course in collaboration with the University of Birmingham; 6 places.

Receive approximately 500 applications for the acting course each year. Accredited by the National Council for Drama Training; students eligible for grants. Prospectus available. Prospective entrants should complete an application form, giving reasons why acting is their chosen profession and why they are applying to the Drama Centre London in particular.

Audition requirements:
one classical piece, chosen from five nominated by the Principal, and one modern piece of the applicant's own choice, plus a lengthy interview. Audition fee: £15.00.

'Before you start your training, you need to have seen something of what exists beyond the confines of school and home. You need to have thought about it and to have formed opinions. Don't go to school too soon, and don't go to a school like the Drama Centre London if you don't feel it a duty to make people ask questions and think about answers . . .

'The training of the actor consists essentially in learning how to bring feeling under control and how to confer form upon it – and, in particular, those especially powerful and especially fruitful feelings that have their origin below the threshold of consciousness. If you have been led to assume that training centres upon the mechanics of expression, speech and movement, you will have to think again. The aim of the Drama Centre London is to provide the student actor with a systematic approach to the problems of acting, which will lead to the eventual acquisition of this control; to teach him to make a proper use of himself as an organic being on the stage and to equip him with the freedom that derives not from the licence to "do his own thing" but from the mastery of his creative resources.'

Drama Studio London

Grange Court, 1 Grange Road, London W5 5QN
Tel (081) 579 3897
Fax (081) 566 2035
Principal Peter Layton (executive director)
Contact Lesley Cockburn (Administrator)

Founded 1966 by Peter Layton.

Courses on offer:
One-year three-term acting course; one-year three-term directing course; one-year three-term theatre administration course. All full-time. 55 places available on the acting course, with 500 applicants each year; 8 places available on the theatre administration and directing courses, with 100 applicants per year. Applicants to both courses must be over the age of 21. The acting course is NCDT accredited, and discretionary grants are available from some authorities. Prospectus available.

Audition requirements:
Acting course: all-day interview, consisting of group and individual acting and improvisation exercises, sight-reading tests and possibly some prepared work (which will be asked for when the appointment is made). Directing and theatre administration courses: interview and practical exercises. Audition fee: £25.00.

'The primary objective of the school is the preparation of the student for a career in the theatre. The student learns to face positively the realities of the profession as it exists . . . The work is serious but not solemn; it requires considerable self-discipline, hard work and a positive commitment from each student. The student must be prepared for searching self-analysis and have an unselfish concern for his fellow students. Drama

Studio London expects its graduates to make a significant contribution to their art, to exercise their best efforts in their professional lives and to establish and abide by their own standards of excellence and integrity.'

Gina van Dyke Stage School

Gina van Dyke Studios, Fairmead, Tolworth, Surrey
Tel (081) 399 9429
Contact Gina van Dyke, Mary McLeish

Founded 1962.

Courses on offer:
Evening and Saturday dance classes for all ages: ballet, tap, modern, jazz.

East 15 Acting School

Hatfields, Rectory Lane, Loughton, Essex IG10 3RU and
Sheriff Hutton Park, Sheriff Hutton, N. Yorks. YO6 1RH
Tel (081) 508 5983 and (03477) 442
Principal Mrs Margaret Walker
Contact Mrs F. C. Stark
(administrator, north)

Founded 1961 to create a school where actors could continue to explore and develop the creative way of working begun by Joan Littlewood at Theatre Workshop.

Courses on offer:
- 3-year full-time acting course.

- 2-year full-time acting course: more pressurized and requiring a good educational background and some acting experience.
- 1-year post-graduate acting course: for mature students and also professionals wishing to extend their range.
- 2-year stage management course.
- Special Courses for Trainee Directors and Drama Tutors

Discretionary grants are available from some local education authorities. Minimum age for application is 18; there is no upper age limit.

Students work at both Hatfields, where there is a TV studio and the fully equipped Corbett Theatre, and at Sheriff Hutton Hall, where performances are given in the historic rooms and in the arena theatre in the grounds.

The school's policy is 'to accept talented and ambitious students of differing ages, backgrounds and nationalities, who, under our demand and tuition, will strive for higher standards of theatre technique and craftsmanship, and aspire to acting as a creative art. Individual coaching is given in preference to class instruction. Training emphasis is on the study of human behaviour and emotions, and on each actor's use of imagery, body and voice. The training challenges the student to recall childhood experiences, to assess the codes of honour and behaviour he has assumed and the effect of his society upon him.'

'It is only through an understanding of oneself that objective assessment of others becomes possible. An actor will only act himself until he can separate his private person from his public self, and when his body, mind and voice are flexible enough as instruments to create the observed truth and reality of others. Only through awareness of reality can theatricality be understood and created.

Actors must first create their characters from observation of life.'

There is a professional company – East 15 Theatre Company – which employs mostly ex-students who have had experience in commercial theatre. The Galtres Theatre Company also consists of East 15 graduates, and works in the historic setting of Sheriff Hutton Park.

East Herts College

Dept of Adult Education, Turnford, Broxbourne, Herts. EN10 6AF
Tel (0992) 466451
Course Tutor Organiser Miss Thelma Tillaney AGSM, LRAM

Course on offer:
- Theatre and Performing Arts Course: two-year full-time preparatory course combining dance, drama and general education.

The aim of the course is to prepare students for entry to an academy of drama/dance or a college of higher education where they can be prepared for careers in theatre, teaching or leisure management.

Entry requirements:
Preferably five 'O' levels including English (special consideration is given to students without these qualifications should they show exceptional ability at audition). Leaflet containing application form is available from the college. Interviews and auditions are held between March and June.

The course is recognised as a Foundation Course for the London Studio Centre, and those students who successfully complete the course are offered a place at the Centre at the discretion of the Artistic Director.

Evening Academy of Dramatic Art

189 Whitechapel Road, London E1
Tel (071) 377 8735
Principal Tim Reynolds

Founded 1985.

Courses on offer:
- 2-year acting course, Monday–Friday 6.30–10.30 pm and Saturday 10.00 am–4.00 pm;
- weekend course, Saturday 4.00–6.30 pm: flexible foundation training, ideal as a pre-drama school preparation.
- medallion course, weekdays: ages 16–19, intended as a bridge between school and drama school.
- company course: a 1-year performance-based course intended for post-graduates or students with previous training and/or experience.
- summer course.

There are 30 places on the full-time evening course, which attracts approximately 400 applications each year. Not eligible for grants. Write for prospectus and application form, and apply between January and July for entry in September.

Audition requirements:
Usually two speeches and a workshop, although this varies. Audition fee: £5–£15.00.

The Academy was set up in response to the large numbers of students who are unable to get grants or to support themselves while at drama school. However, the evening course is not an easy option, as it is very intensive and daytime work must take second place. It is vital that students see themselves as *actors* who earn money in their spare time. All tutors are working professionals, both actors and directors. No one method or theory is taught; students are offered a wide range of techniques and encouraged to develop their own style.

Stella Greenfield School

41 Bush Grove, Stanmore, Middx.
Tel (081) 952 1805
Fax (081) 952 1032

Affiliated to the Stella Greenfield Agency. Run evening classes in speech and drama for children up to the age of 15. Mostly attended by local children.

Guildford School of Acting and Dance (GSA)

20 Buryfields, Guildford, Surrey
GU4 5DA
Tel (0483) 60701
Fax (0483) 35431
Principal Michael Gaunt
Contact Admissions officer

Founded 1964.

Courses on offer:
- acting course: 3-year full time
- musical theatre course: 3-year full time
- post-graduate acting course
- stage management course: 2-year full time

All courses are NCDT accredited. Grant eligibility from appropriate LEA. Ask for prospectus.

Audition requirements:
Full day, to include two pieces, improvisation, learned song, taught dance routine and interview. Stage management admission is by interview. Audition fee: £20.00. Auditions are held in Guildford, New York and Santa Barbara, California:

'Prepare all aspects for the audition as fully as possible: we want to see you at your best.'

The school believes that its training will provide the theatre with disciplined, balanced actors, stage managers and musical theatre specialists with a sense of responsibility to the theatre and community.

Guildhall School of Music and Drama

Barbican, London EC2Y 8DT
Tel (071) 628 2571
Principal Ian Horsbrugh
Contact Drama Department

Founded 1880.

Courses on offer:
- Associate in Music Diploma (AGSM), 4-year full time.
- Diploma in Music (DipGSM), 3-year full time.
- Graduate in Music (GGSM), 3-year full time.
- Professional Acting (AGSM), 3-year full time; NCDT accredited; 24–26 places (700 applicants).
- Certificate in Stage Management (CSMGSM), 2-year full time; NCDT accredited; 24 places (180 applicants).

The following higher diplomas may be obtained on the satisfactory completion of not less than one year's full-time tuition on the appropriate courses: Concert Recital Diploma; Certificate of Advanced Solo Study; Diploma in Music Therapy. Discretionary grants available. Ask for prospectus.

Audition requirements:
Acting course: three contrasting pieces (including one Shakespeare or Jacobean verse piece, one comic piece) and an unaccompanied song. Stage management course: interview. Audition fee: £25.00.

The school follows a policy of classical theatre training.

Ernest Hopner Studios of Voice, Speech and Drama

34/35 Bluecoat Chambers, School Lane, Liverpool L1 3BX
Tel (051) 709 1966
Principal Ernest Hopner, LLAM

Founded 1952.

Courses on offer:
Voice production (singing and speech); dialects; microphone technique; audition technique; movement and mime; characterization; verse speaking; public speaking and self presentation; stage make-up.

All students are taught individually and privately by the Principal. Grants not available; no prospectus.

Audition requirements:
Students must show intelligence, imagination and capacity for hard work. Actors should memorize two pieces, one comedy and one dramatic. A short impromptu mime and a sight-reading are also given at the audition. There is no audition fee. 'Make sure you know your pieces *thoroughly* – that includes the play from which the extract has been taken. Be prepared to be asked searching questions on *why* you want to act. Don't let your nerves run away with you!'

The school has adopted the following policy: 'To develop to the full the student's abilities through a thorough

mastery of technique so as to enable them to produce work of first-class professional standard.'

Italia Conti Academy of Theatre Arts

Italia Conti House, 23 Goswell Road, London EC1M 7BB
Tel (071) 608 0044
Principal Mrs E. M. Sheward
Contact Mrs Beverley Thomas

Founded 1911 by Italia Conti, an actress. She was succeeded by her niece, Ruth Conti, in 1946 and by the present principal in 1967.

Courses on offer:
- junior course: 9–16 years of age; general education to GCSE and vocational training in dance, drama and singing;
- performing arts course: 3-year vocational course from 16 years of age, majoring in dance with drama and singing, designed to teach the student to accept direction and to extend his/her individual potential in all aspects of drama, dance and singing. ISTD Associate examinations and LAMDA ALAM and LLAM examinations may be taken within the course by suitable applicants if required.
- drama course: 1-year foundation course for students aged 16+ who wish to specialize in drama.
- 3-year actors course: the course is designed for young adults of 18 years and above who wish to pursue a career in the classical and modern theatre and will include all aspects of the Recorded Arts, Film, Television, Radio and Sound Recording.

Grants available. There are 70 places available on both the performing arts and the drama courses, and 700 applicants each year. Applicants should write for prospectus and application form. Entry is by written application with photograph, and audition.
Audition fee: £20.00.

Desmond Jones School of Mime & Physical Theatre

St Luke's Church Hall, 450a Uxbridge Road, London W12
Tel (081) 747 3537
Principal Desmond Jones
Contact Registrar (20 Thornton Avenue, London W4 1QG)

The longest-established school of mime in Britain. Course on offer: 3-month intensive study of mime technique and the arts of physical acting (9.30 am–12.30 pm, Monday to Friday). Grants not available. Applicants are asked to attend an interview, which is not an audition, but is to help select those who would benefit most from the course. Those accepted range between the ages of 18 and 35, sometimes older. They will be largely beginners, mostly actors and actresses but also painters, sculptors, puppeteers and people with some mime experience who want to extend their technique.

'The technique is based on that of Etienne Decroux, the originator of modern mime. Through it, students will learn a sense of style and precision indispensable to the modern mime. They will be made aware of the body and how to use it, and of the infinite subtlety that the body is capable of.

The acting techniques draw on a variety of sources that have influenced modern theatre, from Jacques Lecoq to Keith Johnstone. It is not the intention of the school to produce carbon-copy performers, but to give the students a language of the body that they can use as they wish, whether it be for pure mime, clowning, the speaking theatre, or for daily life.'

The bulk of the teaching is undertaken by Desmond Jones himself. He has performed regularly throughout England and Europe, has choreographed for television and the English National Opera, and was Head of Movement on the films *Quest for Fire* and *Greystoke*. He lectures widely and is an adviser on mime not only to the Arts Council but to all the central organizations promoting mime and mime training.

Laine Theatre Arts Ltd

The Studios, East Street, Epsom, Surrey KT17 1HH
Tel (0372) 724648
Principal Betty Laine
Contact The administrator

Courses on offer:
3-year full-time course comprising dance, drama and singing. Individual timetables are prepared for each student. All students are required to enter for the Associate teaching examinations of the Imperial Society of Teachers of Dancing in the third year. There is also a musical theatre course designed for the student who wishes to specialize in drama and singing, with dance as a subsidiary.

The school is accredited by the Council for Dance Education and Training. Discretionary grants available from many local authorities. Ask for prospectus.

Audition requirements:
Girls: one-hour ballet class; modern dance solo; optional two-minute singing and drama pieces. Boys: one-hour jazz class; modern/jazz solo; optional two-minute singing and drama pieces. College policy is to audition students regularly throughout the year.

London Academy of Music and Dramatic Art

Tower House, 226 Cromwell Road, London SW5 0SR
Tel (081) 373 9883
Principal Roger Croucher

Founded 1861.

Courses on offer:
- acting course: 3-year full-time; NCDT accredited; audition fee: £20.00.
- overseas course, with emphasis on Shakespeare and the classics for overseas students: 1-year full-time; audition fee: £35.00.
- stage management/technical theatre course: 2-year full-time; NCDT accredited; interview fee: £15.00.

Discretionary grants available. Ask for prospectus. Age of entry: 18–26.

Audition requirements:
Two pieces: one Shakespeare and one modern, lasting not more than three minutes.

The school's policy is 'to train actors and stage managers to meet the demands and opportunities of the contemporary professional theatre, and to equip them with a strong technical basis for their craft. Directors and specialist technicians from the professional theatre contribute to the training and life of the school throughout the year.'

London Academy of Performing Arts

861–863 Fulham Road, London SW6 5HT
Tel (071) 736 0121
Principal Cecilia Hocking
Contact Faith Sutherland

Founded 1985.

Courses on offer:
- 2-year full-time acting course.
- 1-year post-graduate acting course.
- summer Shakespearean acting course: 4 weeks.
- summer Acting course: 4 weeks.
- evening Introduction to Acting course: 2 evenings per week.

24 places are available on the one- and two-year courses, but there are several hundred applicants each year. Minimum age for entrance is 18, except for post-graduate course, which is 21. Discretionary grants available. Ask for prospectus.

Audition requirements:
two contrasting speeches of candidate's own choice: one classical and one modern of 2 minutes each. Candidates may also be asked to sight-read a passage or to perform a short improvisation. Audition fee: £25.00.

The school's policy is

'to concentrate on the basic studies of voice and movement, to develop the individual resources of each student, to stimulate the imagination and to free the creative instincts. The aim is to lay the foundations for a secure and firm technique for the actor's future role in the theatre, or for film and video.'

Tutors and directors are experienced professionals; finalists' productions are at the Lyric Theatre, Hammersmith.

London and International School of Acting

LISA House, 138 Westbourne Grove, London W11 2RR
Tel (071) 727 2342
Fax (071) 221 7210
Principal Brian Lidstone,
Contact Administration (please write; do not telephone)

Founded 1983.

Courses on offer:
2-year diploma course; 1-year postgraduate course; 3-year career launching course; short-term courses from time to time. There are 20 places available. Students with grants do attend.

Audition requirements:
Prepared presentations. Audition fee £20.00.
Aimed strictly at training professionally orientated aspirants for classical and modern theatre.

London Studio Centre

42–50 York Way, London N1 9AB
Tel (071) 837 7741
Founder Bridget Espinosa
Director Nicholas Espinosa
General Manager Francis Yeoh

Founded 1978.

Course on offer:
3-year full time, including dance and drama and individually structured from a curriculum of over 350 classes a week. The course accredited by Council for Dance Education and Training; grants available from most authorities. Entry is by audition, or by successful completion of the performing course at East Herts College. Audition fee: £25.00. Minimum age 16. In some cases, where students have already attended a dance or drama school, the course may be shortened.

'The London Studio Centre trains students who are dedicated to the pursuit of excellence in all aspects of theatre, with special emphasis on dance, drama, singing, film and TV techniques. The Studio Centre provides a bridge between school leaving and entry into the professional theatre. The majority of teaching staff are actively engaged in the theatre, thus enabling students to be aware of new techniques and trends.'

A classical graduate course has been designed to meet the needs of advanced ballet students who wish to make their careers in classical ballet companies. The London Studio Centre has close links with the London City Ballet, who train selected students to understudy roles for them.

London Theatre School

Memorial Hall, Chapel Yard, 121b Wandsworth High Street, London SW18 4HZ
Tel (081) 874 5852
Principal Barbara Buckmaster, CSTD, LUD
Contact Administrator

Founded 1984 by Barbara Buckmaster and Belinda Quirey with colleagues from major drama schools and the professional theatre, who share the belief that a strong basis in classical theatre best equips an actor for all forms of drama.

Courses on offer:
- 2-year acting course: full time; minimum age 18.
- 1-year post-graduate and mature student acting course: full time; minimum age 21.
- 6-month course: for the more academically mature student, or the professional actor seeking a refresher course.
- foundation course: 1 year, for 16–18-year-olds.

Students eligible for grants. Applicants should write for prospectus and application form.

Audition requirements:
Two pieces (one Shakespeare, one 20th-century), not more than three minutes each; sight-reading, unaccompanied singing and possibly an acting exercise. Good health is considered essential.

Mary Lynch

322 Endsleigh Court, Upper Woburn Place, London WC1
Tel (071) 387 8023
Principal Mary Lynch RAM, LRAM

Courses on offer:
Individual and group sessions for anyone who has to perform or speak in public. Stage, spotlight and camera work are used to allow people to experience being on show. Improvement of English speaking, pronunciation, conversation, speech-making, voice production and business presentation. Personal tuition can be arranged at offices and hotels. All sessions under the direction of Mary Lynch.

Morley Theatre School

Morley College, 61 Westminster Bridge Road, London SE1 7HT
Tel (071) 928 8501
Principal David Normand-Harris (Acting Principal of College)
Contact Brian Croucher (Director of Theatre School) or General Office for enquiries

Founded 1939.

Course on offer:
An intensive part-time theatre course, ideal for those with little background who need a foundation before applying for full-time courses. All students involved in productions, all of which take place at the college studio theatre. There are approximately 30 places available, with 100–150 applicants. No grants. Fees are low. Concessionary rates available. The college prospectus is available in the summer. Enrolment is by interview/audition just before the start of the course in September.

Audition requirements:
To be able to sight-read.

Mountview Theatre School

104 Crouch Hill, London N8 9EA and Ralph Richardson Memorial Studios, Clarendon Road, Wood Green, London N22
Tel (081) 340 5885/881 2201
Contact Flicky Ridel, Graham Caws

Mountview is dedicated to producing vigorous, intelligent and well informed performers, stage technicians and directors who will bring to any performance solid technique, thoughtfulness, energy and commitment. The school equips students artistically as well as practically and is very conscious of the need to be in contact with the profession. Throughout the courses lectures are given by prominent members of the theatre world and guest professional directors work with students from the 1st year.

Courses on offer:
- Acting & musical theatre: 3 year full-time; 9 terms of about 10 to 11 weeks (The year is divided into four terms – autumn, spring, summer and late summer. January and October intakes.)*
- Post-graduate acting & musical theatre: 1 year full-time; 4 terms.*
- Stage management, technical theatre & design course: 2 year, full-time. January and October intakes.*
- Summer course: Four weeks over July and August.

*Courses accredited by the National Council for Drama Training and eligible for student grants. Mountview is a member of the Conference of Drama Schools. Prospectus available on request. Entry requirements: Acting and Muscial Theatre Courses – Prepare one modern and one classical speech and one song. Sessions will be held in movement and voice. Audition Fee £25.00. Technical and Directors Courses – Interview, bring any relevant work with you. Interview Fee £20.00.

Scholarships: Mountview *Acting and Stage Management*. Ralph Richardson *Acting*. Somerset Award, *Acting/Stage Management*. Graucob Award, *Acting*. Mountview/Stage and Television Today, *Acting*. Lawrence Attwell Charity, *Stage Management/Acting*. Thelma Holt, *Acting*. Margaret Rutherford, *Acting*. Penny Blackburn Prize, *Stage Management/Acting*. The Kobler Trust, *Acting*. Singing Scholarships.

New Era Academy of Drama And Music

137b Streatham High Road, London SW16 1HJ
Tel (081) 769 0384
President Michael Bentine
Contact Bernard Price, Principal

Not a drama school as such, but an examining body with a wide ranging syllabus including Speech and Drama, Spoken English, Interview Technique, Public Speaking, Solo Verse Speaking, Reading, Choral Speaking, Bible Reading, English as a Second Language, Mime, Stage Technique. Exams in these subjects can be taken at centres all over the UK in the presence of one or two of the Academy's Board of Directors. Adults and children are catered for and the Senior exams in Stage Technique are helpful for those wishing to take up theatre work as a career. No full time courses are available, but tutors attend the Academy on Wednesday evenings. Write for a syllabus which gives details of exams in all subjects.

The Oxford School of Drama

Samsomes Farm Studios, Woodstock, Oxford OX7 1ER
Tel (0993) 812882
Patron Denholm Elliott, CBE
Principal George Peck
Contact The Administrator

Founded 1982. Developed from summer courses run by professional actors and directors.

Courses on offer:
- Diploma acting course: 2-year full time; minimum age 17.

- Diploma acting course: 1-year full time; minimum age 20.
- Summer courses: introduction to acting, advanced acting, Edinburgh Festival performance course.
- Diploma arts administration/stage management course: 2-year full time; minimum age 17.

28 places on full time courses. The school is applying for National Council for Drama Training accreditation. Discretionary grants are available from some authorities. A prospectus is available.

Audition requirements:
One Shakespeare piece and one modern piece (2 minutes). Improvisation is required at recall auditions. Audition fee: £12.00.

Teaching policy: to develop existing potential by encouraging the imagination and liberating the individual physically.

Jackie Palmer Stage School

30 Daws Hill Lane, High Wycombe, Bucks. HP11 1PW
Tel (0494) 20978
Principals Jackie Palmer, Marylyn Phillips
Contact Marylyn Phillips

Founded 1981.

Courses on offer:
Classes for boys and girls in all subjects, from the age of 3 upwards; 300 places available. No prospectus available; write or telephone the principals for details and to apply.

Audition requirements:
To show some potential in the work that has been learned, suitable for the child's age.

The school attempts to provide an all-round training for those interested in working in the theatre or TV, or who wish to go on to full-time further education in drama.

Rosina Pulley School of Stage Dancing

5 Lancaster Road, London E11
Tel (081) 539 7740
Contact Rosina Pulley

Courses on offer:
Evening and weekend classes for children aged 4–16; ballet, tap, acrobatic and modern. No straight drama classes, though some dance classes include mime. Children are entered for examinations.

Redroofs Theatre School

Littlewick Green, Maidenhead, Berks.
Tel (062882) 2982
Principal June Rose

Courses on offer:
- 2-year full-time student course; performance-orientated professional training in acting, singing and dance. Minimum age of entry: 16.
- children's co-educational day school with education to GCSE level and drama and dance training; from 7 years.
- 1-year Stage Management Course.
- part-time classes in all branches for adults and children.

Prospectus available.

Richmond Drama School

Richmond Adult & Community
College, Parkshot, Richmond
TW9 2RE
Tel (081) 940 0171
Director David Whitworth, BA

Founded 1956, as De Leon Drama
School. A previous course director,
Sam Walters, is now artistic director of
the Orange Tree Theatre.

Course on offer:
1-year full-time acting course; 24
places (70 applicants each year). Some
authorities will give grants. The fees
are low compared to other drama
schools. A prospectus is available.

Audition requirements:
One Shakespeare and one modern
piece. Audition fee: £10.00.
This is a small school with excellent
facilities. Students have the advantage
of belonging to one of the largest adult
education colleges in Europe. High
professional standards are demanded,
and a lot is packed into one year. For
some students, a further course of
study is advisable. Applicants are welcomed from a wide variety of backgrounds, the only criterion being
whether they show potential for
development to a professional standard of acting. Students have many
opportunities to work with professional actors and directors, and
strong links are maintained with the
Orange Tree Theatre. The course is
validated by the Oxford University
Delegacy of Local Examinations. A
diploma is awarded at the end of the
year. The outside Moderator is Ian
Talbot, Artistic Director of the New
Shakespeare Company.

Royal Academy of Dramatic Art

62–64 Gower Street, London
WC1E 6ED
Tel (071) 636 7076
Principal Dr O. Neville
Contact The Secretary

Founded 1904 by Sir Herbert
Beerbohm Tree, and has functioned in
Gower Street since the following year.
Has two fully equipped theatres – the
Vanbrugh and the GBS – and a small
studio theatre.

Courses on offer:
• Diploma in acting: 9 terms, full
  time; 28 places per annum; minimum age 18; NCDT accredited.
• Diploma in stage management: six
  terms, full time; 6 places; minimum age 17; NCDT accredited.
• specialist diploma courses: usually
  four terms, may be taken in stage
  carpentry, scene painting and
  design and property-making; one
  person per course; minimum age
  19.

Audition requirements:
Two pieces, one contemporary and
one Shakespeare. Audition fee:
£20.00.

'The training is vocational. A very favourable
student/staff ratio enables the acquired skills
of the actor, both vocal and physical, to be
taught at an intensive level. Great emphasis
is given to this part of the course. However,
the acquiring of these skills is clearly
directed towards our central purpose, which
is to develop in the actor an ability to understand and communicate a playwright's
intentions. Throughout the course, these in-
terpretative and imaginative skills are also
developed by working with professional directors whose teaching is integrated with an
active career outside the Academy.
Performances take place in three kinds of
acting space. These circumstances combine

to enable the student to explore his/her work from as many angles as possible, and to keep in touch with contemporary theatre.'

Royal Scottish Academy of Music & Drama

School of Drama, 100 Renfrew Street, Glasgow G2 3DB
Tel (041) 332 4101
Principal Edward Argent (Director, School of Drama)
Contact Valerie Parker (Administrative assistant)

Founded 1950, as College of Dramatic Art. Took present title in 1968, and moved to purpose-built accommodation in 1987.

Courses on offer:
● Diploma in dramatic art: 3-year full time; 22 places (300 applicants).
● Diploma in stage management studies: 2-year full time; 14 places (90 applicants).
● BA in dramatic studies: 3-year full time; 30 places (200 applicants).
Both diploma courses are NCDT accredited, and eligible for grants; there is mandatory granting for the degree course, which is validated by the University of Glasgow. A prospectus is available. Applicants should write for an application form, and for details of the auditioning process.

Audition requirements:
Diploma in dramatic art: two pieces – one Shakespeare and one contrasting; candidates who are successful at this stage will be recalled for an interview, and then for group improvisation. BA in dramatic studies: two contrasting pieces, sight reading of texts, interview and improvisation session. Audition fee: £15.00.

St Catherine's Drama Studio

26a Portsmouth Road, Guildford, Surrey GU2 5DH
Tel (0483) 68788
Managing and Artistic Director Richard Winter MPhS
Contact the Secretary

Founded 1977 by June Cooper LGSM (Hons).

Courses on offer:
● Acting diploma course: 2-year full-time.
● Acting diploma course: 1-year full-time.
● Stage management & technical course: 1-year full-time.
Some part time courses for adults and children. All full-time courses include Television Training, an area in which the Studio has been a leader for some time. There are 20 places on the 1-year course, 30 places on the 2-year course and 6 for Stage Management. Discretionary grants available from some education authorities.
Master Classes and Workshops for professional performers, given by established directors and tutors, commence in September 1991.
The Studio/Theatre and Television Studio is available to professionals for private and public work.

Audition requirements:
Usually a workshop. Separate audition pieces. Audition fee: £15.00.
Only tutors with recent professional experience are employed to teach. The Studios are closely associated with the

Strolling Players, a professional company set up to employ students who have become members of Equity.

Sandown College

Greenbank Annexe, Mossley Avenue, Liverpool L18
Tel (051) 733 5511
Principal R. A. Humphries
Contact M. Lloyd

Founded 1986, from the reorganization of the City of Liverpool's further education colleges.

Courses on offer:
- Preparatory course in drama: 1-year full-time.
- Diploma in theatre studies: 2-year full-time.
- Preparatory course in dance: 1-year full-time.
- Diploma in dance: 2-year full-time.
- General course in performing arts (GCSE A-levels in dance, drama, music).
- Diploma in performance technology: 2-year full-time.
- BTEC National Diploma in Performing Arts: 2-year full-time.
- Foundation Course Commercial Music: 1-year full-time.
- Graduate diploma in music: 3-year full-time.
- Diploma in light music: 2-year full-time.
- Preparatory course in music: 1-year full-time.
- Preparatory course in rock: 1-year full-time; intended for the 16–18-year-old performer who cannot read music or who needs to widen his or her skill to progress.

Grants are available for Liverpool residents attending full-time courses, and discretionary grants may be available from other local authorities.

Audition requirements:
Applicants for all performing courses are auditioned, but requirements vary. Policy: 'If it's to do with the arts – WE DO IT!'

Anna Scher Theatre

70–72 Barnsbury Road, London
N1 0ES
Tel (071) 278 2101
Principal Anna Scher
Contact Harriett Dye (administrator)

Founded 1968, as a schools' drama club. Now attended by over 900 children and young people. Classes are divided into Junior (6–11), Secondary (11–16) and Youth (16–21+). There are also two professional groups. Fees are paid per session or per term, with reductions for families. There is a long waiting list, and it takes about three years to get in. As well as classes, productions are put on for parents and for friends of the theatre. There are opportunities for members to work in films, on TV and on the stage under Anna Scher Theatre Management Ltd; see Agents section. (Children under 16 do not do modelling or advertising for commercial products.) 'Our motto is "Talent thrives on training together." ' Emphasis is placed on professionalism, learning to share and being a good audience.

Shandy Stage School

56a Livingstone Road, Hove,
E. Sussex BN3 3WL
Tel (0273) 822244/822238
Principal Andrew Cameron

Founded 1984.

Courses on offer:
Full-time academic and performing arts education for young people aged 6–16. There are 9 places available each year, with 68 applicants. No grants are available.

Audition requirements:
To attend the school for a day for assessment. No audition fee.
The school aims to produce well-accomplished and confident young adults with the best possible knowledge of the performing arts and high academic qualifications.

Barbara Speake Stage School

East Acton Lane, London W3 7EG
Tel (081) 743 1306/6096 (day); (081) 998 6596 (night)

Founded in 1945 as a dancing school and became a full-time educational establishment for 5–16 year olds in 1963. Academic curriculum with one daily non-academic class in drama, singing, tap or modern dancing. Telephone or write for details.
Also see Barbara Speake Agency and C.S.M. (Artistes) Ltd in Agents section.

Stardust Children's Theatre Workshop

43 Marlands Road, Clayhall,
Redbridge, Essex IG5 0JL
Tel (081) 550 7224
Principal Phyllis Borden

Founded 1983.

Courses on offer:
Drama workshops, singing, speech, disco, ballet, tap, modern dance. Classes for all ages of children and adults. Phone or write in to apply. No audition requirements.
Policy: 'Learning through an educative yet fun approach.'

Dacia Stevens Stage School

Glenavon Lodge, Lansdowne Road,
South Woodford, London E18 2BE
Tel (081) 989 0166
Principal Dacia Stevens RAD, RADA, LRAM

Founded 1970.

Courses on offer:
All types of drama and stage training for children, 4–9 pm each day. Pupils entered for examinations and prepared for full-time stage school. 'Children need to be taught to speak correctly. They love to act. I teach them both.' Classes for older pupils by arrangement.

Webber Douglas Academy

30 Clareville Street, London SW7 5AP
Tel (071) 370 4151
Principal Raphael B. Jago
Contact Jacqui Burns (Academic Secretary)

Founded 1906, in Paris. In 1926, moved to London where it became an opera school; became a fully fledged drama school in 1945.

Courses on offer:
- Diploma course: 3-year full-time; 30 places (900 applicants).
- Diploma course: 2-year full-time; 12/14 places (300 applicants).
- Post-graduate course: 1-year full-time; 12/14 places (300 applicants).

All courses are NCDT accredited and eligible for student grants. A prospectus is available. Prospective students should complete an application form, attaching a small photograph.

Audition requirements:
One Shakespeare piece, one modern piece. It is recommended that one piece should be comedy, one should include some movement, and that only one should be a direct address to the panel. Applicants may also be asked to sing unaccompanied and to improvise. Audition fee: £18.00.

Teaching policy: 'To create a professional well-equipped actor with a good working method.'

'The demands made on actors with the development of the range of the media since the middle 1950s, and the requirement that the modern actor should be able to sing, dance and stage fight as well as act, make great demands on the modern drama school. Nevertheless, the core of the course remains the development of skills primarily to enable the student actor to cope with the demands of the classical stage. Once this is achieved, the needs of the modern theatre, films, TV and radio can be satisfied by building on these foundations.'

Welsh College of Music & Drama

Castle Grounds, Cathays Park, Cardiff CF1 3ER
Tel (0222) 342854/5/6
Principal Edmond Fivet
Contact Paul Clements

Founded 1949.

Courses on offer:

Acting
- Performer's course: 3-year full-time.
- Graduate diploma course: 3-year.
- Advanced certificate course: 1-year; for graduates or those with appropriate experience.

All the above acting courses are fully accredited by the NCDT.

Design & stage management
- Graduate diploma course: 3-year full-time.
- Advanced certificate course: 1-year.
- Directing: 1-year advanced certificate course.

Education
- B Ed (Hons) course: 4-year full-time, designed primarily for those who wish to qualify as teachers of drama, but also useful for radio and TV work with young people, and Theatre-in-Education.

Minimum age for all 3-year courses is 18; for 1-year courses, 21. Grants are mandatory for the degree and graduate diploma courses, and discretionary for the acting courses and the 1-year courses. A prospectus is available.

Audition requirements:
Candidates will be selected by audition and interview. A reference is required, which must be sent with the application form.

Policy: 'The acting courses are practical in philosophy and emphasis. They aim to:

- equip the student with control of both inner and external resources for acting.
- encourage the development of the actor as a thinking, feeling, passionate and self-confident individual.
- help the actor become aware of the opportunities for employment and expression which exist in the theatre and its related industries.
- build a foundation of commitment and care about the work and the arts, which will assist the individual to make the most of the profession and, in particular, the opportunities it presents for further development, learning and growth.'

White Rose Studio

Castle Hill House, 21 Otley Road, Leeds LS6 3AA
Tel (0532) 757514
Principals Mr S. J. Armstrong, Mrs J. M. Armstrong
Contact Miss J. A. Turner (secretary)

Courses on offer:
Part-time tuition in speech, drama, and public speaking. Different classes to suit the needs of each individual, including private and small group lessons and group workshops. All ages catered for. A prospectus is available. No auditions, just a brief interview. There are lots of opportunities for taking examinations and for taking part in festivals. Coaching is given for drama school entrance.

3 Universities and Further Education Courses

The City Literary Institute

Stukeley Street, Drury Lane, London
WC2B 5LJ
Tel (071) 430 0455
Principal William Tyler
Contact Valerie Colgan (joint head of department)

Founded 1919. The City Lit Drama, Dance and Speech Department has a high reputation for all aspects of acting, different dance forms, mime, clowning and circus skills, as well as speech skills taught by professional actors and teachers at low cost to students. Prospectus available (two are usually issued each year). An average of 180 courses per year, with between 25 and 20 applicants for each course.

Audition requirements:
Entry is by personal interview. Open auditions are held for specified dance classes where evidence of training is required, and prepared speeches may be asked for entry into some performance classes. There are no audition fees.

'The two-year part-time drama course aims to give a good introduction to acting skills for students who may hope to become professional actors. Other, more advanced courses are designed to extend performance skills and refresh working performers and teachers. Numerous professional actors/performers have entered the City Lit as beginners seeking to test a vocation/skill for work in the theatre and in other branches of entertainment. It is possible to begin in an introductory class and then proceed by carefully monitored stages to advanced classes, and to Equity only professional classes. The low fees are made possible by the educational policies of this registered charity, which seeks to make educational opportunities available to all in accordance with its equal opportunities statements.'

The City University

Dept of Arts Policy & Management,
Level 12, Frobisher Crescent,
Barbican, Silk Street, London
EC2Y 8HB
Tel (071) 628 5641/2
Head of Department Professor John Pick BA, PGCE, MA PhD, FRSA

Courses on offer:
- Diploma in Arts Administration: one-year full-time course in professional skills associated with administration in the arts. Candidates should hold a degree and have professional experience in arts administration.

- MA in Arts Administration: one-year full-time or two-year part-time course. For practising arts administrators.
- MA in Arts Criticism: one-year full-time or two-year part-time course. For those with experience of criticism and evaluation in the arts.
- MA in Museum & Galleries Administration: one-year full-time or two-year part-time course.
- MA in Arts Management in Education: one-year full-time or two-year part-time course.

Applicants for all courses should have an honours degree or equivalent and working experience in the arts.

- short course programme runs from time to time.

Loughborough University of Technology

Loughborough, Leics. LE11 3TU
Tel (0509) 231983
Head of English & Drama
Department W.J. Overton, BA PhD
Director of Drama M.G. Robinson, BA PhD

Courses on offer:
- BA Single Honours in Drama: three-year full-time course, designed to offer the opportunity of studying the subject both in practice on stage and in theory through the detailed examination of a wide range of dramatic texts.
- BA Joint Honours in English & Drama: three-year full-time course. During the third year, students may concentrate on either the practical or the theoretical elements of the drama side of the course.

Students intending to become teachers may take an alternative four-year course that leads to the award of a degree and a Certificate in Education.

Facilities for practical drama work include a 300-seat theatre and a multi-purpose drama workshop with 150 seats. Professional theatre companies often visit these, and the university is well situated for visits to theatres at Leicester, Nottingham, Derby, Coventry, Stratford, Birmingham and Sheffield.

Manchester Polytechnic, School of Theatre

Dept of Communication Arts & Design, Capitol Building, Didsbury, Manchester M20 0HT
Tel (061) 247 2000 Ext 7123
Principal Nicolette Lee (Head of School of Theatre)

Course on offer:
BA (Hons) Acting Course, 3 year full-time. Annual intake: 25. NCDT and CNAA accredited. Minimum age: 18. Grants mandatory. Prospectus available from school address above. Apply through PCAS.

Audition requirements:
Maximum of three set-pieces, an improvisation and, when relevant, a hearing test. Selected applicants are asked to return.

A training course for professional actors that provides training both in basic skills, and in creative technique. Stanislavski's observation of the relationship between relaxation, concentration and imagination forms the basic creative principle of the training, which students learn to apply with flexibility depending on the style of the play. As well as preparing students for a tough and disciplined profession, the course aims to encourage students to develop a set of values against which to measure their work.

Middlesex Polytechnic

Bounds Green Road, London
N11 2NQ
Tel (081) 368 1299
Director Dr R. M. W. Rickett CBE
Contact Leon Rubin (Head of School of Drama).

Trent Park College and the New College of Speech and Drama joined Middlesex Polytechnic in 1975.

Courses on offer:
- BA (Hons) Performance Arts: 3-year full-time, with core of performance studies and choice of first study in dance, drama or music.
- BEd (Hons): 4-year full-time, with study areas in dance and music.
- MA Performance Arts: 2-year part-time.
- Post-graduate Certificate in Education: music or drama, 1-year full-time.
- under the 'modular scheme', which offers 400 modules in 28 different subject areas: BA (Hons) in History of Art, Design and Film; BA (Hons) Contemporary Cultural Studies; DipHE in dance, drama and music. All three courses can be full- or part-time.

(The Diploma in Dramatic Art, the Certificate in Stage Management and Technical Theatre and the Certificate in Drama Skills have been suspended due to lack of funding, and at present, their future is unclear.)

Grants available. Normal entry requirements for degree courses are five GCSE passes including two at A-level, or four GCSE passes with three at A-level, or an equivalent standard of education. Applications from mature students with appropriate experience but no formal qualifications will be considered.

Audition requirements:
Vary for the different courses. No audition fees.

'Middlesex Polytechnic has a reputation for excellence in all the performing arts. This is based on the strengths of two of the Polytechnic's constituent colleges: Trent Park College of Education and the New College of Speech and Drama. Both became part of the Polytechnic in 1975, offering staff expertise and specialist facilities for what is now a major centre for the teaching of dance, drama and music at degree, diploma and certificate levels.

'Students at Middlesex have ample opportunity for involvement with performance in both academic work and extra-curricular activities. Concerts, plays, dance programmes and multi-media productions are staged throughout the year. In one academic session alone, student productions included dance workshops and dance programmes in the community, lunchtime recitals, major opera productions, Greek and Roman drama, Japanese Noh plays, performances of electronic music, major modern plays, musicals, revues and productions of the classics.'

Nene College

Moulton Park, Northampton NN2 7AL
Tel (0604) 715000

BA and BSc (Hons) degrees in combined studies include drama, which can be taken for one, two or three years. Offers 'a unique blend of academic study and practical experience'. Those who take drama as a minor three-year subject study a selected element of the course in Modern British and European Drama and the practical course in its entirety. Prospectus available.

Newark Technical College

Chauntry Park, Newark on Trent,
Notts. NG24 1PB
Tel (0636) 705921
Principal Mr G. Williams
Contact Mrs G. Dicks BA, Cert Ed
(Section head)

Course on offer:
- Foundation course in theatre arts: 1-year, full-time or part-time; 15–20 places (20–30 applicants).

Free to students living in Nottingham-shire. Other local education authorities may give grants. Application should be made to Mrs G. Dicks.

Audition requirements:
Interview and workshop audition. No audition fee.

The course is based on modules – e.g. acting technique, voice production, dance, text study, etc. English and Drama can be taken at GCSE level, and Drama at A-level.

Newcastle upon Tyne Polytechnic

Squires Building, Sandyford Road,
Newcastle upon Tyne NE1 8ST
Tel (091) 232 6002
Contact Tony Goode, Dept of Visual and Performing Arts

Course on offer:
- BA (Hons) Creative Arts.

Drama is available as a substantial, practical area of study within the BA (Hons) Creative Arts Course. The Course provides a vocationally oriented training in the uses of arts in a variety of community settings. It aims to develop the student's practical creative skills to a professional level in one art form – Drama, Music or Visual Art – and to provide the opportunity for the development of multi-media work. It aims also to develop the student's theoretical understanding of the different roles the arts can play in the lives of the majority of people.

The Course is engaged in increasing popular access to the arts. It is also involved in extending the social accountability of the artist. The majority of people in Britain have little or no direct contact with the live arts. The Course trains students in methods of presenting art to those people, and is equally concerned with encouraging their participation in the production of their own art.

We are interested in mature applicants with relevant experience in community-based work and/or the arts, and in other types of non-standard candidates.

Queen Margaret College

Clerwood Terrace, Edinburgh
EH12 8TS
Tel (031) 317 3542
Principal Donald Leach
Contact Clive Perry (Head of drama)

Founded 1971. The Department of Drama, which is part of a multi-discipline college, was formed after the closure of a private school called the Edinburgh College of Speech & Drama.

Courses on offer:
- Diploma in drama (acting): 3-year full-time.
- Diploma in drama (stage management): 3-year full-time.

There are approximately 25 places available, with 250–300 applicants per course. Grants are mandatory for Scottish students. A prospectus is available.

Audition requirements:
(*Acting*); An audition/interview with staff for which the candidate is asked to prepare two 2/3 minute speeches – one classical and one modern, and to prepare a song.

Interview requirements:
(*Stage Management*): An interview with staff at which the candidate is invited to bring proposals to a design brief specified by the college. Candidates are also hosted by a current S.M. student during the visit.

Policy: 'To train students, both acting and stage management, for work in the professional theatre and related media. We are looking for people who have talent and who are *totally committed* to the job.'

Stockton–Billingham Technical College

The Causeway, Billingham, Cleveland TS23 2DB
Tel (0642) 552101
Principal A. Oyston, MA LRAM LTCL
Cert Ed
Contact Anne Attwood
(Section Head)

Courses on offer:
- BTEC First Diploma in Performing Arts (1 year).
- BTEC National Diploma in Performing Arts (2 years).
Both courses allow specialisation in drama, dance or music.

For National Diploma students, GCE Advanced examinations are available in English Literature, Theatre Studies, Dance, Music.

University of Birmingham

Dept of Drama & Theatre Arts,
University of Birmingham, Birmingham B15 2TT
Tel (021) 414 5994
Admissions Tutor for Faculty of Arts R. B. Leach, MA

Courses on offer:
- BA Special Honours: 3-year full-time course in drama and theatre arts.
- BA Combined Honours: 3-year full-time course in drama and theatre arts, with one other subject: English, French, German, Greek (ancient or modern), history, Italian, Latin, music, physical education, Russian, sociology or Hispanic studies.

The Drama & Theatre Arts Department at Birmingham is a leader in the field of practical drama, having pioneered a course which puts at its centre the actor in performance. At the core are the complementary dramatic medium and theatre practice courses which all students follow, and from this stem the optional courses which aim to develop more specialized skills.

The Department also runs a special honours degree course in music, drama and dance in conjunction with the Music Department, and a unique MA in Playwriting.

University of Bristol

Drama Dept, Senate House, Bristol BS8 1TH
Tel (0272) 303030
Professor of Drama Professor E. Braun, MA, PhD (Cantab)

Courses on offer:
- BA Single Honours: 3-year full-time course in drama, designed to provide students with a training in

the theory, criticism and history of dramatic literature and performance (including film and TV drama), together with an introduction to practical aspects of the dramatic arts.

- MA in Drama Studies: 1-year full-time or 2-year part-time course for those seeking an advanced qualification in drama.
- Certificate in Film and Television: post-graduate 1-year course that is an introduction to the skills in practical work in these three media.

Facilities for research work leading to the degrees of M.Litt. and PhD are also offered by the Department.

University of Essex

Dept of Literature, Wivenhoe Park, Colchester, Essex CO4 3SQ
Tel (0206) 872624
Course director Roger Howard

Course on offer:

- MA in Drama: 1-year full-time (or possibly 2-year part-time at the course director's discretion). Chiefly concerned with modern dramatic literature world-wide, with options available in English plays of the late medieval, Elizabethan and Jacobean stages. There are currently two main components to the course: 'The Theatre and Social Change' and 'Naturalism and Beyond'. Instead of a final written dissertation, students may offer: an original stage play of at least one hour's duration; the production and direction of a play of at least one hour's duration; or a prompt book for the production of a full-length play.

The Dept of Literature has initiated a theatre writer's residency to provide students with an opportunity to work with a professional theatre writer during the writing of a play, usually leading to a production. Recent writers have included Edward Bond, Nick Dear, Steve Gooch, Michele Celeste and Michele Roberts.

University of Exeter

Department of Drama, Thornlea, New North Road, Exeter EX4 4JZ
Tel (0392) 264580
Head of Department John Rudlin

Courses on offer:

- BA Single Honours: 3-year full-time course in drama, which has a national reputation for innovation and experiment. The studio-based project system of teaching and learning obliterates any final distinction between practical and academic work. Continuous assessment, a dissertation, a practical 'essay' (devised and performed, not written) and portfolios take their place alongside examination papers in the degree scheme.
- BA Combined Honours: 3-year full-time course in drama and English, Drama and German, or Drama and Spanish.
- BA (Ed) Honours: 3-year full-time teaching course in English and drama. Offers opportunities to those who have equal interest in both subjects, or to those who prefer to concentrate on one or the other. The work seeks to involve students in the kinds of approaches they can readily adapt to teaching in schools.

University of Glasgow

Dept of Theatre, Film & Television
Studies, Glasgow G12 8QQ
Tel (041) 339 8855
Head of Department Professor Janet
B. I. McDonald, MA

Courses on offer:
- Theatre Studies: *1st year*: an introduction to the nature of the theatrical art. *2nd year*: a study of the major theatrical genres, current trends in non-text-based theatre, practical classes in direction and design. *Honours courses (3rd & 4th years)*: students may choose from a wide range of options. Entry to the 1st-year class is limited to 100, preference being given to those who want to pursue the subject to honours level.
- Film & Television Studies: *1st year*: introductory course on film and TV. *2nd year*: two subjects – 'Genre in Film and Television' and 'Film, Television and British National Culture'. *Honours courses (3rd & 4th years)*: a variety of topics are studied, and there is a substantial practical course in the 3rd year. Entry to 1st-year class limited to 90 (40 intending Honours).

University of Hull

Dept of Drama, Cottingham Road, Hull
HU6 7RX
Tel (0482) 46311 ext 6210
Director of Drama Donald H. Roy,
MA, Dip Ed, FRSA

Courses on offer:
- BA Special Honours: 3-year full-time course, designed for the student who wishes to concentrate on the study of drama in all its aspects.

- Joint Honours: 3-year full-time course, designed for the student who wishes to read drama and one other subject.
- MA in Theatre Production: 1-year full-time course designed to take advantage of the practical opportunities afforded by the Gulbenkian Theatre.

University of Kent

Drama & Theatre Studies, Rutherford
College, The University, Canterbury,
Kent CT2 7NX
Tel (0227) 764000
**Chairman of Drama & Theatre
Studies** Alan Pearlman

Courses on offer:
- BA Single Honours: 4-year full-time course in drama and theatre studies. The fourth year of this course is devoted to one specialist subject: directing; devising; or the funding and organization of the British theatre.
- BA Combined Honours: 3-year full-time course, with half the degree work in drama and half in another subject in the Faculty of Humanities.
- Visual & Performed Arts: 3-year full-time course. A package of courses may be chosen, related to film, drama and the history and theory of art.

'At this university, we start from the rejection of the notion (which dies hard in the English theatre) that skills of an intellectual and analytical kind are incompatible with skills of a creative and imaginative kind. We believe that the best theatre has always been created by people with developed minds as well as natural theatrical talent.

'At a drama school, you will be trained as an actor. If you are absolutely certain that you want to study acting exclusively, then perhaps a drama school is the better choice – university drama departments do not give specialist acting training. But if your interest in the theatre is more broad-based, if you want to study its literature and its history, if you are interested in writing and directing and design – if, in short, you want to study theatre in its widest sense, then a university drama course is the wiser choice . . . The kind of training a degree in drama offers is relevant to all worlds of work: learning to meet work deadlines; learning to find and use information; learning to present coherent arguments; learning to work cooperatively in group projects . . . Also bear in mind that people do much better at things that interest and stimulate them, than at things that they "ought" to be doing.'

The recently published Gulbenkian Enquiry into Directors' Training *A Better Direction*, singled out Kent's course structure and the Directing Programme for special commendation. The Department of Drama from University College of North Wales (Bangor) has been transferred to Kent, and a new Drama Studies Theatre has recently been built.

University of Lancaster

Drama Dept, University House, Bailrigg, Lancaster LA1 4YW
Tel (0524) 65201
Head of Department K. M. Sturgess, MA, B.Litt (Oxon)

Courses on offer:
- BA (Hons) Single Major in Theatre Studies: 3-year full-time. Based entirely around the Theatre Studies Department and involving the study of subjects and options which include: theatrecrafts; Stanislavski and Brecht; arts administration; medieval English theatre; one theatre, its Company and repertoire; TV drama; ritual theatre; feminist theatre.

- BA (Hons) Combined Major: 3-year full-time, in theatre studies and one other subject: education; religious studies; English; French; German; sociology.
- MA in Contemporary Theatre Practice: 1-year full-time. 'This course aims to provide laboratory facilities for and guidance into a variety of aspects of contemporary theatre.'

University of Leeds

Leeds LS2 9JT
Tel (0532) 334720
Director Professor Martin Banham (at The Workshop Theatre)

Courses on offer:
- MA Theatre Studies: normally 1-year full-time. Students will be required to attend three courses: theory and practice of performance; history of theatre and methods of theatrical analysis; theatre practice. Applicants will be expected to have made some significant study of drama or theatre during the course of their studies at first-degree level.
- BA Theatre Studies and English Literature.

'The Workshop Theatre is the laboratory for the academic programme in theatre studies in the School of English. Much of the work that is to be seen in the Workshop Theatre is directly related to teaching programmes within the university, specifically the MA programme in theatre studies and the BA in Eng. Lit. and Theatre Studies; but the Workshop Theatre also has a responsibility to the university as a whole, and originates a range of general theatrical activities that are designed to complement academic programmes and provide a richer cultural life for the university community.'

University of London: Goldsmiths' College

New Cross, London SE14 6NW
Tel (081) 692 7171 (enquiries to The Registry)
Admissions Tutor for Drama and Theatre Arts Christopher Baugh
Admissions Tutor for English and Theatre Arts William Naismith
Admissions Tutor for MA Professor Vera Gottlieb
Admissions Tutor for M.Phil & Ph.D Simon Trussler, Reader in Drama
Admissions Tutor for Postgraduate Teaching Certificate Brian Roberts

Courses on offer:
- BA Drama and Theatre: 3-year full-time – (also offered part-time).
- BA English and Drama: 3-year full-time.
- MA Drama (Process of Production): 2-year part-time.
- Research degrees (full-time or part-time) leading to the award of M.Phil or Ph.D.
- Postgraduate Teaching Certificate in drama as a subject for secondary school teaching: 1-year full-time.

Goldsmiths' is a unique institution, in which the creative and performing arts co-exist at a high level of achievement with more traditional studies in the humanities, education, science and the social services.

University of London: Royal Holloway & Bedford New College

Dept of Drama & Theatre Studies, Egham Hill, Egham, Surrey TW20 0EX
Tel (0784) 434455
Professor & Head of Department D. Bradby

Courses on offer:
- BA Single Honours in Drama & Theatre Studies: 3-year full-time course, established 1980. Designed to extend knowledge and deepen critical appreciation of drama from the classical period to the present day. Practical work is undertaken with this end in view.
- BA Combined Honours: 3-year full-time course in drama and theatre studies combined with Classical Studies, English, French or music.
- MA in Drama & Theatre Studies: 1-year full-time or 2-year part-time study.

All of the above courses include training in and use of theatre skills, production work, critical analysis, and study of the history of film and theatre, with many optional subjects. There is a Departmental Studio Theatre, and radio and TV facilities are available at the London University Audio-Visual Centre in central London. The Department also houses the Centre for the Study of Japanese Noh Theatre, which is building up a specialist library of videotapes and books.

University of London: Queen Mary and Westfield College

Kidderpore Avenue, London NW3 7ST
Tel (071) 435 7141
Director of Drama J. Redmond, MA
Ed B (Glasgow), BA (Cantab), B.Litt
(Oxon)

Courses on offer:
- BA Combined Honours Degrees as follows:
  English & Drama (3 years, full-time)
  French & Drama (3 and 4 years, full-time)
  German & Drama (3 and 4 years, full-time)
  Hispanic Studies & Drama (3 and 4 years, full-time)
- Graduate students are accepted for the degrees of M.Phil and PhD in Drama, and receive personal supervision.

Drama classwork for the combined degrees involves a wide variety of lectures, seminars, tutorials and practical studio and production work. Students are registered as undergraduates at Queen Mary and Westfield University of London, but they also have membership of the Central School of Speech & Drama (*see* Drama schools), and take practical classes and mount productions there.

University of Manchester

Dept of Drama, The University,
Manchester M13 9PL
Tel (061) 275 2000
Head of Department Professor Kenneth Richards

Courses on offer:
- BA Single Honours: 3-year full-time course in drama. Largely an academic course, with a practical element.
- BA Double Honours: 4-year full-time courses in English and drama; French and drama; German and drama.
- BA Joint Honours: 3-year full-time course in Italian and drama. Other combinations of subjects are also available on some occasions.
- Diploma in Drama: 3 terms. Occasionally the Department is able to offer supervised study for the Diploma in select areas of practical theatre work (e.g. design, playwriting).
- Facilities are also available for study for PhD and M.Phil degrees.

The Drama Department at Manchester is one of the largest in Britain, with approximately 90 undergraduates. There are a number of professional theatre companies in the city, and opera, ballet and contemporary dance flourish in the region.

University of Ulster at Coleraine

Faculty of Humanities, University of Ulster, Coleraine, Co. Londonderry BT52 1SA
Tel (0265) 44141   Fax (0265) 40903
Dean Professor P. R. Roebuck

Courses on offer:
- BA (Hons) Theatre Studies: 3-year full-time course. This new degree has a strongly practical and skills based emphasis. All students do production units and take supporting units which explore modern approaches to theatre; theatre and society; the use of space; the actor and the role; the actor and the audience; stage management and

its wider application to general management. The work on stage management includes an introduction to basic computer skills and applications; and to basic stage lighting.

All students take a placement in the second year. This is an attachment to a professional theatre, company or organisation relevant to the individual student's career interests. There is a choice of specialist options in the final year.

- BA (Hons) Humanities Combined Degree: 3-year full-time course. Theatre Studies may be taken as a Major, Joint or Minor programme, in conjunction with the student's choice of other subjects offered within the degree. The course shares units on the theory and practice of Theatre with the BATS, described above. As with that degree, the methodology stresses teamwork in collective practical activity.

Students taking theatre studies as a major option take a placement in their second year. This is a six-week period of attachment, usually to a leading producing theatre in Britain or Ireland.

University of Warwick

Coventry CV4 7AL
Tel (0203) 523523
Professor of Theatre Studies & Dramatic Arts D. B. Thomas MA, PhD (Cantab)

Courses on offer:
- BA Single Honours: 3-year full-time course in theatre studies and dramatic arts. Allows students to emphasize, in their second and third years, either a practical or an

historical and analytical approach to theatre.
- BA Joint Honours (English & Theatre Studies): 3-year full-time course. Approaches drama from two directions: through the literary analysis of texts, and via the understanding of playing places and performance. The degree provides no training for actors or directors, but does have a special concern with the role of the writer in the theatre: as critic and dramatist, in theory and practice.
- BA Combined Honours: 3-year full-time course in theatre studies with either French or Italian.
- BA Joint Honours (Film & Literature): 3-year full-time course. The only course of its kind at a British university.

University College of Wales Aberystwyth

The Old College, King Street,
Aberystwyth, Dyfed SY23 2AX
Tel (0970) 623177
Head of Department Mrs E. Closs Stephens

Courses on offer:
- BA Single Honours: 3-year full-time course in drama.
- BA Joint Honours: 3-year full-time. Drama with a wide range of Arts and non-Arts subjects.

After following a one-year Part 1 course made up of a number of courses from different departments, students decide on their Part II course at the beginning of the second year. In the case of Single Hons Drama they then follow the equivalent of eight fully weighted courses over two years. These may include courses in film or television studies. Joint Hons students select four courses from Drama, with four from another department.

'Drama at Aberystwyth is characterized academically by its emphasis on the indivisibility of theory and practice. Practical work is seen as illuminating and deepening the student's understanding of the written text; similarly, theoretical approaches are tested in the workshop of creative work.'

4 Film and Video Courses

Bournemouth & Poole College of Art & Design

Wallisdown, Poole, Dorset BH12 5HH
Tel (0202) 533011
Head of School of Film, Television & Audio Visual Production
Nick Wright

Courses on offer:
- BTEC Higher National Diploma in film and television: 2 years, full time.
- BTEC Diploma in audio visual design: 2 years, full time.
- Advanced Diploma in media production: 1 year, full time; specifically devised to offer an opportunity to 'especially gifted students' to extend and develop a chosen specialization within certain categories such as writing/direction, production management, editing, etc.
- In preparation – BTEC HN Dip in Arts and Events Administration: 2 years full time.

Prospectus available.

Gwent College of Higher Education

Faculty of Art and Design, Clarence Place, Newport, Gwent NP9 OUW
Tel (0633) 259984
Contact Les Mills

Course on offer:
BTEC Higher National Diploma in film and television: 2 years, full time; devised to provide vocational training in the practical skills of handling film and video equipment and materials and to encourage a creative yet professional attitude towards the film and television media.

Harrow College, Polytechnic of Central London

Northwick Park, Harrow, Middx HA1 3TP
Tel (071) 911 5000

Offer a BA (Hons) CNAA (Council for National Academic Awards) degree course in photography, film and video (3 years full time). Prospectus available.

Kent Institute of Art and Design

Oakwood Park, Oakwood Road,
Maidstone, Kent ME16 8AG
Tel (0622) 757286
Head of Time-based Studies
A.L. Rees

Course on offer:
BA (Hons) communication media–
time based studies: 3 years, full time.
Time based studies is for students
with a particular interest in the exploration of new developments in the
field. The practical and theoretical
thrust aims to inform, encourage and
develop a broad approach to video/TV
production with special attention to
creative authorship and visual innovation.

King Alfred's College of Higher Education

Sparkford Road, Winchester
SO22 4NR
Tel (0962) 841515
Contact Peter Sykes

Course on offer:
BA (Hons) (CNAA) in drama, theatre
and television: 3 years. The focus is
on the practice of communication
through live performance and television with approximately equal integrated practical and theoretical units.

London College of Printing

School of Media, Elephant & Castle,
London SE1 6SB
Tel (071) 735 9100 ext 2064
Contact Linda Swanell

Courses on offer:
3–year full-time course leading to a
Council for National Academic

Awards BA (Hons) degree in film and
video. A production course with a
strong theoretical input, concentrating
on independent, new and innovative
production. Students study all stages
of film and video production within
the context of past and current media
structures and institutions. The course
has a special interest in popular culture, women's cinema and Third
World cinema, and prepares students
for the possibilities of cross-ethnic,
cross-cultural co-productions in the
European and international context.
2-year part-time course leading to
CNAA MA in Independent Film and
Video. The course is aimed at people
working or wishing to work in film
and video production. The year group
shares and exchanges ideas about
their work and its context within the
framework of theory, history and context of cinema and video. In the
second year students take part in an
attachment scheme.

London International Film School

24 Shelton Street, London WC2H 9HP
Tel (071) 836 9642/240 0168
Administrator Phil Mottram
Principal Martin M Amstell

Diploma course, 2 years full time. The
syllabus includes: basic principles for
film-makers; scripting and planning;
organization and production; directing
and acting; photography; lenses;
camera; lighting and special effects;
animation and titling; projection and
presentation; editing; sound; music;
art department and design; make-up
and wardrobe; film analysis and
appreciation; written work, tests, etc.;
dissertation. Prospectus available.

Manchester Polytechnic School of Television Production and Design

Faculty of Art and Design, Dept of Communication Arts & Design, Capitol Building, School Lane, Didsbury, Manchester M20 OHT
Tel (061) 434 3331
Head of School Wally Butler – Directors Guild of Great Britain

Course on offer:
BA (Hons) Design for communication media/television production and design: 3 years, full time with options in television production or television production design (set design). General audio–visual design and animation 2D and 3D is also available. The course is 60% practical and the main study is on television production and design with emphasis towards broadcasting.

Middlesex Polytechnic

Cat Hill, Barnet, Herts. EN4 8HT
Tel (081) 368 1299

MA Video 1 year, full-time: 16 students. DES Bursaries and European Social Funding available. Candidates should be graduates and have experience of video production.

National Film & Television School

Beaconsfield Studios, Station Road, Beaconsfield, Bucks. HP9 1LG
Tel (0494) 671234 Fax (0494) 674042
Contact Admissions secretary

Offers a full-time 3-year training programme to professional standards in all aspects of film-making. The School's departments cover Animation, Art Direction, Camera, Direction, Documentary, Music Composition, Producers, and Sound. Deadline for applications: mid-January. A 1-year course in Script Writing is also available. Application deadline for Script end October.

The National Short Course Training Programme operates as a separate unit with the NFTS and offers courses for those directly working in the film and television industry. Contact: Hilary Coote.

Newcastle upon Tyne Polytechnic

Faculty of Art and Design, Squires Building, Sandyford Road, Newcastle upon Tyne NE1 8ST
Tel (091) 232 6002
Contact Peter Leake, Faculty of Art and Design

Course on offer:
BA (Hons) Media Production: 3 years, full time. The course aims to produce graduates who will become professional practitioners whose basic technical proficiency is informed by firmly established critical perspectives. The film and video area offers an opportunity to engage in the processes of film and video production and criticism and seeks to develop individual and group skills, perceptions and roles to a level satisfying professional standards.

Polytechnic of Central London

18 Riding House Street, London
W1P 7PD
Tel (071) 911 5000
Contact Communication School
Office

Undergraduate courses:
Offer the following 3-year full-time
courses: BA (Hons) degree in media
studies; BA (Hons) degree in film,
video and photographic arts; BSc and
BSc (Hons) degrees in photographic
and electronic imaging sciences.

Postgraduate courses:
Linked MA and postgraduate diploma
in film and TV studies (part-time evening). These courses lead to the post-
graduate diploma of the CNAA
(Council for National Academic
Awards) in film and TV studies after
six terms of study, and to the MA in
film and TV studies of the CNAA after
a further three terms of study.
Students with previous film and/or TV
study experience may be directly
admitted to year two.

'The Faculty of Communication is concerned
with the study and practice of the modern
media of communication – principally broadcasting, film, journalism and photography. It
embraces a wide variety of academic disciplines. Our courses deal with the technology
of the media, creative professional practice
and the aesthetic and social implications of
media products . . .'

Royal College of Art

Kensington Gore, London SW7 2EU
Tel (071) 584 5020

Postgraduate 2-year full-time course in
film and TV production, direction and
design. Candidates should be over 21
and under 40 years old and have
obtained the BA in art and design or a
first degree of a British university or an
equivalent overseas qualification.

St Martin's School of Art

Film and Video Unit, 27–29 Long Acre,
London WC2E 9LA
Tel (071) 753 9090 ext 414
Advanced Course Tutor David
Parsons

Course on offer:
MA in independent film and video: 2
years, part time. An intensive programme of lectures and seminars
which are designed to meet the needs
of film and video–makers.

Suffolk College of Higher and Further Eduction

School of Art & Design, Rope Walk,
Ipswich, Suffolk IPA 1LT
Tel (0473) 55885
Head of Dept J R Lowe

Courses on offer:
- BTEC Higher National Diploma in
  visual communication: 2 years, full
  time. Includes options in film/TV
  graphics, animation and film/video
  production.
- BA (Hons) Degree in *Design
  Studies*. 1-year top-up following
  the course above (or equivalent): 3
  years full-time in total. Includes
  options in:
  – Interior Design
  – Exhibition and Museum
    Design
  – TV and Theatre Set Design
  – Corporate Graphic Design

— Advanced TV Graphics
— Illustration
— Animation
— Photography
— Design History
— Film/Video Production

West Surrey College of Art & Design

Falkner Road, Farnham, Surrey
GU9 7DS
Tel (0252) 722441
Contact Art & Design Admissions
Registry

Offer 3-year full-time CNAA (Council for National Academic Awards) BA (Hons) degree courses in photography; film and video; or animation. Prospectus available.

5 Directors' Courses and Awards

BAC Young Director's Award

Battersea Arts Centre, Old Town Hall, Lavender Hill, London SW11 5TF
Tel (071) 223 6557
Fax (071) 978 5207
Administrator Judith Hibberd

Annual Award for Young Directors under the age of 35. Entry is by written application to the above address in response to adverts in the national press. A list of applicant directors is narrowed down to a finalist by a two-day directing workshop watched and judged by leading theatre critics, directors, and professionals. The Award Winner goes on to direct a professional production at BAC, receiving an Arts Council of Great Britain Bursary to allow them to train in a regional British theatre later that year.

Bournemouth & Poole College of Art & Design

Wallisdown, Poole, Dorset BH12 5HH
Tel (0202) 533011

See **Film & Video Courses** above.

Bristol Old Vic Theatre School

2 Downside Road, Clifton, Bristol BS8 2XF
Tel (0272) 733535

Trainee directors' attachment (not a structured course).
See **Drama Schools** above.

East 15 Acting School

Hatfields, Rectory Lane, Loughton, Essex IG10 3RU
Tel (081) 508 5983

See **Drama Schools** above.

National Film & Television School

Beaconsfield Studios, Station Road, Beaconsfield, Bucks. HP9 1LG
Tel (0494) **671234**

See **Film & Video Courses** above.

Regional Theatre Young Director Scheme

Independent Television Association,
56 Mortimer Street, London W1N 8AN
Tel (071) 636 6866
Administrator Jack Andrews

Founded 1960. A training scheme for those between the ages of 20 and 26 who have had some experience in theatre (professional or amateur) or the allied arts and who wish to make a career as directors in the professional theatre. Funded by the ITV companies, there are four vacancies each year. Applications should be made by early February (the closing date can be obtained from the Television Fund Secretary and is advertised in *The Stage*). The list of former trainees is long and distinguished, including Pip Broughton, Bill Bryden, Giles Havergal, Gregory Hersov, Barry Kyle, Kenneth Loach, Adrian Noble, Trevor Nunn, Michael Rudman, Sue Wilson.

Part 2 *The Opportunities of Acting*

6 Agents

A good agent will help you to find regular work, develop your career prospects, boost your status, increase your earnings, and take over all the unpleasant business of searching out work, negotiating fees, and securing payment for work you have done. And all for around 10–15% of your earnings. It's not a bad deal. A competent agent is necessary for any access to the vast majority of jobs in film and television. A competent agent will negotiate a decent contract for you, and pursue proper payment through the labyrinth of details attached to the constantly changing standards of agreements with theatre, television, advertising, etc. The complexity of these beggars belief. For example, payments for commercials are based on an initial daily fee (currently a minimum of £95.00) a percentage of which becomes due each time an advert is repeated. The percentages vary widely from region to region, from one company to another, and from one channel to another. The average actor is certainly not equipped to deal with such contracts on their own.

Finding an agent is for many at least as difficult as obtaining an Equity card. Most responsible agents try to restrict their client list to actors who they think will have a reasonable chance of regular work. They may also have a limit on the number of clients in any one range of age, general physique, and character-type. Most will want to see some evidence of ability and employment potential. It's obviously a help for them to see you performing, but bear in mind that it's a buyer's market and it can be quite difficult to persuade agents to attend a show that you're in. In most cases agents prefer to be contacted initially by letter, with accompanying CV and photograph. It is most important that this letter is carefully prepared and presented, and that your photograph is of professional quality. Directors can sometimes be helpful by recommending actors to agents.

In recent years there has been a growth of actors' co-operative agencies, in which groups of actors take on the running of an agency to represent each other. Co-operatives require not only a commitment of considerable time and energy, but also some level of office-management ability. Inevitably they are hampered by lack of continuity and of high-powered negotiating ability, and their quality varies considerably depending on their membership, but they can help the inexperienced to learn the intricacies of the business and many actors find them more appealing than the relative anonymity of commercial agencies with large client-lists. The total number of actors in any one co-operative is likely to be very restricted, and a substantial joining-fee may be required to help off-set running costs. Commerical agents meet with such costs by representing larger numbers of actors and do not normally ask for such a fee: be wary of any who do.

Once registered with an agent it is sensible to establish exactly what is expected of you. Agents need to be able to contact clients easily and quickly, and you should know how often to call in without making a nuisance of yourself. It is up to you to ensure that your agent knows what you can do. It is astonishing how easily an actor can be categorised mistakenly within a very narrow stereotype by casual impressions of dress and mannerism. Common sense suggests that your agent should not always see you in jeans and T-shirt. If you were first seen by them when playing a mass-murderer, make sure you display a lighter side when visiting for coffee.

Voice Over

Voice-over work for commercials, dubbing for film, and the like, is a highly lucrative area. Consequently it is fiercely competitive and very difficult to break into. A demo-tape is crucial, and to be effective this must be professionally produced. This will not be cheap. If the demo tape is successful, and work comes your way (normally through the efforts of a specialist agent) you will need to be a brilliant sight-reader capable of instant performance without direction or rehearsal. Great powers of concentration, stamina, inventiveness and unflappability are required.

A & B Personal Management Ltd

5th floor, 114 Jermyn Street, London SW1Y 6HJ
Tel (071) 839 4433

Represent actors, writers, directors and a choreographer. Welcome queries from actors seeking representation. Send CV and photograph initially. Will consider video tapes of work done, not set-up demos.

AC Management

38 Mount Pleasant, London WC1X 0AH
Tel (071) 837 2413   Fax (071) 833 5593

Founded 1976. Cooperative management. Represent actors only, and welcome queries from those seeking representation. Approach in writing in the first instance (with SAE). No unsolicited demo tapes or video show reels.

AIM (Associated International Management)

5 Denmark Street, London WC2H 8LP
Tel (071) 836 2001
Fax (071) 379 0848
Contact Derek Webster, Les Hines

Founded 1984. Represent actors and film and TV directors. Welcome queries from actors seeking representation. Approach in writing in the first instance. No unsolicited demo tapes or video show reels.

A & J Management

551 Green Lanes, London N13 4DR
Tel (081) 886 3159
Contact Jackie Michael

Founded 1984. Represent actors and children (small number of adult clients). Do not welcome queries from actors seeking representation.

ANA (Actors Network Agency)

55 Lambeth Walk, London SE11 6DX
Tel (071) 735 0999

Founded 1985. Cooperative management. Represent actors only, and welcome casting queries from those seeking representation.

Actors Network Agency

See **ANA**.

ART Casting

2 Mount Pleasant, Liverpool L3 5RY
Tel (051) 207 2868
Contact Tom Mack

Founded 1980. Represent actors only, and welcome queries from those seeking representation. Send letter in the first instance, with CV and photograph. Welcome demo tapes and video show reels.

Abacus Agency

31 Chesfield Road, Kingston upon Thames, Surrey KT2 5TH
Tel (081) 546 3463
Contact Jean Darnell

Founded 1985. Represent child actors, and welcome queries from under 16s, or 16–18 with Equity if able to play down. Approach by telephone in the first instance. No unsolicited demo tapes or video show reels.

Marjorie Abel Ltd

50 Maddox Street, London W1R 9PA
Tel (071) 499 1343
Contact Marjorie Abel

Founded 1972. Represent actors. Welcome queries from actors seeking representation. Approach in writing in the first instance. No unsolicited demo tapes or video show reels.

Acting Associates

Unit F10, 28 Tooting High Street, London SW17 0RG
Tel (081) 672 7801

Founded 1987. Cooperative management. Represent actors only, and welcome queries from prospective clients. Write in the first instance, stating interest in a cooperative agency.

Actor Factor (Barbara Pemberton Associates)

Imex House, 40 Princess Street, Manchester M1 6DE
Tel (061) 228 6616
Contact Barbara Pemberton

Founded 1987. Represent actors only, and welcome queries from those seeking representation. Approach in writing in the first instance, enclosing CV and photograph. Do not welcome

unsolicited demo tapes or video show reels.

The Actors Agency

13 Gardners Crescent, Edinburgh EH3 8DE
Tel (031) 228 4645
Fax (031) 228 4040
Contact Douglas Stiven

Founded 1984. Represent actors, directors, writers, producers, and also involved in co-productions, investment, etc. Welcome queries from actors seeking representation. Approach in writing in the first instance. Will consider demo tapes and video show reels.

Actors Alliance

Bon Marché Building, 444 Brixton Road, London SW9 8EJ
Tel (071) 326 0070

Founded 1976. Cooperative management. Represent actors only. Currently not considering requests for representation. No unsolicited demo tapes or video show reels.

The Actors' Exchange Ltd

Unit 503, 69/71 Bondway, London SW8 1SQ
Tel (071) 793 0028

Founded 1983. Cooperative management. Represent actors only. Usually advertise in *The Stage* when seeking new members, but will consider queries from actors wanting representation. Approach by telephone in the first instance. Photographs and CVs should always be accompanied by an SAE. No unsolicited demo tapes or video show reels.

Actors Management Wales Ltd (Rheolaeth Actorion Cymru CYF)

House One, The Maltings, East Tyndall Street, Cardiff CF5 5EA
Tel (0222) 489032

Founded 1987. Cooperative management. Represent actors only, and welcome queries from those seeking representation. Approach in writing in the first instance, although 'if someone rings, we are happy to send information.' Will consider demo tapes and video show reels. 'It is vital to send a good photograph and informative CV as well as a letter stating interest. As we are a cooperative agency, it is essential that applicants are willing and able to man the office on a rota basis when not working. We would advise any actor who wants more control over his/her career to join a cooperative.'

ADS Agency

Reform Road, Maidenhead, Berks.
SL6 8BT
Tel (0628) 39758/29346
Fax (0628) 777101
Contact Betty Curtis

Founded 1983. Represent children and some adults. Welcome queries from actors seeking representation. Write in the first instance, sending photograph and CV. Demo tapes and video show reels welcome.

Alpha Management

London House, 68 Upper Richmond Road, London SW15 2RP
Tel (081) 870 7066

Founded 1983. Cooperative management. Represent actors only, and welcome queries from those seeking representation. Approach in writing in the first instance, enclosing photograph and CV. No unsolicited demo tapes or video show reels.

Amber Personal Management Ltd

28 St. Margaret's Chambers, 5 Newton Street, Manchester M1 1HL
Tel (061) 228 0236

Founded 1987. Cooperative management with permanent manager. Represent actors only, and very much welcome queries from those seeking representation. Approach in writing in the first instance – 'your letter will be discussed at our monthly meeting.' Will consider demo tapes and video show reels. 'As Amber is a cooperative agency, we are interested in the reasons why a particular actor is searching for this kind of management as opposed to a commercial management.

Susan Angel Associates

1st floor, 12 D'Arblay Street, London W1V 3FP
Tel (071) 439 3086
Contact Susan Angel

Founded 1978. Represent actors; one designer on the books. Welcome queries from actors seeking representation. Approach in writing in the first instance. Do not welcome telephone calls, unsolicited demo tapes or video show reels.

Angel Star Theatrical Employment Agency

5 Lancaster Road, London E11
Tel (081) 539 7740

Represent children and adults. Do not welcome queries from actors seeking representation as they are handling only their established clients at the moment.

Anglian Casting

Burgh Castle, Great Yarmouth, Norfolk NR31 9QH
Tel (0493) 780793/780465
Contact Carl Adams

Founded 1980. Represent actors and supporting and crowd artists for TV, films and commercials. Specialize in location work in East Anglia including an Edwardian Theatre, so handle mostly clients who live there. Welcome queries from actors seeking representation. Write in the first instance with CV and photograph. Demo tapes and video show reels welcome. All letters acknowledged.

Arena Personal Management Ltd

Bon Marché Building, 444 Brixton Road, London SW9 8EJ
Tel (071) 274 4000 ext 268
Contact Simon Williamson

Founded 1985. Cooperative management. Represent actors only, and welcome queries from those seeking representation, 'especially from those over 40 years, those under 23 years and ethnic actors of all ages – all must

be Equity members or from recognized drama schools'. Send letter with CV, photograph and SAE. No unsolicited demo tapes or video show reels.

Mary Arnold Management

12 Cambridge Park, East
Twickenham, Middx TW1 2PF
Tel (081) 892 4860
Contact Mary Arnold

Founded 1965 as a variety agency; now deal only with actors. Some voice-over work. Welcome queries from actors seeking representation. Approach in writing with CV and photograph. Telephone calls and unsolicited demo tapes and video show reels not welcome.

Arts Management

Redroofs, Littlewick Green,
Maidenhead, Berks.
Tel (0628 82) 2982

Represent actors and children. Do not welcome queries from actors seeking representation.

Avenue Artistes Ltd

47 The Polygon, Southampton, Hants SO1 2BP
Tel (0703) 227077
Contact Terry Rolph

Founded 1963. Represent actors and 'offer a full entertainment service covering every aspect of the entertainment industry'. Welcome queries from those seeking representation. Initial approach by either telephone call or letter. Will consider demo tapes and video show reels.

AZA Artistes Ltd

652 Finchley Road, London
NW11 7NT
Tel (081) 458 7288
Contact Morris Aza, Sheila Aza

Founded 1958. Represent actors, comedians, writers and musicians. Not taking new clients. Do not welcome queries.

Paul Bailey Agency

22 Wolsey Road, East Molesey,
Surrey KT8 9EL
Tel (081) 941 2034

Represent variety artists. No actors.

Julian Belfrage Associates

68 St James's Street, London SW1
Tel (071) 491 4400
Contact Julian Belfrage

Founded 1985 (previously Leading Artists). Represent actors only, and welcome queries from those seeking representation. Approach in writing in the first instance, with CV and photograph. Demo tapes and video show reels will be considered.

Billboard Personal Management Ltd

The Co-Op Centre, 11 Mowll Street,
London SW9 6BG
Tel (071) 735 9956

Founded 1987. Cooperative management. Represent actors and directors. Welcome queries from actors seeking representation. Approach in writing in the first instance. Will consider demo tapes and video show reels.

Boden Agency

13 Essex Road, Enfield, Middx
EN2 6TZ
Tel (081) 367 1836/2692
Contact Tony Boden

Founded 1979. Represent actors only, and welcome queries from those seeking representation. Approach in writing in the first instance. Will consider demo tapes and video show reels. To newcomers: 'Try to get qualifications for something apart from acting before going to drama school.'

Sheila Bourne Management

2-2-3, Greenwich Business Centre,
49 Greenwich High Road, London
SE10 8JL
Tel (081) 469 2726
Contact Sheila Bourne

Founded 1987. Represent actors and directors. Welcome queries from actors seeking representation. Send letter with CV, photograph and SAE (large enough for the return of the photograph). No unsolicited demo tapes or video show reels.

Michelle Braidman Associates

Third floor suite, 10/11 Lower John
Street, London W1R 3PE
Tel (071) 437 0817
Fax (071) 439 3600
Contact Michelle Braidman, Alan Turner, Amanda King, Wim Hance

Founded 1984. Represent actors, directors and designers. Welcome queries from actors seeking representation. Approach in writing in the first instance, enclosing CV, 10×8 photograph and SAE. Video show reels must always be accompanied by large enough SAE.

Braithwaite's Theatrical Agency

8 Brookshill Avenue, Harrow Weald, Middx HA3 6RZ
Tel (081) 954 5638

Linked with Braithwaite's Acrobatic School.

Barry Brown Management

47 West Square, Southwark, London SE11 4SP
Tel (071) 928 1229
Contact Barry Brown, Carrie Simcocks

Founded 1972. Represent mostly actors, one or two 'personalities'. Welcome queries from actors seeking representation. Write with CV and photograph initially. Will not consider unsolicited demo tapes or video show reels. 'Let us know what you are doing, and when and where you're doing it; don't write at the end of a run. Be different – agents get around 25 queries every week.'

Darryl Brown Associates Ltd

Thornton House, Thornton Road, London SW19 4NG
Tel (081) 944 6688
Contact Darryl Brown

Founded 1981. Represent actors only, and welcome queries from those seeking representation. Write in the first instance with SAE. Will not consider

unsolicited demo tapes or video show reels.

Pete Brown Artist Management

37 Marshall Street, London W1V 1WL
Tel (071) 734 8346
Contact Pete Brown, Karen Andrews, Judith Clough

Represent actors, musicians, bands, writers, producers and directors. Welcome queries from actors seeking representation. Approach in writing in the first instance. Will consider demo tapes and video show reels.

Brunskill Management Ltd

Suite 8a, 169 Queens Gate, London SW7 5EH and The Courtyard, Edenhall, Penrith, Cumbria CA11 8ST
Tel (071) 584 8060/(076881) 430   Fax (071) 589 9460/(076881) 850
Contact Ms Aude Powell

Represent actors, directors, producers, writers and musicians. Welcome queries from actors seeking representation. Approach in writing in the first instance. Will consider demo tapes and video show reels.

Barry Burnett Organisation Ltd

Suite 42, Grafton House, 23 Golden Square, London W1
Tel (071) 437 7048
Fax (071) 437 1098

Founded 1968. Represent actors only, but do not welcome queries from those seeking representation.

CCA Personal Management

4 Court Lodge, 48 Sloane Square, London SW1W 8AT
Tel (071) 730 8857 Fax (071) 730 6971
Contact Howard Pays

Founded 1965. Represent actors, directors, technicians. Welcome queries from actors seeking representation. Write in the first instance. Will not consider unsolicited demo tapes or video show reels.

C & S Personal Management

Picardy House, 4 Picardy Place, Edinburgh EH1 3JT
Tel (031) 557 0790
Fax (031) 557 0790
Contact Linda Crooks, Liz Smith

Founded 1986. Represent actors, directors and choreographers. Welcome queries from actors seeking representation. Approach in writing in the first instance.

CSM (Artistes) Ltd

49 Churchfield Road, London W3 6AY
Tel (081) 992 8668
Contact Carole Deamer

Founded 1984. Represent actors, but welcome queries from teenagers only seeking representation.

Calypso Voice Agency

25–26 Poland Street, London W1V 3DB
Tel (071) 734 0410
Contact Ann Dawson, Jane Savage

Founded 1983. Represent actors for voice work only. Welcome queries from experienced voice-over artists seeking representation. Will not consider unsolicited demo tapes or show reels.

Sara Cameron Management

1 Aberdeen Lane, London N5 2EJ
Tel (071) 359 8178
Contact Sara Cameron

Founded 1990. Represent actors and presenters. Welcome queries from actors seeking representation, but have limited list of clients. Write, with SAE. Will consider demo tapes and video show reels.

Cameron, Hayward & Co. Ltd

3 Lord Napier Place, London W6 9UB
Tel (081) 748 9974
Fax (081) 741 1428
Contact Clodagh Wallace

Founded 1973. Represent actors and recording artists. Do not welcome queries from actors seeking representation.

Sarah Cape

2 Hinde Street, London W1M 5RH
Tel (071) 486 3312
Contact Sarah Cape

Founded 1968. Primarily a model agency, although they do handle actors of Asian, African and Oriental ethnic origin for commercials. Welcome queries from actors interested in representation for commercials. Write in the first instance. Will not consider unsolicited demo tapes or video show reels.

Cardiff Casting

Unit 15, Royal Stuart Workshops, Adelaide Place, Cardiff CF1 6BR
Tel (0222) 494465   Fax (0222) 481623

Founded 1984. Cooperative management. Represent actors only, and welcome queries from those seeking representation – 'from time to time, we do increase our membership.' Send letter with CV and photograph. No unsolicited demo tapes or video show reels. 'Cardiff Casting is by no means a purely Welsh agency. However, due to the nature of our organization, it would be impractical to consider anyone for membership who is not within reasonable travelling distance.'

The Central Agency

112 Gunnersbury Avenue, London W5 4HB
Tel (081) 993 7441
Fax (081) 992 9993
Contact Hazel Hemmings

Founded 1980. Represent actors. Welcome queries from actors seeking representation. Write or telephone in the first instance. Will consider demo tapes and video show reels.

The Central Line

11 East Circus Street, Nottingham NG1 5AF
Tel (0602) 412937   Fax (0602) 508087

Founded 1984. Cooperative management. Represent actors only, and welcome queries from those seeking representation. Send letter enclosing CV and photograph. No unsolicited demo tapes or video show reels.

Characters Agency

106 Wilsden Avenue, Luton LU1 5HR
Tel (0582) 456213
Contact Ron O'Brien, Sussette O'Brien

Founded 1983. Represent actors only, and welcome queries from those seeking representation. Send letter with photograph and CV in the first instance. Will consider demo tapes and video show reels. 'Ron O'Brien is also a casting adviser/director for many video production companies specializing in corporate and training videos.'

Peter Charlesworth Ltd

2nd floor, 68 Old Brompton Road, London SW7 3LQ
Tel (071) 581 2478
Fax (071) 589 2922
Contact Peter Charlesworth, Marilyn Collis

Represent actors, directors, writers, designers, etc. Welcome queries from actors seeking representation – strictly by letter with SAE. No unsolicited demo tapes or video show reels.

Chatto & Linnit Ltd

Prince of Wales Theatre, Coventry Street, London W1V 7FE
Tel (071) 930 6677
Fax (071) 930 0091
Contact Rosalind Chatto

Founded 1970. Represent actors, designers and directors. Take for granted queries from actors seeking representation. Write in the first instance. Will not consider unsolicited demo tapes or video show reels.

City Actors' Management Ltd

5 Leonard Street, London EC2A 4AQ
Tel (071) 251 0917

Founded 1981. Cooperative management. Represent actors only, and always welcome queries from those seeking representation. Send brief letter, photograph, CV and *photo-size* SAE. No unsolicited demo tapes or video show reels – 'there just isn't time.'

Clarion/Seven Muses

64 Whitehall Park, London N19 3TN
Tel (071) 272 4413
Telex 918774 SEVMUS G
Contact Nicholas Curry

Founded 1983. Represent classical musicians (soloists and ensembles), as well as well-known actors in words-and-music programmes. Do not welcome queries from actors seeking representation.

Elspeth Cochrane Agency

11–13 Orlando Road, London SW4 0LE
Tel (071) 622 0314
Fax (071) 622 9456

Founded 1959. Actors, designers, writers and directors represented.

Shane Collins Associates

24 Wardour Street, London W1V 3HD
Tel (071) 439 1976
Contact Shane Collins

Founded 1986. Represent actors only, and welcome queries from those seeking representation. Send letter with full CV and photograph. No unsolicited demo tapes or video show reels.

Company Call

27 Romford Road, London E15 4LJ
Tel (081) 519 5909

Founded 1986. Cooperative management. Welcome queries from actors seeking representation. It is better to write in the first instance with photo, CV and SAE, as this is easier for the members to deal with. Will not consider unsolicited demo tapes or video show reels.

Elison Combe Associates, Personal Management

16 Evelyn Gardens, Richmond, Surrey TW9 2PL
Tel (081) 940 7863
Contact Timotny Combe (managing director)

Founded 1981. Represent actors, producers and presenters. Welcome queries from actors seeking representation

– 'many of our enquiries are by personal recommendation.' Approach in writing in the first instance. Will consider demo tapes and video show reels – 'we use these as a back-up to the interview'. 'Our policy is always to reply to applications, but a quicker response will be given to those with an SAE.'

Jeremy Conway Ltd

109 Jermyn Street, London
SW1Y 6HB
Tel (071) 839 2121
Fax (071) 930 3272
Contact Jeremy Conway, Nicola van Gelder, Valerie Hoskins

Represent actors, directors and writers. Will consider queries from actors seeking representation. Approach in writing in the first instance. No unsolicited demo tapes or video show reels.

Vernon Conway Ltd

5 Spring Street, London W2 3RA
Tel (071) 262 5506
Contact Vernon Conway

Founded 1977. Represent actors and writers. Welcome queries from actors seeking representation. Write in the first instance with photo and CV. Send SAE for reply and return of photo. Will not consider unsolicited demo tapes or video show reels.

Lou Coulson

37 Berwick Street, London W1
Tel (071) 734 9633
Contact Lou Coulson

Founded 1978. Represent actors only. Not actively seeking new clients – do not welcome unsolicited queries. Usually work on personal recommendation.

Crawfords

2 Conduit Street, London W1R 9TG
Tel (071) 629 6464
Contact Nicholas Young, Veronica Pieters

Founded 1981. Represent actors only, and welcome queries from those seeking representation. Approach in writing in the first instance. Will consider demo tapes and video show reels. 'Crawfords is the only agency specializing in representing actors and actresses for TV commercials.'

Crouch Associates

59 Frith Street, London W1V 5TA
Tel (071) 734 2167

Founded 1959. Represent actors only, and welcome queries from those seeking representation. Write in the first instance with photo and CV. Will not consider unsolicited demo tapes or video show reels.

Culbertson Reeves Ltd

44 Monmouth Street, London WC2
Tel (071) 497 2540
Contact Carrie Culbertson, Fenella Reeves

Founded 1985. Represent actors only, and welcome queries from those seeking representation – 'but it is difficult to get on to our deliberately small list.' Approach in writing in the first instance. No unsolicited demo tapes or video show reels. 'When sending a CV, always say what part played, which production and *where* (e.g. not just "*Romeo and Juliet*"). Not only is it important, but we may have seen it on our numerous theatre visits. Also, the director's name is helpful.'

DACS Management

Rusthall Avenue, London W4 1BP
Tel (081) 995 1995
Contact Rashna Homji-Jefferies

Founded 1983. Specialise in musical theatre and commercial theatre. Represent actors with dancing and singing abilities, choreographers, designers and dancers, and welcome queries from such actors seeking representation. Approach in writing in the first instance. Will consider demo tapes and video show reels.

Liam Dale Associates Ltd

3 Culvers Avenue, Carshalton, Surrey SM5 2BN
Tel (081) 647 6627
Fax (081) 647 6628
Contact Liam Dale, Vanessa Anstey

Founded 1984. Represent actors, light entertainment, presenters and writers. Welcome queries from actors seeking representation – however, 'we are a personal management company dealing with artists accustomed to high-profile exposure; the company limits its responsibilities to 14 artists.' Approach in writing in the first instance. Will consider demo tapes and video show reels.

Daly Gagan Associates

68 Old Brompton Road, London SW7 3LQ
Tel (071) 581 0121 Fax (071) 589 2922
Contact David Daly, Hilary Gagan

Founded 1978. Represent actors, but do not welcome queries from them – 'our list is full.'

Larry Dalzell Associates Ltd

Suite 12, 17 Broad Court, Covent Garden, London WC2B 5QN
Tel (071) 379 0875 Telex DALMAR LONDON
Contact Larry Dalzell, Jean Clarke, Sarah Osborne

Founded 1970. Represent actors, directors and designers. Welcome queries from actors seeking representation. Approach in writing in the first instance, enclosing SAE. Will consider demo tapes and video show reels if accompanied by SAE.

Caroline Dawson Associates

Apt 9, 47 Courtfield Road, London SW7 4DB
Tel (071) 370 0708

Founded 1978. Represent actors only.

Denman Casting Agency

Commerce Chambers, Elite Buildings, Parliament Street, Nottingham NG1 2BP
Tel (0602) 418421/473257
Contact Jack Denman, Alison Hope

Founded 1958. Represent actors, walk-ons, supporting artists. Very large agency, operating countrywide with the largest casting directory in the country. Welcome queries from actors seeking representation. Write in the first instance with photo and CV. Will not consider unsolicited demo tapes or video show reels.

Denmark Street Management

Room 122, Canalot Production Studios, 222 Kensal Road, London W10 5BN
Tel (081) 960 8204

Founded 1985. Cooperative management. Represent actors only, and welcome queries from those (particularly older actors) who are seeking representation. Approach in writing in the first instance. No unsolicited demo tapes or video show reels. 'We are 15 members and, to date, are looking to expand to 18. Our main casting gap is men and women 40+.' Advice to newcomers: 'When dealing with an agent or casting director, an actor should never generalize – be specific: what roles you want to do, who you want to work with, which companies you want to try for, what work you do not want to do. Know your material; try and know what work directors have done. Ask direct questions and give direct answers. Be adroit and persevere. When dealing with agents, do not be frightened of chasing up your letter by phone – when agents get busy, it is very helpful to be reminded about people and what's going on; in a busy week, a new application will simply get left lying around.'

Felix de Wolfe

Manfield House, 376/378 The Strand, London WC2R 0LR
Tel (071) 379 5767   Fax (071) 836 0337   Telex 931770 A/B W1BU G
Contact Felix de Wolfe

Founded 1938. Represent actors, writers, designers, directors, composers, musical directors and producers. Welcome queries from *established* actors seeking representation. Approach in writing in the first instance. Will consider demo tapes and video show reels.

Direct Line Personal Management

35 The CHEL Centre, 26 Roundhay Road, Leeds LS7 1AB
Tel (0532) 444991

Founded 1985. Cooperative management. Represent actors only, and welcome queries from those seeking representation. Approach in writing in the first instance. Will consider demo tapes and video show reels.

Donna Maria Management

16 Bell Meadows, Dulwich Wood Avenue, London SE19 1HP
Tel (081) 670 7814

Linked to Donna Maria Children's Theatre Company of London. Represent children and adults.

Bryan Drew Limited

Mezzanine, Quadrant House, 80–82
Regent Street, London W1R 6AU
Tel (071) 437 2293
Fax (071) 437 0561
Contact Bryan Drew & Dulcie Huston
(theatre, film, TV); Bryan Drew
(writers, directors); Suzie Wooton &
Nicki McArdle (voice-overs)

Founded 1963. Represent actors,
writers and directors. Welcome queries from actors seeking representation.
Approach in writing in the first instance. Will consider demo tapes and
video show reels.

Evan Dunstan Associates/EDA (TV) Ltd

1b Montagu Mews North, London W1
Tel (071) 486 3479/0
Contact Evan Dunstan

Founded 1973. Represent actors,
singers and dancers. Welcome queries
from actors seeking representation.
Approach in writing in the first
instance. Will consider demo tapes
and video show reels. 'Where possible, it is always handy if artists have a
play (even one in fringe) where we can
see their performance before accepting
them on to the books.'

Elliman's Agency

Flat 1, 10 Westbourne Villas, Hove,
East Sussex BN3 4GQ
Tel (0273) 728307
Contact Sonia Elliman

Founded 1983. Represent actors, directors. Welcome queries from actors
seeking representation. Approach
either by telephone or in writing. No
unsolicited demo tapes or video show
reels.

Emanco Ltd

8 Great Russell Street, London
WC1B 3NH
Tel (071) 323 0821

Do not represent actors. Technical
people only.

June Epstein Associates

62 Compayne Gardens, London
NW6 3RY
Tel (071) 328 0864
Contact June Epstein

Founded 1973. Represent actors only,
and welcome queries from prospective
clients. Write in the first instance with
SAE for reply. Will consider demo
tapes or video show reels, but only if
requested.

Kate Feast Management

43a Princess Road, London NW1 8JS
Tel (071) 586 5502

Represent actors and the occasional
director. Do not generally welcome
queries from actors seeking representation.

Sheridan Fitzgerald Management

69b Credon Road, Upton Park,
London E13 9BS
Tel (081) 471 9814
Contact Sheridan Fitzgerald

Founded 1987. Represent actors, and
will act on their behalf for any writing
or directing they may do in addition to
acting. Welcome queries from actors
seeking representation. Send letter
with SAE and follow up with a telephone call. No unsolicited demo tapes
or video show reels. 'Always consult

Spotlight for advice, and always have a *Spotlight* entry. Photos that are not honest to the subject are a total waste of time and money.'

Fletcher & Boyce

1 Kingsway House, Albion Road, London N16 0TA
Tel (071) 923 0606
Fax (071) 241 2313
Contact Wendy Fletcher, Sandra Boyce

Represent mostly actors, a couple of directors. Welcome queries from actors seeking representation. Write in the first instance, with CV, photo and SAE. Will consider unsolicited demo tapes and video show reels.

Focus Management Ltd

Unit 314, Bon Marché Building, 444 Brixton Road, London SW9 8EJ
Tel (071) 737 7713

Founded 1982. Represent actors and technicians, and welcome queries from those seeking representation. Send letter with CV, photograph and SAE. Will consider demo tapes and video show reels.

Aida Foster Ltd

33 Abbey Lodge, Park Road, London NW8 7RJ
Tel (071) 262 2181
Contact Anita Foster

Founded 1945. Represent actors only, and welcome queries from those seeking representation. Approach in writing in the first instance. Will consider video show reels. 'Always send a truly representative photo, an up-to-date

CV, including age and playing age, and an SAE.'

Fraser & Dunlop Ltd

503, The Chambers, Chelsea Harbour, Lots Road, London SW10 0XF
Tel (071) 376 7676
Contact Ginette Chalmers, Maureen Vincent

Founded 1951. Represent actors, writers, directors and producers. Welcome queries from actors seeking representation, although they tend to take on only people whose work they know and are interested in, or those who will fill a gap on their client list. Write in the first instance. Will not consider unsolicited demo tapes or video show reels.

Frazer Skemp Management Ltd

34 Bramerton Street, Chelsea, London SW3 5LA
Tel (071) 352 2922/3771
Fax (071) 352 1969
Contact Norma Skemp & Howard Cooke (directors)

Founded 1972. Represent actors working in theatre, films and TV, and welcome queries from those seeking representation. Approach in writing in the first instance. Will consider demo tapes and video show reels. 'It is important that artists appreciate that, however talented they may be, we cannot represent them if we already have a similar actor or actress on our books, or if our books at the time are already full.'

Patrick Freeman Management

4 Cromwell Grove, London W6 7RG
Tel (071) 602 4035
Contact Patrick Freeman

Founded 1973. Represent actors only. Write in the first instance with SAE; *no* telephone calls. Will consider unsolicited demo tapes and video show reels.

French's

52 Holland Park Mews, London
W11 3SP
Tel (071) 629 4159
Contact John French

Founded 1974. Represent actors, directors and writers. Welcome queries from actors seeking representation. Write in the first instance.

Frontline Management

Bon Marché Building, 444 Brixton Road, London SW9 8EJ
Tel (071) 326 1382

Founded 1985. Cooperative management. Represent actors only, and welcome queries from those seeking representation. Approach in writing in the first instance. No unsolicited demo tapes or video show reels.

Joy Galloway Management

15 Lexham Mews, London W8
Tel (071) 376 2414
Contact Joy Galloway

Represent actors only, and welcome queries from those seeking representation. Write in the first instance with CV and photograph.

Galloways Ltd

14 Rocks Lane, London SW13 0DB
Tel (081) 392 1313/1818
Fax (081) 878 2213
Contact Hugh Galloway

Founded 1971. Represent actors only, and welcome queries from those seeking representation. Send letter with current photo, *Spotlight* number and CV in the first instance. Video show reels/demo tapes only required at an interview. Advice to newcomers: 'Take as many classes/workshops as possible to gain experience and confidence.'

Kerry Gardner Management

15 Kensington High Street, London
W8 5NP
Tel (071) 937 4478/3142
Fax (071) 376 2587
Contact Kerry Gardner, Angela Collins, Lorna Dolan, Shawn McEnaney

Founded 1975. Represent actors, directors, producers and a voice coach. Welcome queries from actors seeking representation. Approach in writing in the first instance – 'always send an SAE if you expect a reply.' No unsolicited demo tapes or video show reels.

Garricks

7 Garrick Street, London WC2 9AR
Tel (071) 240 0660/379 7476
Fax (071) 497 9242
Contact Megan Willis

Do not welcome queries from actors seeking representation.

Noel Gay Artists

24 Denmark Street, London
WC2H 8NJ
Tel (071) 836 3941
Fax (071) 379 7027
Telex 21760

Represent actors, presenters, composers, directors, writers and producers. Welcome queries from actors seeking representation. Approach in writing in the first instance.

Keith Gilbey Personal Management

11/15 Betterton Street, Covent
Garden, London WC2H 9BP
Tel (071) 379 0344
Fax (071) 379 0801
Telex 265639 BETTS G
Contact Keith Gilbey

Founded 1987. Represent actors, scriptwriters, directors, and act as freelance casting director to film/TV/corporate sectors. Welcome queries from actors seeking representation. Send letter with CV and 10×8 photograph. No unsolicited demo tapes or video show reels. Advice to newcomers: 'Pay attention to photographs; they are the window to the profession. Learn about your profession, and understand that it is a business and treat it as such.'

Eric Glass Ltd

28 Berkeley Square, London
W1X 6HD
Tel (071) 629 7162
Telex 296759 KALLIN G
Contact Eric Glass, Janet Crowley

Founded 1934. Represent actors, directors, authors and playwrights. Welcome queries from actors seeking representation. Favour initial approach in writing. Will consider demo tapes and video show reels.

Jimmy Grafton Management

9 Orme Court, London W2 4RL
Tel (071) 221 9364
Fax (071) 221 3907
Telex 268312 WESCOM G

Founded 1950. Represent actors and light entertainment artists. Welcome queries from actors seeking representation. Write or telephone. Will consider unsolicited demo tapes and video show reels.

Peter Graham Associates

59 Frith Street, London W1V 5TA
Tel (071) 734 2203   Fax (071) 494 0315
Contact Peter Graham, Mo Lane

Founded 1980/1. Represent actors only. Also voice-over agent. No unsolicited demo tapes or video show reels.

Joan Gray Personal Management

29 Sunbury Court Island, Sunbury on
Thames, Middx TW16 5PP
Tel (081) 979 1789
Contact Joan Gray

Founded 1960. Represent actors only. 'I have a complete list and am not taking on anyone else.'

Grays Management Ltd

Panther House, 38 Mount Pleasant,
London WC1X 0AP
Tel (071) 278 1054
Fax (071) 837 6391

Founded 1986. Cooperative management. Represent actors only, and welcome queries from those seeking representation. 'A phone call can be a quick check to see if your category is already covered by someone in the agency.' No unsolicited demo tapes or video show reels.

Green & Underwood (in association with Essanay)

2 Conduit Street, London W1R 9TG
Tel (071) 493 0308
Contact Nicholas Young, Louise Hillman

Founded 1937 (Essanay), 1962 (Green & Underwood). Represent actors, costume designers and theatre directors. Sometimes welcome queries from actors seeking representation: 'It is basically a matter of luck. If a letter arrives when we are looking for someone and they fill a gap, we will probably see them. Always approach by letter, unless an established actor.' No unsolicited demo tapes or video show reels. 'Always send an SAE; good photographs are a real asset.'

Stella Greenfield Agency

41 Bush Grove, Stanmore, Middx
HA7 2DY
Tel (081) 952 1805
Fax (081) 952 1032
Contact Stella Greenfield

Founded 1970. Represent actors, children and teenagers. Welcome queries from actors seeking representation (teenagers should have Equity membership). Write in the first instance, with CV and photograph. Will consider demo tapes and video show reels, but please enclose an appropriate SAE for their return.

Carl Gresham Presentations

P.O. Box 3, Bradford, W. Yorkshire
BD1 4QN
Tel (0274) 735880
Fax (0274) 370313
Contact Carl Gresham

Founded 1970. Represent actors and general entertainers. No unsolicited demo tapes or video show reels.

Hamilton & Sydney Ltd

21 Goodge Street, London W1P 1FD
Tel (071) 323 1162
Contact Margaret Hamilton

Founded 1960. Represent mostly actors, and will consider queries from those seeking representation. Write in the first instance with CV and photograph. Will not consider unsolicited demo tapes or video show reels.

Sue Hammer Management

Otterbourne House, Chobham Road,
Ottershaw, Chertsey, Surrey
KT16 0QF
Tel (0932) 874111/2
Fax (0932) 872922
Contact Sue Hammer, Verne Richins

Founded 1980. Represent actors only, and welcome queries from those seeking representation. Send a letter with CV and photograph. No unsolicited demo tapes or video show reels.

Louis Hammond Management Ltd

Golden House, 29 Great Pulteney Street, London W1R 3DD
Tel (071) 734 1931   Fax (071) 437 0887
Contact Louis Hammond, Saskia Nowell

Founded 1982. Represent actors only, and welcome queries from those seeking representation ('It is something agents must expect'). Approach in writing in the first instance. Will consider demo tapes and video show reels.

Hamper–Neafsey Associates

4 Great Queen Street, London WC2
Tel (071) 404 5255
Fax (071) 831 1524
Contact Sharon Hamper (managing director)

Founded 1976. Represent actors, directors and designers. Welcome queries from actors seeking representation, but only 'when they are in a showcase where we can see their work before any interview is granted. Send photograph that looks like the actor and mention what parts played in what productions.'

Harbour & Coffey

9 Bleinhem Street, New Bond Street, London W1Y 9LE
Tel (071) 499 5548
Fax (071) 629 6923
Contact Gillian Coffey, Harry Harbour

Founded 1969. Represent actors only, and will consider queries from those seeking representation, especially if they have been recommended. Write in the first instance, with CV, photograph and SAE. Will not consider unsolicited demo tapes and video show reels, although 'it is worth mentioning that you have these available.'

Val Hastings Management

8 Wynfield Gardens, Birmingham B14 6EY
Tel (021) 443 3166
Contact Val Hastings (manager)

Founded 1981 as Val Hastings Casting Ltd; changed name 1988. Represent Midlands-based actors only. Welcome queries from actors (Equity only) seeking representation. 'I only recruit once a year in Autumn for 12-month contracts starting the following January.' Send letter with good CV and photograph. Will not consider unsolicited demo tapes and video show reels. 'Actors must have good CVs, well printed and readable; good photos in black and white, head shots only. In our case, we do not represent actors who undertake walk-on work, so we are selective in whom we see. Actors must be able to talk well at interviews, and sight reading is of paramount importance for television auditions.'

Richard Hatton Ltd

18 Jermyn Street, London SW1Y 6HN
Tel (071) 439 2971
Fax (071) 439 7633
Telex 263026

Represent actors and writers. Welcome queries from actors seeking representation. Write in the first instance with CV and photograph. Will not consider unsolicited demo tapes or video show reels.

Duncan Heath Associates Ltd

162 Wardour Street, London W1V 3AT
Tel (071) 439 1471   Fax (071) 439
7274   Telex 263361

Founded early 1970s. Represent actors, directors, writers, producers, technicians, composers. Welcome queries from actors seeking representation. Write in the first instance. Will not consider unsolicited demo tapes or video show reels.

Hill–Urwin Associates (incorporating The Singers Agency)

22 Inverness Street, London NW1 7HJ
Tel (071) 267 6845/482 1831
Fax (071) 267 7188
Contact David Urwin, Stephen Hill

Founded 1980. Represent actors, musical directors and singers. Welcome queries from actors seeking representation. Send letter with photograph and CV. Will consider demo tapes from singers. 'We are principally a musical theatre-orientated agency, representing Equity members only.'

Hills Personal Management

1st floor, 7 Childwall Valley Road,
Childwall Fiveways, Liverpool L16 4PB
Tel (051) 737 1939
Contact Jonathan Swain, Sally Moss

Founded 1986. Represent actors only; cooperative management. Welcome queries from actors seeking representation. Send a letter enclosing CV, photograph and details of any forthcoming performances where your work can be seen. Will consider demo tapes and video show reels.

Hope & Lyne

108 Leonard Street, London
EC2A 4RH
Tel (071) 739 6200
Contact Sally Hope, Dennis Lyne, Ann Hope, John Wood

Founded 1975. Represent actors, directors and designers. Welcome queries from actors seeking representation, 'but it is only possible to take on a very few each year as our client list is small.' Approach in writing in the first instance. No unsolicited demo tapes or video show reels – 'we prefer to see actors working in theatre.'

The Bill Horne Partnership

15 Exmoor Street, London W10 6BA
Tel (081) 960 8281
Contact Bill Horne, Peter Walmsley

Founded 1970. Represent actors, directors, musical directors and choreographers. Welcome queries from actors seeking representation. Approach in writing in the first instance – 'no telephone calls please.' Will consider demo tapes and video show reels.

Howes & Prior Ltd

66 Berkeley House, Hay Hill, London
W1X 7LH
Tel (071) 493 7570/7655
Contact Rupert Prior

Founded 1969. Welcome casting queries from actors seeking representation. Approach in writing in the first instance. No unsolicited demo tapes or video show reels.

Jane Hughes Management

Suite 21, Rex Buildings, Alderley
Road, Wilmslow, Cheshire SK9 1HY
Tel (0625) 530787
Fax (0625) 528064
Contact Jane Hughes, Amanda
Brown

Founded 1968. Represent actors, presenters and voice-over artists. Welcome queries from actors seeking representation. Write in the first instance, with CV and photograph. Will not consider unsolicited demo tapes or video show reels.

Hutton Management Ltd

200 Fulham Road, London SW10 9PN
Tel (071) 352 4825
Contact Anne Hutton, Christina
Shepherd

Represent actors only, but do not welcome queries from those seeking representation. Do not consider unsolicited demo tapes and video show reels.

ICM Ltd

388/396 Oxford Street, London
W1N 9HE
Tel (071) 629 8080
Fax (071) 493 6279
Telex 885974 ICMLON G
Contact Laurence Evans, Dennis
Selinger, Michael Anderson, Ronnie
Waters

Represent actors, producers, directors and writers. Welcome queries from actors seeking representation. Approach in writing in the first instance. No unsolicited demo tapes or video show reels.

Inspiration Management

Room 140, Southbank House, Black
Prince Road, London SE1 7SJ
Tel (071) 587 0947/735 8171

Founded 1986. Cooperative management. Represent actors only, and welcome queries from those seeking representation. Send letter with CV and photograph. Will consider demo tapes and video show reels. 'Inspiration is a cooperative agency which means helping with office duties and being the other members' agent. Being involved makes you feel you have a much stronger hold on your own career even when you are out of work.'

Inter-City Casting Ltd

383 Corn Exchange Building, Fennel
Street, Manchester M4 3DH
Tel (061) 832 8848
Contact Hilary Jones

Founded 1984. Cooperative management. Represent actors only, and welcome queries from those seeking representation. Approach in writing in the first instance. Will consider demo tapes and video show reels. 'As a coop agency, we need applicants who have good administrative skills – though abilities as an actor are the prime consideration. We have a personal manager, and we believe this is the future for coop agencies. We would warn new actors that London agents are not always the "be all and end all" of good management since often a new actor finds he is a small fish in a very big sea.'

International Artistes Ltd

235 Regent Street, London W1R 8AX
Tel (071) 439 8401   Fax (071) 409 2070   Telex 295061 INTAM G
Contact Hugh J. Alexander, Jean Mirylees (actors), Laurie Mansfield, Bob Voice, Stuart Littlewood (variety)

Founded 1946. Represent actors and variety performers. Welcome queries from actors seeking representation. Approach in writing in the first instance (addressed to Jean Mirylees). Will consider demo tapes and video show reels.

Italia Conti Agency Ltd

Italia Conti House, 23 Goswell Road, London EC1M 7BB
Tel (071) 608 0044/5
Contact Gaynor Sheward

Founded 1911. Specialize in young people (10 years to early 20s) in all branches of the media, mainly those training at the Italia Conti Academy of Theatre Arts. But 'opens its books from time to time to outsiders.'

Approach in writing in the first instance. Will consider demo tapes and video show reels.

Richard Jackson Personal Management Ltd

59 Knightsbridge, London SW1X 7RA
Tel (071) 235 3671
Contact Richard Jackson

Founded 1959. Represent actors, and also a play director from France, a fight director and one after-dinner speaker. Also involved in play production, mainly on London's Fringe (*see separate entry*). Welcome queries from actors seeking representation; 'all applicants are given serious consideration and some are granted interviews.' Approach in writing in the first instance. Will consider demo tapes and video show reels.

Jaclyn Agency

Thackeray House, Hempnall, Norwich NR15 2LP
Tel (050842) 241
Contact Marilyn Sandiford (proprietor), Julie Parker, Peggy Brown

Founded 1952. Represent actors who are mainly TV supporting artists, extras and walk-ons, background artists for TV commercials, audiovisuals and training films. Do not handle theatre work. Welcome queries from those seeking representation 'only if they are within the East Anglian/East Midlands region'. Approach in writing in the first instance. No unsolicited demo tapes or video show reels. 'The nature of the work we handle excludes those who do not have Equity membership.'

Carole James Management

2 Water Lane House, Water Lane,
Richmond, Surrey TW9 1TJ
Tel (081) 940 8154
Contact Carole James

Represent actors only, and welcome
queries from those seeking representation. Send letter with CV and photograph. Will consider demo tapes for
actors who also sing, but these are not
essential.

Joseph & Wagg

Studio One, 2 Tunstall Road, London
SW9 8BN
Tel (071) 738 3026
Contact Tod Joseph

Founded 1964. Represent actors only,
and welcome queries from those seeking representation. Write in the first
instance. Will not consider unsolicited
demo tapes or video show reels.

Chuck Julian Agency

3rd floor, Cecil House, 41 Charing
Cross Road, London WC2H 0AR
Tel (071) 437 4248
Telex 21120 Ref 2745
Contact Chuck Julian, Sue Yager,
Carl Carpenter, Anita Alraun

Represent actors and a couple of directors. Welcome queries from actors
seeking representation.

KD Management

64 Sussex Road, Harrow, Middx
HA1 4LX
Tel (081) 861 0240

Represent Afro-Asian artists.

Roberta Kanal Agency

82 Constance Road, Twickenham,
Middx TW2 7JA
Tel (081) 892 2277
Contact Roberta Kanal

Founded 1968. Represent actors, directors, musical directors, etc., and
welcome queries from those seeking
representation. Write in the first instance. Will not consider unsolicited
demo tapes or video show reels.

Kean & Garrick

6–8 Paved Court, The Green,
Richmond, Surrey TW9 1LZ
Tel (081) 940 5559
Contact Jane Ball, Ralph P. Ball

Founded 1982. Represent actors only –
comedy, straight and musical – and
directors, and welcome queries from
those seeking representation. Write in
the first instance, with photograph
and CV. Will not consider unsolicited
demo tapes or video show reels.

Ivor Kimmel Casting

7 Andover Place, London NW6
Tel (071) 328 3125
Contact Ivor Kimmel

Founded 1973. Represent actors, stunt
men and supporting artists. Do not
welcome queries from actors seeking
representation.

Rolf Kruger Management Ltd

121 Gloucester Place, London
W1H 3PJ
Tel (071) 224 4493
Fax (071) 224 4273
Contact Rolf Kruger, Rachel Kurger

Founded 1969. Represent actors, directors (theatre, film, TV), theatre designers, action coordinators. Welcome queries from actors seeking representation. Approach in writing in the first instance. 'We are only interested in well-trained theatre actors with good theatre background, and only take on artists after we have seen a considerable amount of their work. Training is essential.'

LA Entertainments

13 Fenswood Mead, Long Ashton,
Bristol BS18 9BL
Tel (0272) 393876
Contact Dave Royal

Founded 1983. Represent actors and walk-ons. Welcome queries from actors seeking representation. Initial approach by telephone. No demo tapes or video show reels.

LWA

52 Wardour Street, London W1V 3HL
Tel (071) 434 3944
Contact Eileen Williams, Jill Williams

Founded 1968. Represent actors and freelance TV directors. Do not particularly welcome queries from actors seeking representation, but any initial contact must be made in writing. No unsolicited demo tapes or video show reels.

Tessa Le Bars Management

18 Queen Anne Street, London
W1M 9LB
Tel (071) 636 3191
Fax (071) 436 0229
Contact Tessa Le Bars

Founded 1983. 'Not an actors agency as such but personal/business management and production for small group of performers/writers in the light entertainment field.' Do not welcome queries from actors seeking representation – 'new clients come through personal contact only.'

Bernard Lee Management

Moorcroft Lodge, Farleigh Common,
Warlingham, Surrey CR3 9PE
Tel (0883) 625667
Contact Bernard Lee

Founded 1968. Represent actors and light entertainment artists. Do not welcome queries from actors seeking representation.

Brian Lidstone Representation

138 Westbourne Grove, London W11
2RR
Tel (071) 727 2342   Fax (071) 221
7210
Contact Brian Lidstone

Founded 1962. Represent actors, directors, writers, composers and teachers. Welcome queries from actors seeking representation. Approach in

writing in the first instance. No unsolicited demo tapes or video show reels.

Links Management

22 Colombo Street, London SE1 8DP
Tel (071) 928 0806/3134

Founded 1984. Cooperative management. Represent actors only, and welcome queries from those seeking
representation. Send letter with CV
and photograph. Will consider demo
tapes and video show reels.

Lipson Tinker Associates Ltd

18–19 Warwick Street, London
W1R 5RB
Tel (071) 439 8195
Fax (071) 434 4478
Telex 263899 GENMAN G
Contact Victoria Tinker

Founded 1985. Represent actors, directors, choreographers and musical
directors. 'Within reason', welcome
queries from actors seeking representation. Approach in writing in the first
instance, enclosing CV and photograph. No unsolicited demo tapes or
video show reels.

London Actors

10 Barley Mow Passage, Chiswick,
London W4 4PH
Tel (081) 994 6477

Founded 1979. Cooperative management. Represent actors only, and
welcome queries from those interested

in being in a cooperative agency.
Approach in writing in the first instance. Will consider demo tapes and
video show reels.

London Management

235/241 Regent Street, London
W1R 7AG
Tel (071) 493 1610
Fax (071) 408 0065
Contact Address letter to the
company

Founded 1959. Represent actors, composers, directors, designers, film technicians, illustrators, producers and
writers. Welcome queries from actors
seeking representation. Approach in
writing in the first instance with SAE:
'Always put name and address on the
back of photographs; do not send a
$3^1/_2 \times 6$ or 9×4 SAE with a 10×8
photograph.' No unsolicited demo
tapes or video show reels.

Look Alikes

46 Clapham Common Northside,
London SW4 0AA
Tel (071) 720 0525
Telex 888941 LCCI
Fax (071) 622 6366
Contact Julia Joseph

Founded 1980. Represent actors,
models, amateurs – anyone who looks
like a personality. Welcome queries
from actors seeking representation.
Send a letter with photograph in the
first instance. Will consider demo
tapes and video show reels.

Pat Lovett Agency

14 Broughton Place, Edinburgh
EH1 3RX
Tel (031) 557 5565
Contact Pat Lovett, Morag Arbuthnot,
Alan McCredie

Founded 1981. Represent actors only,
and welcome queries from those seeking representation. Approach in writing in the first instance. No unsolicited
demo tapes or video show reels.

McKenna & Grantham

1B Montague Mews North, London
W1H 1AJ
Tel (071) 224 4434
Contact John Grantham

Founded 1987. Represent actors only,
and welcome queries from those seeking representation. Send letter enclosing photograph and CV. Send SAE for
a reply. No unsolicited demo tapes or
video show reels.

Bill McLean Personal Management

23b Deodar Road, Putney, London
SW15 2NP
Tel (081) 789 8191
Contact Bill McLean

Founded 1972. Represent actors,
directors, authors, musical directors
and composers. Welcome queries
from actors seeking representation.
Approach in writing in the first instance. No unsolicited demo tapes or
video show reels.

Magnet Personal Management

111/119 Bishop Street, Birmingham
B5 6JL
Tel (021) 622 5938
Fax (021) 622 1554
Contact Kim Durham, Amanda Loy-
Ellis, Karen Benjamin

Founded 1986. Cooperative management. Represent actors only, and welcome queries from those seeking
representation. Approach in writing in
the first instance. Will consider demo
tapes and video show reels.

Magnus Management

155 Park Road, Teddington, Middx
TW11 0BP
Tel (081) 977 5471/2
Fax (081) 943 1024
Telex 9222958 SCHUF G

Founded early 1960s. Represent children and teenagers for acting and
modelling. Welcome queries from
prospective clients. Write in the first
instance, with SAE. Will consider demo
tapes and video show reels.

John Mahoney Management

Lower ground floor, 94 Gloucester
Place, London W1H 3DA
Tel (071) 486 2947
Contact David Gretton, Ann Mahoney

Founded 1960s. Represent actors, a
fight director and several TV directors.
Welcome queries from actors seeking
representation; write in the first instance. Will consider unsolicited demo
tapes and video show reels.

Hazel Malone Management Ltd

26 Wellesley Road, London W4 4BW
Tel (081) 944 2992

Founded late 1950s. Personal management. Welcome queries from actors seeking representation. Write in the first instance. Will not consider unsolicited demo tapes or video show reels, as they like to meet prospective clients first.

Markham & Froggatt Ltd

4 Windmill Street, London W1P 1HF
Tel (071) 636 4412
Fax (071) 637 5233
Contact Peter Froggatt, Pippa Markham

Founded 1965. Represent actors only, and welcome queries from those seeking representation. Write in the first instance. Will not consider unsolicited demo tapes or video show reels.

Marmont Management Ltd

Langham House, 308 Regent Street, London W1R 5AL
Tel (071) 637 3183
Contact Patricia Marmont, Rose Streatfield

Founded 1983. Represent actors and directors. Client list is full. No unsolicited demo tapes or video show reels.

Ronnie Marshall Agency

66 Ollerton Road, London N11 2LA
Tel (081) 368 4958
Contact Ronnie Marshall, Shelana Marshall

Founded 1970. Represent actors 'with song and dance skills of a very high standard, and with full Equity status'. Welcome queries from prospective clients. Approach in writing in the first instance. Will consider demo tapes and video show reels, 'providing the recording is of good quality and, in the case of video, VHS system'. 'New actors should furnish themselves with good photographs and, if possible, advertise in *Spotlight*.'

Scott Marshall Personal Management

44 Perryn Road, London W3 7NA
Tel (081) 749 7692
Fax (081) 749 7692
Contact Scott Marshall, Denise Marshall, Wendy Brayington, Helen Ashby

Founded 1968. Represent actors and directors (TV & theatre). Welcome queries from actors seeking representation. Approach in writing or by telephone in the first instance. Will consider demo tapes and video show reels.

Marina Martin Associates Ltd

6A Danbury Street, London N1 8JU
Tel (071) 359 3646
Fax (071) 359 7759
Contact Marina Martin, Pam Ashmann

Founded 1972. Represent actors only, but do not welcome queries from those seeking representation. 'Ours is a personal management, and I am attempting to keep the list at around 50 actors only.'

Nigel Martin-Smith Personal Management

Half Moon Chambers, Chapel Walks,
Manchester M2 1HN
Tel (061) 834 3403
Contact Ying

Founded 1980. Represent actors, writers, directors, musicians, singers and photographic models. Welcome queries from actors seeking representation. Send letter enclosing CV and photograph. Will consider demo tapes and video show reels.

Masque Management

38 Mount Pleasant, London
WC1X 0AP
Tel (071) 278 7449
Fax (071) 278 3608

Founded 1986. Cooperative management. Represent actors only, and welcome queries from those seeking representation. Write in the first instance with CV and photograph, and an SAE if you would like them returned. Will consider unsolicited demo tapes and video show reels.

Mayer Management Ltd (in association with James Sharkey Associates Ltd)

Grafton House, 2–3 Golden Square,
London W1R 3AD
Tel (071) 434 1242
Fax (071) 494 1547
Telex 295251 JSA
Contact Cassie Mayer, Clare Eden

Founded 1985. Represent actors and directors. Very few actors taken on each year.

Janet Mills Associates

1 Thetis Terrace, Westerly Ware, Kew Green, Richmond, Surrey TW9 3AU
Tel (081) 948 4549
Contact Janet Mills

Founded 1987. Represent actors, and also have a composer/lyricist, voice and dialogue coach and a choreographer on their books. Will consider queries from actors seeking representation. However, 'I prefer to keep a small list, so I am not anxious to add to it by more than two or three for the foreseeable future.' Approach in writing in the first instance. Will consider demo tapes and video show reels. 'I would not consider taking on any person whose work I had not seen, preferably in theatre.'

Montagu Associates

3 Bretton House, Fairbridge Road,
London N19 3HP
Tel (071) 281 4658
Contact Beverley Montagu, Helen Watts

Founded 1987. Represent actors only, and welcome queries from those seeking representation. Approach in writing in the first instance. Will consider video show reels.

Morgan & Goodman

1 Old Compton Street, London
W1V 5PH
Tel (071) 437 1383

Mainly represent actors, but also have directors and musical directors on their books.

William Morris Agency (UK) Ltd

31/32 Soho Square, London
W1V 5DG
Tel (071) 434 2191
Fax (071) 437 0238
Telex 27928
Contact 'Too complex to list –
address letter to the agency'

Founded 1965. Also literary agents.
Represent actors, directors, choreographers, designers (theatre & costume),
dramatists and producers. Although
innundated with queries from actors
seeking representation, will consider
letters. No unsolicited demo tapes or
video show reels.

Elaine Murphy Associates Ltd

1 Aberdeen Lane, London N5 2EJ
Tel (071) 704 9913
Fax (071) 704 8039
Contact Elaine Murphy

Founded 1985. Represent actors only,
and welcome queries from those seeking representation. Write in the first
instance. Will not consider unsolicited
demo tapes or video show reels.

The Narrow Road Company

22 Poland Street, London W1V 3DD
Tel (071) 434 0406
Contact Tim Brown, Richard Ireson

Founded 1986. Represent actors,
directors, writers, designers and
lighting designers. Welcome queries
from actors seeking representation.

Approach in writing in the first
instance.

1984 Personal Management Ltd

5 Leonard Street, London EC2A 4AQ
Tel (071) 251 8046
Contact Robin Browne, Susan
McGoun

Founded 1984. Cooperative management. Represent actors only, and welcome queries from those seeking
representation. Approach in writing in
the first instance. Will consider demo
tapes and video show reels if accompanied by covering letter and CV.

'North of Watford' Actors Agency Ltd

Bridge Mill, Hebden Bridge, West
Yorks. HX7 8EX
Tel (0422) 845361

Founded 1984. Cooperative management. Represent actors only, and welcome queries from those seeking
representation. Approach in writing in
the first instance. Will consider demo
tapes and video show reels.

North One Management

Unit C20, Metropolitan Workshops,
Enfield Road, London N1 5AZ
Tel (071) 254 9093

Founded 1987. Cooperative management. Welcome queries from actors
seeking representation. Send letter
with CV and photo in the first instance. Will consider video show reels.

Oriental Casting Agency Ltd

60 Downton Avenue, Streatham Hill,
London SW2 3TR
Tel (081) 674 9304
Fax (081) 674 9303
Contact Peggy Sirr

Founded 1963. Represent Afro/Asian actors, walk-ons and supporting artists only. Do not welcome queries from actors seeking representation.

Otto Personal Management Ltd

Regency House, 75–77 St Mary's Road, Sheffield S2 4AN
Tel (0742) 752592
Contact Chris Wilkinson, John Graham Davies, Robin Polley

Founded 1985. Cooperative management representing actors only. Welcome queries from actors seeking representation (Equity members only). Initial approach by letter preferred, with CV, photograph and SAE. If work is not known to members of the agency, give details of current/forthcoming performances, broadcasts, etc.; 'For economic and practical reasons, we favour actors living locally.' 'Otto expects actors to provide their own 10×8 photos; new members pay £100 joining fee plus £1 share purchase. Current pay commissions: 12% – TV, film and commercial; 10% – voice-over, training and video; 8% – radio and theatre. Members to attend six-weekly business meetings. The agency has an annual brochure launch of 250; circulates members' availability monthly; issues weekly newsletter to members.'

PBR Management

138 Putney Bridge Road, London
SW15 2NQ
Tel (081) 871 4139
Fax (081) 874 4847
Contact Simon Cutting

Founded 1986. Represent actors and a couple of choreographers. Write in the first instance. Will not consider unsolicited demo tapes or video show reels.

PTA

Bugle House, 21a Noel Street, London
W1V 3PD
Tel (071) 439 2282
Fax (071) 439 7649
Telex 8955398
Contact Roxane Vacca, Louisa Stevenson

Founded 1986. Represent actors and technicians. Welcome queries from actors seeking representation. Approach in writing in the first instance. Will consider demo tapes and video show reels.

Pan Artists Agency

Ingleby, 1 Hollins Grove, Sale,
Cheshire M33 1RR
Tel (061) 969 7419   Fax (061) 973 9724

Founded 1973. Represent actors, supporting artists and walk-ons. Welcome queries from actors seeking representation; experience preferred. Write in the first instance. Will not consider unsolicited demo tapes or video show reels.

Park Personal Management Ltd

111 Thames House, 566 Cable Street,
London E1 9HB
Tel (071) 790 6060

Founded 1986. Cooperative management. Represent actors only, and welcome queries from those seeking
representation. Send letter with CV
and photograph. No unsolicited demo
tapes or video show reels.

Performance Actors Agency

137 Goswell Road, London EC1V 7ET
Tel (071) 251 5716/3974

Founded 1984. Cooperative management. Represent actors only, and welcome queries from those seeking
representation. Write in the first instance. Will not consider unsolicited
demo tapes or video show reels.

Performer and Choreographic Enterprises

Flames Studio, Galena Road,
Hammersmith, London W6 0LT
Tel (081) 977 1115   Fax (081) 977
1171   Telex 934386 BMS G
Contact Catriona Keenan, Jaquie
Grace

Founded 1986. Represent actors,
dancers, singers, and stage production
shows and cabaret. Welcome queries
from prospective clients. Approach in
writing in the first instance: 'Always
send a well-prepared CV and letter.'
Will consider demo tapes and video
show reels.

Performing Arts

6 Windmill Street, London W1P 1HF
Tel (071) 255 1362
Fax (071) 631 4631
Telex 266708 AJHLDN (Ref: Perfar)
Contact Richard Haigh

Founded 1983. Represent directors,
designers, lighting designers, choreographers and conductors – do not represent actors.

Frances Phillips

Laynes House, 526/528 Watford Way,
London NW7 4RS
Tel (081) 906 1200/0911
Fax (081) 906 0261
Contact Frances Phillips

Founded 1986. Represent actors, choreographers and directors. Welcome
queries from actors seeking representation. Approach in writing in the first
instance. Will consider demo tapes
and video show reels 'if a meeting is
agreed'. Member of the Personal
Managers' Association (PMA).

Hilda Physick

78 Temple Sheen Road, London
SW14 7RR
Tel (081) 876 0073
Contact Hilda Physick

Represent actors only, but do not welcome queries from those seeking
representation.

Piccadilly Management Actors' Cooperative

Unit 123, 23 New Mount Street,
Manchester M4 4DE
Tel (061) 953 4057
Fax (061) 953 4001

Founded 1986. Cooperative management. Represent actors only, and welcome queries from those seeking representation. Send letter with CV, photograph and any show dates. No unsolicited demo tapes or video show reels. 'We welcome applications from actors of all ages and backgrounds who are Equity members based in or around Manchester. We expect a high degree of commitment from our members, as well as a willingness to work in a cooperative environment.'

Pineapple Agency

6 Langley Street, London WC2H 9JA
Tel (071) 836 9477

Represent dancers. No actors.

Peter Pitts Management

6 South Parade, Headingley, Leeds
LS6 3LF
Tel (0532) 789789
Fax (0532) 743946
Contact Peter Pitts

Founded 1964. Represent actors and organize outdoor events such as the first commercial *It's a Knockout*, beer competitions, etc. (Member of National Outdoor Events Association and Institute of Entertainment and Arts Management.) Also represent bands and groups. Welcome queries from actors seeking representation, 'preferably from the northern provinces'. Approach in writing in the first instance. No unsolicited demo tapes or video show reels.

Plunket Greene Ltd

4 Ovington Gardens, London
SW3 1LS
Tel (071) 584 0688
Contact Mr. Plunket Greene

Founded 1952. Represent actors only, and welcome queries from those seeking representation. Write in the first instance, with SAE. Will consider video tapes and demo show reels, if they are of work done and not set-up 'audition pieces'.

Gordon Poole Ltd

Kingston House, Pierrepont Street,
Bath BA1 1LA
Tel (0225) 469884
Fax (0225) 442777
Telex 449212 LANTEL G
Contact Gordon Poole, Jill Poole

Founded 1965. Represent actors, and also are general booking agents for all types of entertainers. Welcome queries from actors seeking representation. Approach in writing in the first instance. Will consider demo tapes and video show reels.

Portfolio Management

58 Alexandra Road, London NW4 2RY
Tel (081) 203 1747
Fax (081) 203 1064

Founded 1984. Represent actor-dancers, singers, musical ensembles. Welcome queries from actors seeking representation. Write in the first instance. Will consider unsolicited demo tapes and video show reels.

David Preston Associates Ltd

9 Blenheim Street, London W1
Tel (071) 495 1812
Contact David Preston

Founded 1965. Represent actors and opera singers. 'Occasionally' welcome queries from actors seeking representation. Approach in writing in the first instance. No unsolicited demo tapes or video show reels.

Profile Management Associates

73 New Bond Street, London
W1Y 9DD
Tel (071) 499 4222
Fax (071) 409 2859
Contact Bill Merrow, George Perry

Founded 1980. Represent actors, dancers/singers. Welcome queries from prospective clients. Send a letter with SAE. Will consider demo tapes and video show reels.

RAP Management

98 Bromley Common, Bromley, Kent
BR2 9PF
Tel (081) 464 2630
Fax (081) 305 2320
Telex 8951182 GCOMS G
Contact Paul Edwards

Founded 1984. Represent actors only, and welcome queries from those seeking representation. Write in the first instance. Will consider demo tapes and video show reels. 'No callers without appointment, please!'

Reactors Management Ltd

London House, 68 Upper Richmond Road, Putney, London SW15 2RP
Tel (081) 870 7357/871 1505

Founded 1985. Cooperative management. Represent actors only, and welcome queries from those seeking representation. Approach in writing in the first instance. Videos welcomed.

Joan Reddin

Hazel Cottage, Wheeler End
Common, Lane End, Bucks
HP14 3NL
Tel (0494) 882729
Contact Joan Reddin

Founded 1954. Represent actors only, but do not welcome queries from those seeking representation.

Redroofs Agency

Littlewick Green, Maidenhead, Berks
SL6 3QY
Tel (062882) 2982

Attached to Redroofs Theatre School. Represent actors, singers, dancers and children, but do not welcome queries from actors seeking representation.

John Redway and Associates Ltd, (in association with A.I.M.)

5 Denmark Street, London WC2H 8LP
Tel (071) 836 2001   Fax (071) 379 0848   Telex 22914 CCC
Contact David Booth

Represent actors, directors and writers, and welcome queries from actors seeking representation. Approach in writing in the first instance.

Will consider demo tapes and video show reels.

Stella Richards Management

42 Hazlebury Road, London SW6 2ND
Tel (071) 736 7786   Fax (071) 731 5082
Contact Paul McGurk, Stella Richards

Founded 1978. Represent actors, directors, designers, musical directors, film editors, choreographers, etc. Do not welcome queries from actors seeking representation. Will 'possibly' consider demo tapes and video show reels. 'Failure to enclose an SAE tends to lead to no reply!'

Rigal Management

109 Albert Bridge Road, London SW11 4PF
Tel (071) 228 8689   Fax (071) 738 1742
Contact Muriel Rigal, Hans Baernhoft

Founded 1985. Represent actors only, and very much welcome queries from those seeking representation. Approach in writing in the first instance. Will consider demo tapes and video show reels.

Rogues & Vagabonds Management

Garden Studios, 11–15 Betterton Street, Covent Garden, London WC2H 9PB
Tel (071) 379 0344
Fax (071) 379 0801
Telex 265639 BETTS G

Founded 1987. Cooperative management. Represent actors only, and welcome queries from those seeking representation. Approach in writing in the first instance. No unsolicited demo tapes or video show reels. 'Anyone accepted by us should be prepared to take a share of the work in manning the office and also to make a financial contribution.'

Jon Roseman Associates Ltd

103 Charing Cross Road, London WC2 0DT
Tel (071) 439 8245

Represent presenters. No actors.

Rossmore Associates

1a Rossmore Road, London NW1
Tel (071) 258 1953
Contact Veronica Foley

Founded 1988. Represent actors only, and welcome queries from those seeking representation. Write in the first instance with CV and photograph. Will not consider unsolicited demo tapes or video show reels.

Royce Management

44 Nasmyth Street, London W6 0HB
Tel (081) 741 4341

Founded 1980. Represent actors only, and welcome queries from those seeking representation. Approach in writing in the first instance. No unsolicited demo tapes or video show reels. 'We carefully consider all applications for representation, but only see people for interview if we feel there is a reasonable possibility that we could move on to offer a proposition. If applicants want photos and CVs returned, they must include an SAE and should never, in any case, send original or indispensable photos.'

Saraband Associates

265 Liverpool Road, Islington, London
N1 1LX
Tel (071) 609 5313/4
Contact Sara Randall, Bryn Newton

Founded 1973. Mainly represent actors, but also directors and choreographers. 'Sometimes' welcome queries from actors seeking representation. Always approach in writing in the first instance. Will consider demo tapes and video show reels.

SCA Management Ltd

23 Goswell Road, London EC1M 7BB
Tel (071) 608 0047/8
Contact Anne Sheward

Primarily represent actors, but also have singers/dancers and particularly specialize in musicals. Welcome casting queries from actors seeking representation. 'We represent a small select number of artists whose playing ages range between 18 and 35 years.' Approach in writing in the first instance. Will consider demo tapes and video show reels.

Anna Scher Theatre Management Ltd

70–72 Barnsbury Road, London
N1 0ES
Tel (071) 278 2101
Fax (071) 833 9467
Contact Anna Scher

Founded 1975. Represent actors only, and welcome queries from those seeking representation. Approach in writing in the first instance. Will consider demo tapes and video show reels. 'New clients must participate in classes at the Anna Scher Theatre. We only represent actors who train or have trained with us.' Anna Scher represents actors of all ages.

Screenlite

Shepperton Film Studios, Studios
Road, Shepperton, Middx TW17 0QD
Tel (0932) 562611 ext 2271/2
Fax (0932) 68989
Telex 929146 MOVIES G
Contact Carlie Tovey, Kerry Tovey

Founded 1982. Represent actors and children, and welcome queries from those seeking representation. Approach in writing in the first instance. No unsolicited demo tapes or video show reels.

Seven Muses

See **Clarion**

James Sharkey Associates Ltd

Third floor suite, 15 Golden Square,
London W1R 3AG
Tel (071) 434 3801/6
Fax (071) 494 1547
Telex 295251 JSALON G
Contact James Sharkey, Sophie James

Founded 1983. Represent actors; also have a literary department (chief executive, Sebastian Born). Welcome queries from actors seeking representation. Approach in writing in the first instance. Will consider demo tapes and video show reels.

Vincent Shaw Associates

20 Jay Mews, London SW7 2EP
Tel (071) 581 8215
Contact Vincent Shaw, Cherry Palfrey

Founded 1958. Represent actors, stage managers, company managers and directors. Welcome queries from actors, but only if they can be seen working. Will consider demo tapes and video show reels if they are of work done.

Elizabeth Shepherd

29 Eversley Crescent, London
N21 1EL
Tel (081) 364-0598
Contact Elizabeth Shepherd

Founded 1986. Represent actors, musical directors and composers. Welcome queries from actors only, and in moderation. Write in the first instance. Will not consider unsolicited demo tapes or video show reels.

L'Epine Smith & Carney Associates

10 Wyndham Place, London W1H 1AS
Tel (071) 724 0739
Contact Terry Carney, Eric L'Epine Smith

Founded early 1960s. Represent actors, directors, writers, technicians. Welcome queries from actors seeking representation. Write in the first instance. Will not consider unsolicited demo tapes or video show reels.

Pamela Simons

9/15 Neal Street, London WC2H 9PU
Tel (071) 240 0228
Contact Pamela Simons

Founded 1961. Represent actors only. No unsolicited demo tapes or video show reels: 'As I have only a limited number of artists, I must see their work before representing.'

Robert Smith Agency

20 Royal York Crescent, Clifton,
Bristol BS8 4JY
Tel (0272) 738265
Contact Robert Smith

Founded 1986 (in present form). Represent actors. Welcome queries from actors seeking representation. Send letter with CV, Equity number, etc. Will consider demo tapes and video show reels.

Snowshaft Theatrical Agency

Room 217, Wickham House, 10
Cleveland Way, London E1 4TR
Tel (071) 791 3373 and (0277) 227271
Telex 932011 GENFING
Contact Aleene Hatchard

Founded 1984. Represent actors, models, promotions people, dancers, singers. Welcome queries from actors seeking representation. Send a letter enclosing CV, recent photograph or Index Card. Will consider demo tapes for voice and vocal ability.

South East Theatrical & Promotion Agency

25 Samos Road, London SE20 7UQ
Tel (081) 778 4101

Represent children. No adult actors.

Barbara Speake Agency

East Acton Lane, London W3 7EG
Tel (081) 743 1306/6096
Contact Mrs June Collins

Mainly represent pupils, aged five to sixteen, of the Barbara Speake Stage School. Graduates of the school are represented by C.S.M. (Artistes) Ltd (see entry).

Barrie Stacey Promotions

9 Denmark Street, London WC2
Tel (071) 836 6220
Contact Barrie Stacey

Founded 1966. Represent actors only. Specialize in musical comedy, panto and commercials. Welcome queries from actors seeking representation. Write in the first instance with photo and CV. Will not consider unsolicited demo tapes or video show reels.

Stage Centre

41 North Road, London N7 9DP
Tel (071) 607 0872
Fax (071) 609 8462

Founded 1982. Represent actors only – cooperative management. Welcome queries from those seeking representation. Send letter enclosing photograph and CV. Will consider demo tapes and video show reels: 'Please

send SAE large enough for return of photos, show reels and video tapes.'

Stellaris Management

47 Greencoat Place, Westminster, London SW1P 1DS
Tel (071) 828 6826
Fax (071) 828 0922
Contact Heidi Cook

Founded 1970. Represent actors, singers and dancers. Welcome queries from actors seeking representation. Approach in writing in the first instance. Will consider demo tapes and video show reels.

Annette Stone Associates

9 Newburgh Street, London W1V 1LH
Tel (071) 734 0626
Fax (071) 434 2014
Contact Annette Stone, Edward Hill

Founded 1983. Represent actors and directors. Do not welcome unsolicited queries from actors seeking representation; rely on personal recommendation. No unsolicited demo tapes or video show reels.

Roger Storey Ltd

71 Westbury Road, London N12 7PB
Tel (081) 346 9411
Contact Roger Storey

Founded 1965. Represent actors only. Welcome queries from those seeking representation, but only if there is a strong possibility of work being seen. Write in the first instance. Will not consider unsolicited demo tapes or video show reels.

Swap Enterprises International Ltd

International House, 2–4 Wendell Road, London W12 9RT
Tel (081) 740 1009
Fax (081) 749 6342
Contact Mr W. Pestano, Denise Brockton

Alongside representation of actors, Swap Enterprises run a promotions company, and stage exhibitions, conferences and trade shows. Welcome enquiries from prospective clients. Approach by telephone or letter. Will consider demo tapes and video show reels.

Talkies

10 St Martin's Court, London WC2
Tel (071) 836 2392
Contact Beth Owen

Founded 1979. Represent actors only, just for voice work. Sometimes welcome queries from actors as prospective clients. Write in the first instance. Demo tapes will only be considered if an interest has been expressed by the agency.

Target Casting Ltd

St Leonard's House, St Leonard's Gate, Lancaster LA1 1NN
Tel (0524) 67354
Fax (0524) 63280
Contact Cooperative management

Founded 1983. Represent actors only, and welcome queries from those seeking representation. Approach in writing in the first instance; will consider video show reels. 'We are a successful actors' cooperative, and acceptance is limited by our geographical position (members should live in the north-west) and by our wish to hold the number of members to a manageable level.'

Ruth Tarko Agency

50/52 Cecil Street, Glasgow G12 8RJ
Tel (041) 334 0555
Fax (041) 434 0151
Contact Ruth Tarko, Arlene Carroll

Founded 1970. Represent mainly actors, and welcome applications by letter with CV, photograph and tapes (if available) from Scottish-based actors.

Theatre World Ltd

Cotton's Farmhouse, Whiston Road, Cogenhoe, Northants NN7 1NL
Tel (0604) 891487
Contact Lena Davis

Founded 1982. Represent actors, writers, directors, singers, etc. 'Sometimes' welcome queries from actors seeking representation. Approach in writing in the first instance. Will consider demo tapes and video show reels.

Thomas & Benda Associates Ltd

361 Edgware Road, London W2 1BS
Tel (071) 723 5509
Fax (071) 724 7287
Contact Miss Thomas, Mr Benda

Founded 1980. Represent actors and a couple of musical directors. Welcome queries from actors seeking representation; write in the first instance. Will not consider unsolicited demo tapes or video show reels.

Jim Thompson

Rivington House, 82 Great Eastern
Street, London EC2 3JL
Tel (071) 739 8410
Contact Jim Thompson

Founded 1980. Represent actors,
writers, directors, children and personalities. Welcome queries from actors
seeking representation. Approach in
writing in the first instance. Will consider demo tapes and video show
reels.

Thornton Agency

72 Purley Downs Road, Croydon,
Surrey CR2 0RB
Tel (081) 660 5588
Contact Leslie Collins, Jaqui
Lillywhite

Founded 1963. Represent actors and
some TV variety artists. Welcome
queries from actors seeking representation. Write in the first instance with
CV and photograph. Will consider
unsolicited demo tapes and video
show reels.

Tobias Management

Regency Court, 62–66 Deansgate,
Manchester M3 2EN
Tel (061) 832 5128
Contact Sharon Tobias, Stephen
Stroud

Formerly Zena Sharpe Personal
Management (founded 1971). Represent actors, directors, choreographers,
and also have a musical director on
their books. Welcome queries – 'in
moderation' – from actors seeking
representation. Approach in writing in
the first instance. Will consider demo
tapes and video show reels.

Top Drawer Management

The Royal Institution, Office 61,
Colquitt Street, Liverpool L1 4DE
Tel (051) 708 7752
Fax (051) 708 0643
Contact Mark Roscoe

Founded 1985. Represent actors and
children. Welcome queries from actors
seeking representation. Either telephone or send letter with CV and
photograph. Will consider video show
reels.

Sheila Tozer Management & Agency

143 Nevill Avenue, Hove, East Sussex
BN3 7NE
Tel (0273) 774388
Contact Sheila Tozer

Represent actors. New clients
acquired mainly through personal
recommendation.

Trapeze

190 Upper Street, London N1 1RQ
Tel (071) 359 3531
Contact Charlotte Kelly, Jane Pearce

Founded 1987. Represent actors and
directors. Welcome queries from
actors seeking representation. Approach in writing in the first instance.
Will consider demo tapes and video
show reels: 'I would not consider
taking anyone on until I had seen their
work first – either live or on a fairly
thorough tape – preferably both.
Circular letters (particularly ones
addressed "Dear Sir"!) go in the bin.'

Trends Management

54 Lisson Street, London NW1 6ST
Tel (071) 723 8001   Fax (071) 258
3591   Telex 912881
Contact Robert Jayes, Julian Ochyra

Founded 1950. Represent actors, dancers and singers. Welcome queries from actors seeking representation. Approach in writing in the first instance. Will consider demo tapes and video show reels.

Gary Trolan Management

30 Burrard Road, London NW6 1DB
Tel (071) 794 4429
Fax (071) 794 4429
Contact Gary Trolan

Founded mix-Sixties. Represent actors and presenters. Welcome queries from actors seeking representation. Write in the first instance with CV and photograph, and enclose SAE.

Joan Underwood

5 Sudbrook Gardens, Ham Common, Richmond, Surrey
Tel (081) 940 8888
Contact Joan Underwood

Formerly Encore Agency Ltd, founded in the 1950s. Represent photogenic teenagers and young, classically trained singers. Approach in writing in the first instance, enclosing a photograph. Will not consider unsolicited demo tapes or video show reels. Also offer a consultation service to help with all aspects of presentation for auditions and interviews, choice of pieces, songs and so forth.

Universal Productions

1 Haggard Road, Twickenham, Middx
TW1 3AL
Tel (081) 892 5530
Contact Elizabeth A. Roberts

Founded 1948. Represent actors and children for television and all types of dancers. Do not welcome queries from actors seeking representation 'at present', but will consider demo tapes and video show reels.

Paul Vaughan Associates

3rd Floor, 146 Strand, London
WC2R 1JH
Tel (071) 240 8851
Fax (071) 379 0089
and Alpha Tower, Paradise Circus,
Birmingham B1 1TT
Tel (021) 643 4011
Fax (021) 633 3947
Contact Mark Hudson (London),
Stephen Pink (Birmingham)

Founded 1978. Represent actors and presenters. Welcome queries from actors seeking representation. Write in the first instance. Will not consider unsolicited demo tapes or video show reels.

Adza Vincent

11a Ivor Place, London NW1 6HS
Tel (071) 262 9356

Founded 1957. Represent actors only, but do not welcome queries from those seeking representation.

Voice Box

Stamford House, Stamford New Road,
Altrincham, Cheshire WA14 1BL
Tel (061) 928 3222

Represent actors for voice work, and
actors and presenters for vision work
on corporate videos. Do not welcome
queries from actors seeking representation.

Voicecall

Apt 2, 12 Cambridge Park, East
Twickenham, Middx TW1 2PF
Tel (081) 891 1264

Represent actors for voice-over work.
Have a long list of established clients,
and do not welcome queries from
actors seeking representation at the
moment.

Voiceover

59 Frith Street, London W1V 5TA
Tel ex-dir.
Contact Heather Fooks

Founded 1974. Represent actors for
voice-over work only. Very rarely take
on new clients; do not really welcome
queries from actors seeking representation.

Voice Shop Ltd

Bakerloo Chambers, 304 Edgware
Road, London W2 1DY
Tel (071) 402 3966
Fax (071) 706 1002
Contact Maxine Wiltshire

Founded 1979. Represent actors for
voice-over work only, and welcome
queries from those seeking representation. Approach in writing in the first
instance, enclosing demo tape.

Voices Ltd

Suite 116, Golden House, 29 Great
Pulteney Street, London W1R 3DD
Tel (071) 734 3934
Fax (071) 287 0064
Contact Jenni Waters

Founded 1984. Represent actors for
voice work only, and welcome queries
from those seeking representation.
Write in the first instance. Will consider unsolicited demo tapes.

Thelma Wade

54 Harley Street, London W1N 1AD
Tel (071) 580 9860
Fax (071) 637 8022
Contact Thelma Wade

Founded 1985. Represent actors and
actor-singers. Welcome queries from
actors seeking representation. Approach in writing in the first instance,
with CV, photograph and SAE. Will
consider demo tapes and video show
reels. 'Good clear presentation of CV
is essential, to include colouring,
height, training, skills, languages,
hobbies.'

Penny Wesson

26 King Henry's Road, London
NW3 3RP
Tel (071) 722 6607
also at: Expresso Ltd, 65 Blandford
Street, London W1
Tel (071) 224 1748
Fax (071) 224 4196

Consultancy and advisory service.

West Central Management (WCM)

Suite 121, Panther House, 38 Mount Pleasant, London WC1
Tel (071) 833 8134

Founded 1986. Cooperative management. Represent actors only, and very much welcome queries from those seeking representation. Send letter with CV and photograph. Will consider demo tapes and video show reels. 'WCM is an actors' cooperative agency. A willingness to participate fully in the life of WCM is essential. This involves office duty (one day a week minimum), attendance at regular meetings and a creative input generally. The constitution of WCM is available on request to all prospective members. All decisions and matters of policy are decided collectively and cooperatively.'

David White Associates

2 Ormond Road, Richmond, Surrey TW10 6TH
Tel (081) 940 8300
Contact David White

Founded 1965. Represent actors and directors. Welcome queries from actors as prospective clients, but only if the first approach is by letter with a photograph and a brief CV so that neither side need waste time. 'The agent might already represent someone of the actor's type, and at least then a gentle rebuff can be sent as opposed to a flat "NOT INTERESTED" if one really is busy.'

Michael Whitehall Ltd

125 Gloucester Road, London SW7 4TE
Tel (071) 244 8466
Fax (071) 244 9060

Founded 1985. Represent actors, directors and writers. Welcome queries from prospective clients. Write in the first instance. Will consider unsolicited demo tapes and video show reels. Have a large voice-over department.

Newton Wills Management

Utopia Studios, 7 Chalcot Road, London NW1
and 17 Church Street, Belton-in-Rutland, Leics. LE15 9JU
Tel (071) 586 3434
Contact Newton Wills

Founded 1980. Represent actors, TV presenters, singers/actors. Welcome queries from actors seeking representation. Contact by telephone or letter in the first instance. Will consider demo tapes and video show reels. 'Send as much information as possible – full CV, good photographs, etc. Never ask an agent to return your call when making enquiries for representation!'

The Wendy Wisbey Agency

2 Rupert Road, London W4 1LX
Tel (081) 994 1210/5378
Contact Dinah Bland, Wendy Wisbey

Founded 1956. Represent actors only: 'We are always prepared to consider enquiries.' Send a letter with an SAE in the first instance. No unsolicited demo tapes or video show reels.

April Young Ltd

The Clock House, 6 St. Catherine's
Mews, Milner Street, London
SW3 2PX
Tel (071) 584 1274
Contact April Young

Founded 1974. Represent actors and
writers. Do not welcome queries from
actors seeking representation, as no
longer in a position to take on any new
clients.

Young Casting Agency

7 Beaumont Gate, Glasgow G12 9EE
Tel (041) 334 2646
Fax (041) 334 0575
Contact Freddie Young

Founded 1967. Represent actors, walk-
ons and supporting artists. Welcome
queries from actors seeking representation if they are based in Scotland and
can be seen working. Write or telephone with details of work. Will consider unsolicited demo tapes and
video show reels.

Sonny Zahl Associates

57 Great Cumberland Place,
London W1
Tel (071) 724 3684
Telex 94014150 ANNZ
Contact Ann Zahl

Founded 1975. Represent actors,
choreographers, light entertainment
artists, designers and directors.
Welcome queries from actors seeking
representation, although a small
agency with not many actors on its
books. Write in the first instance. Will
consider unsolicited demo tapes and
video show reels.

Peter Zander Artist &
Concert Management

22 Romilly Street, London W1V 5TG
Tel (071) 437 4767
Contact Peter Zander

Founded 1983. Represent actors,
musical directors, musicians and
singers. Also a promoter of opera,
plays, concerts and concert seasons,
music competitions, arts festivals.
Counsel actors on the handling of
their careers and self-promotion.
Commercial sponsorship of the arts.
Welcome queries from actors seeking
representation – 'but telephone first;
do not send bumph uninvited.' No
unsolicited demo tapes or video show
reels.

7 *Independent Casting Directors*

The casting director is employed by a theatre or production company to present a package of likely candidates to fit a particular script, for final selection by a director, producer, or, in the case of advertising, client. For details of such a casting session, see the introduction to the chapter on Film, Video and Independent Production Companies (p 000). It is important for actors to assist the casting director by representing their abilities accurately. The opinion of a casting director is trusted automatically and being helpful and biddable may lead to what can be highly lucrative work.

Casting directors need to have elephantine memories for names, faces and performances. Make sure they're supplied with a good photograph and up-to-date CV, and certainly notify them of any production where they might see you perform. If you have particular abilities and skills, don't conceal them. However, take care not to exaggerate them as you are bound to be caught out. Such embarrassing situations reflect badly on the casting director, and may well prevent future offers of work.

Casting directors generally conduct their business by telephone. Casual callers are unlikely to be welcome, and in the course of a busy day may be dealt with rather brusquely. As a rule, it is better to write enclosing your details.

Whatever the circumstances of the casting-session, the casting director should be on your side and will do their best to help you prepare. Follow their advice, particularly about clothes, and do not be put off your stride if the session seems brief or uninspiring. Despite all your instincts, you may discover the following day that the job is yours, after all. If not, your professionalism is being noted, along with your suitability for other roles which may be on offer in the future.

Tony Arnell

93 Fowlers Walk, London W5 1BQ
Tel (081) 991 5988   Fax (081) 998 8258

Head of Casting *The Bill* Unit – Thames TV (1990–1991). Will consider CVs, photographs and performance notices. Does not welcome telephone enquiries from individual actors, unsolicited demo tapes or video show reels.

Derek Barnes

26 Danbury Street, London N1
Tel (071) 354 6616

Television, films, commercials and training films. Will consider CVs, photographs and performance notices, but no reply without SAE.

Michael Barnes Ltd

Suite 201, Golden House, 29 Great Pulteney Street, London W1R 3DD
Tel (071) 439 9716
Fax (071) 437 0824
Contact Michael Barnes, Karin Stretford-Grainger

TV, films, commercials and training videos. Do not welcome casting queries from actors, but will consider demo tapes and video show reels.

Laura Cairns

Flat 2, 7 Streathbourne Road, Tooting Bec, London SW17 8QZ
Tel (081) 767 8607

Films, TV, video and theatre. Welcomes casting queries from actors; approach in writing in the first instance. 'I try and see as many shows as I can if the contact is made in writing, but of course, I cannot see everyone. The main reason for contacting a casting director is in the hope that he/she may be able to see you working. If I had sufficient secretarial assistance, I should certainly want to set aside more time to interview actors personally. I do not think actors need to include an SAE with a CV and photograph. However, it is necessary in the case of returning a video.'

Di Carling

52 Wardour Street, London W1V 3HJ
Tel (071) 437 0841

TV films, commercials and training films. Very occasionally holds general interviews, but does not particularly welcome casting queries from actors. No unsolicited demo tapes or video show reels. Credits include: *The Birmingham Six Appeal*.

Maggie Cartier

Pinewood Studios, Iver Heath, Bucks.

Feature films and films for TV. Credits include: *Empire of the Sun*, *Valmont*, *Amadeus*, *Ragtime*, *Jack the Ripper* (Euston Films), and *Indiana Jones And The Last Crusade*. CVs, photographs and performance notices welcomed. No unsolicited demo tapes or video show reels. Do not telephone.

The Casting Company

9 Newburgh Street, London W1V 1LH
Tel (071) 734 4955
Contact Michelle Guishe, Debbie McWilliams

Feature films, TV and some commercials. Do not welcome general letters, but will try to see actors' work if performance notices sent. Credits include: *Queen of Hearts* (feature film) and *Des Res* (Michelle Guishe); *Danny, the Champion of the World* and the feature film of Kenneth Branagh's *Henry V* (Debbie McWilliams).

Beth Charkham

122 Wardour Street, London W1V 3LA
Tel (071) 734 0202
Fax (071) 439 8568
Contact Beth Charkham, Emma Goldman

TV films and commercials. Do not welcome casting queries from actors. Will consider demo tapes and video show reels. Hold general interviews. Credits include: *Robin of Sherwood* and *Pulaski*.

Jackie Coote

27 Britannia Road, London SW6 2HJ
Tel (071) 731 1061

Stills advertisements and commercials. Will consider CVs and photographs. No unsolicited demo tapes or video show reels.

Kathy Curshen

26 Ulundi Road, Blackheath, London SE3 7UG
Tel (081) 858 9291

Approach by letter in the first instance. No unsolicited demo tapes or video show reels.

Davis & Zimmerman Casting

31 King's Road, London SW3 4RP
Tel (071) 730 9421
Contact Noel Davis, Jeremy Zimmerman

Feature films, TV films and commercials, training films. Approach by letter in the first instance. No unsolicited demo tapes or video show reels. 'Forty-five per cent of photographs have no name on the back. Needless to say, they go into the bin. Letters, photographs and CVs should be stapled or clipped together. Actors should learn that casting directors are not agents. We do not answer letters from actors, but we file the information and refer to it when casting. Every actor must advertise in *Spotlight*; otherwise, they are dead.' Credits include: *The Dresser* and *Madame Sousatzka*.

Gillian Diamond

22 Burghley Road, London NW5 1VE
Tel (071) 485 6522

Mainley theatre. No unsolicited photographs or CVs. Telephone calls welcome. No tapes or videos.

Liz England Casting

34 Connaught Street, London W2 2AF
Tel (071) 723 1332
Contact Simone Ireland

Commercials, films and TV. Prefer to
be approached in writing in the first
instance. Will consider demo tapes
and video show reels, but 'We like to
be told in advance that they're going
to be sent. Videos that arrive unasked
for can sometimes be put to one side
until we have time to view them.' 'It is
very important to have an agent for
numerous reasons – e.g. money nego-
tiations, availability checks. It is very
time-consuming chasing actors without agents.'

Richard Evans Casting

10 Shirley Road, London W4 1DD
Tel (081) 994 6304   Fax (081) 742
1010

Theatre, commercials, voice-overs and
training films. Holds occasional general interviews. Approach in writing
with CV and photograph. Welcomes
performance notices (attends theatre,
London, regional and drama schools,
3–9 times weekly). Considers unsolicited video show reels and voice-over
demo cassettes, if accompanied by an
SAE with sufficient return postage.

Ann Fielden Casting

36 Wardour Street, London W1V 3HJ
Tel (071) 434 1331

TV, film, corporate video, commercials. Approach by letter in the first
instance. No unsolicited demo tapes
or video show reels. Credits include:
The Fear, The Monocled Mutineer and
Shanghai Surprise.

Susie Figgis

12 Flitcroft Street, London WC2
Tel (071) 379 7808

Feature films. Welcomes letters and
performance notices from actors.
Credits include: *Ghandi, The Killing
Fields, The Mission, Mona Lisa, Local
Hero, Wish You Were Here.*

Bernice Fildes

56 Wigmore Street, London W1
Tel (071) 935 1254

General casting – films, TV, etc. Will
consider CVs, photographs and performance notices; also demo tapes and
video show reels. Very occasionally
holds general interviews.

Allan Foenander

59 North Eyot Gardens, St Peters
Square, London W6 9NL
Tel (081) 748 9641

Films, TV, commercials and documentaries. Credits include: *Deadline* and
The Most Dangerous Man in the World
(both BBC); *Friendships in Vienna* (Disney TV); *Shirley Valentine* (Paramount);
Great Expectations (Walt Disney Prime-
time). Will consider CVs, photographs
and performance notices. No unsolicited demo tapes or video show reels.

Celestia Fox

5 Clapham Common Northside,
London SW4
Tel (071) 720 6143

Feature films. Credits include: *A Room
with a View, Maurice, A Handful of Dust,
Mountains of the Moon.* Does not wel-

come unsolicited photographs and CVs, but will consider performance notices. No unsolicited demo tapes or video show reels.

Paul de Freitas

3rd floor, 2 Conduit Street, London W1R 9TG
Tel (071) 434 4233/4

TV commercials and training films. Will consider letters from actors, but no unsolicited demo tapes or video show reels. Does not usually hold general interviews.

Jane Frisby Casting

51 Ridge Road, London N8 9LJ
Tel (081) 341 4747

Commercials, training films, TV drama, theatre. Approach by letter in the first instance. No unsolicited demo tapes or video show reels.

Joyce Gallie

37 Westcroft Square, London W6 0TA
Tel (081) 741 4009

Feature films, commercials and some TV. Does not particularly welcome unsolicited letters from actors – 'we are inundated' – nor demo tapes and video show reels.

Lesley Grayburn

74 Leigh Gardens, London NW10 5HP
Tel (081) 969 6112

TV commercials and corporate videos. Approach in writing in the first in-

stance, enclosing CV and photograph. No unsolicited demo tapes or video show reels.

Anne Henderson Casting Ltd

93 Kelvin Road, Highbury, London N5 2PL
Tel (071) 354 3786

Films, TV, commercials. Does not welcome casting queries from actors, or unsolicited demo tapes or video show reels. 'Only contact casting directors by letter when you have something to be seen in, either TV or theatre.' Credits include: *A Very British Coup*, *Porterhouse Blue* and *Taggart*.

Rebecca Howard

37 Wharton Street, London WC1X 9PG
Tel (071) 837 2978
Contact Rebecca Howard, Cathy Bell

Film and TV. Approach by letter in the first instance. No unsolicited demo tapes or video show reels. Credits include: *A Very Peculiar Practice* and *Salome*.

Sharon Howard Field

27 Neal Street, London WC2H 9PR
Tel (071) 240 0388

Feature and TV films. Does not particularly welcome letters from actors; prefers to receive performance notices. No unsolicited demo tapes or video show reels. Credits include: *The Attic* (YTV) and *Drowning by Numbers*.

Hubbard Casting

6 Noel Street, London W1
Tel (071) 494 3191
Fax (071) 437 0559
Contact John Hubbard, Ros Hubbard,
Sue Needleman

Feature and TV films, plays and commercials, theatre. Approach by letter in the first instance. Hold general interviews. Will consider demo tapes and video show reels. Credits include: *Out of Order* and *Twins*. 'Get known by all casting directors. Keep them posted about progress. Persevere.' Do not welcome telephone enquiries from individual actors.

Priscilla John

22 Cardross Street, London W6 0DR
Tel (081) 741 9615

Feature films and TV. Credits include: *A Fish Called Wanda* and *Who Framed Roger Rabbit?* Happy to receive CVs, photographs and performance notices. No unsolicited demo tapes or video show reels.

Marilyn Johnson

The Basement, 115 Chesterton Road,
London W10 6ET
Tel (081) 969 7128/9

TV and films. 'Rarely see people for general interviews.' Does not welcome letters from actors; prefers to receive performance notices. No unsolicited demo tapes or video show reels. Credits include: *Piece of Cake, Inspector Morse* and *Slipstream*.

Doreen Jones

107 Warwick Road, London SW5 9EZ
Tel (071) 373 0171
Contact Doreen Jones, Amanda
Fisher

TV and film (was Head of Casting for Granada TV until 1987). Approach by letter in the first instance. No unsolicited demo tapes or video show reels. Credits include: *Game, Set and Match* and *Shake Hands Forever*.

Just Casting

128 Talbot Road, London W11 1JA
Tel (071) 229 3471
Contact Leo Davis

Feature films and TV. Performance notices, but no unsolicited demo tapes or video show reels. Credits include: *Absolute Beginners, For Queen and Country*.

Suzy Korel

20 Blenheim Road, London NW8 0LX
Tel (071) 624 6435

Approach by letter in the first instance. No unsolicited demo tapes or video show reels. 'I like letters to be sent, and then I try to meet the actor.' Sometimes considers demo tapes and video show reels, but 'only after I have met the actor'.

Irene Lamb

Flat 4, Avenue House, 97 Walton
Street, London SW3 2JY
Tel (071) 589 6452

Feature films and TV. Approach in writing in the first instance, enclosing CV and *Spotlight* number. No unsolicited demo tapes or video show reels.

Credits include: *Brazil*, *The Lonely Passion of Judith Hearne* and *Eric the Viking*.

Jane L'Epine Smith

2 Chertsey Road, St Margaret's,
Twickenham, Middx
Tel (081) 891 1685

Corporate videos. Tries to see as many actors as possible. Welcomes letters and performance notices (sees at least three shows per week). No unsolicited demo tapes or video show reels.

Sharon Levinson

48 Yale Court, Honeybourne Road,
London NW6 1JG
Tel (071) 435 3329

Commercials, corporate video, TV. Occasionally holds general interviews. No unsolicited demo tapes or video show reels.

Julia Lisney

c/o 'The Bill' office, Thames
Television, 85 Barlby Road,
London W10
Tel (081) 969 6699

TV, films, commercials, training films. Credits include: *The Bill*, *The Gemini Factor*, *Gems*.

Joyce Nettles

16 Cressida Road, London N19
Tel (071) 263 0830

Film, TV and theatre. Will consider CVs, photographs and performance notices. Does not welcome telephone enquiries from individual actors, unsolicited demo tapes or video show reels.

Diana Parry

58 Mysore Road, London SW11 5SB
Tel (071) 223 0226

Performance notices welcome, but please no unsolicited CVs, photos or videos.

Jill Pearce

Suite 16, 6 Langley Street,
London WC2
Tel (071) 240 0316

TV and cinema commercials. Performance notification – preferably by phone. No unsolicited demo tapes or video show reels.

Lesley de Pettitt

2 Parkview, The Ride, Hatfield, Herts.
AL9 5HG
Tel (07072) 64301
Contact Lesley de Pettitt

Film, TV and commercials. Approach in writing in the first instance, enclosing CV and photograph.

Poole and Crowley Casting

2nd floor, 82 Wardour Street, London
W1V 3LS
Tel (071) 437 4444
Contact Gilly Poole, Suzanne
Crowley

Founded 1988 (formerly with The Casting Company). Feature films, commercials, TV, theatre, etc. No demo tapes or video show reels.

Simone Reynolds

60 Hebden Road, London SW17 7NN
Tel (081) 672 5443

Film, TV, theatre and some commercials (for directors such as John Mackenzie). Credits include: *Chariots of Fire*, *The Long Good Friday*, *We Think the World of You* and *The Firm* (BBC Screen on 2). Does not welcome letters; performance notice cards preferred. No unsolicited demo tapes or video show reels.

Maggie Sangwin

61 Flanders Mansions, Flanders Road, London W4 1NF
Tel (081) 995 7523

Feature films, TV, commercials and photographic work. Welcomes letters and performance notices from actors. Enclose CV and photograph. Will consider demo tapes and video show reels. Credits include: *The Bill* (Thames TV) and *Tank Malling* (film).

Mary Selway

Twickenham Film Studios, The Barons, St Margaret's, Twickenham, Middx TW1 2AW
Tel (081) 892 4477

Feature films. Credits include: *Out of Africa*, *White Mischief*, *Dry White Season*, *Gorillas in the Mist*, *Strapless*, *Paris by Night*. Is happy to receive CV, photograph and performance notices.

Hazel Singer

1 Newcastle House, Luxborough Street, London W1

Mainly corporate videos and training films.

Michelle Smith

34 Willow Way, Didsbury, Manchester M20 0JS
Tel (061) 445 9613

Films, TV, commercials and training films. Will consider CVs, photographs and performance notices. Does not welcome telephone calls from individual actors.

Maude Spector

16 Upper Brook Street, London W1Y 1PD
Tel (071) 493 3478

Feature films and TV. Does not welcome unsolicited letters or demo tapes and video show reels. Prefers to deal only through agents.

Gail Stevens & Janey Fothergill

37 Berwick Street, London W1
Tel (071) 437 1562

Films, TV, commercials, etc. Do not hold general interviews. No demo tapes or video show reels; send letter with CV and photograph. Credits: *The Lair of the White Worm*, *Resurrection*, *The Rachel Papers* and two projects for Jim Henson.

Sylvia Taylor

40 Brookville Road, London SW6 7BJ
Tel (071) 385 9716

Commercials and stills. Will consider CVs and photographs. Demo tapes and video show reels *only on request*.

Rose Tobias Shaw

219 Liverpool Road, London N1 1LX
Tel (071) 607 0762
Contact Rose Tobias Shaw

Film, TV and commercials. Approach in writing in the first instance, enclosing CV and photograph. Will try to cover a show if performance notice sent. Does not hold general interviews. No unsolicited demo tapes or video show reels. Credits include: *Voice of the Heart* and *Around the World in 80 Days*.

Valerie Van Ost

57 Oakwood Court, Kensington,
London W14 8JY
Tel (071) 602 0088

Commercials and some TV films. Welcomes letters, including *Spotlight* number and CV. Does not hold general interviews. No unsolicited demo tapes or video show reels.

The Vocal Casting Company

25–26 Poland Street, London
W1V 3DB
Tel (071) 437 4492
Contact Alan Fitter

Voice-over casting service and consultancy. Welcome demo tapes for consideration.

Sue Whatmough

34 Cadogan Road, Surbiton, Surrey
KT6 4DJ
Tel (081) 390 6225

TV and feature films. Credits include: *Gentlemen and Players*. Photographs, CVs and performance notices will be considered. No phone calls and no unsolicited demo tapes or video show reels.

8 Repertory and Regional Theatres

The system of repertory, in which a theatre presents a regularly changing programme of widely varying plays, once provided the backbone of the British acting profession. Repertory provided young actors with a start in the profession, however humble, in the company of older and more experienced performers. In a company hired for a season, an actor could expect a variety of roles in a broad selection of plays of different periods and styles, and the chance to work with different directors. There would always be the possibility of gaining a very good role which could give an individual career a major boost.

Today many repertory theatres are struggling for survival. Most hire casts for particular plays, rather than companies for a season; seasons themselves are noticeably shorter than even a few years ago; and there is a marked tendency towards caution in the choice of programme.

They still offer the possibility of working in well-equipped theatres with well-organised professional support. Actors can concentrate on their work, get to know the people they are working with, develop a common vocabulary and the confidence to experiment in rehearsal. It remains the best way to experience variety in scale and style of play, and size and significance of role. There is a good chance of quality work being recognised and noted by future employers from theatre and television, and there is always the possibility of conspicuously successful productions transferring to the West End.

The pay, as with most theatrical work, is at bare survival rates, especially for those who have a permanent home in another town and family or other responsibilities. Rehearsal periods are often quite insufficient for the task in hand. Avoid depression during a longish contract by working hard to find decent and convenient digs.

Yvonne Arnaud Theatre

Millbrook, Guildford, Surrey GU1 3UX
Tel (0483) 64571
Artistic director Val May

Founded 1965. Seating capacity: just under 600. Mostly co-produce with managements such as Triumph and Bill Kenwright for pre-and post-West End productions and nationwide tours. 20–25 shows per year. Recent productions: *The Royal Baccarat Scandal* (Val May; Chichester Festival production), *Dear Charles* (directed by Val May), and *Who's Afraid Of Virginia Woolf?* (directed by Val May). Do not welcome casting queries from actors. Recommend that the actors contact the co-producing company as unlikely to hold auditions at the Yvonne Arnaud.

Touring company:
Millstream (*see* **Touring companies**).

Belgrade Theatre

Belgrade Square, Coventry CV1 1GS
Tel (0203) 256431
Artistic director Robert Hamlin

Founded 1958. Seating capacity: 866. Two seasons: September to July. Nine productions: musicals, classics, revivals, premières and pantomime. Cast sizes range from four to 25. Recent productions: *Noises Off, Curse of the Baskervilles, Coventry Mystery Plays* (triennial event), *Tess of the D'Urbervilles* (directed by Robert Hamlin), *Pack of Lies* (directed by John Durnin), *Accidental Death of an Anarchist* (directed by Peter Fieldson), *A Chorus of Disapproval* (directed by Sue Wilson). Do not advertise for actors, but welcome casting queries. Approach by letter in the first instance. Hold auditions mainly for specific casting.

Studio theatre with a seating capacity of 60. Seven plays annually with a maximum cast size of five. Recently closed for refurbishment. First production since re-opening *It's A Girl* (directed by Robert Hamlin) in January 1991. TIE company (*see* **Theatre-in-Education companies**).

Comment:
The West Midlands is extremely well served with high-quality theatre, and the Belgrade is no exception. This lively rep theatre offers an adventurous and varied programme. Named after the Yugoslav capital, which presented the timber used in its interior, The Belgrade, built in 1958, was Britain's first civic theatre.

Birmingham Repertory Theatre

Broad Street, Birmingham B1 2EP
Tel (021) 236 6771
Artistic director John Adams
Associate directors Gwenda Hughes, Tony Clark

Founded 1913 by Barry Jackson; moved to present modern home 1970. Seating capacity: 834–899 (flexible stage). Autumn and spring seasons of approximately four to five plays per season. Recent productions: *All My Sons* (Gwenda Hughes); *The Ragged Trousered Philanthropists* (John Adams); *Saturday, Sunday, Monday* (Tony Clark); *Antony and Cleopatra* (John Adams); *Translations* (Gwenda Hughes). Welcome casting queries, either by telephone or letter: 'But please do not follow up a letter with a telephone call. We carefully file all photographs and CVs for the season.'

Studio theatre: seating capacity 109–140. Touring productions as well as home-produced contemporary and classical works. Recent production: *The Seagull* (Tony Clark).

Comment:
The launching pad for many leading actors – Olivier, Richardson, Scofield – the Birmingham Rep has a long-established reputation for unusual and avant-garde drama going back to its beginnings in 1913. The Rep was the first British theatre to introduce a subscription ticket scheme and, in 1976, was the first regional rep to present productions at the National Theatre (*Measure for Measure* and *The Devil is an Ass*). One of the foremost rep theatres in the country.

Brunton Theatre Company

Ladywell Way, Musselburgh, East
Lothian EH21 6AA
Tel (031) 665 9900
Fax (031) 665 7495
Artistic director Charles Nowosielski

Founded 1979. Seating capacity: 312. One season (August–March) of eight plays, one pantomime. Wide range of productions: musicals, Scots plays, new work. Average cast size of ten (including musicians). Recent productions: *The Diary of Anne Frank, Wizard of Oz, The Hollow, Good, Animal Farm, St. Joan, Pinocchio.* Hold auditions in May/June. Advertise in *SBS, The Stage* and Scottish national daily papers. Welcome casting queries; approach by letter only. 'Persevere with applications and know about the theatre to which you are applying to join.'

Byre Theatre Company

Byre Theatre, Abbey Street, St
Andrews, Fife KY16 9LA
Tel (0334) 76288
Artistic director Maggie Kinloch

Founded 1933. Seating capacity: 174. Produce six to seven plays annually with an average cast size of five. 'The mainstage season is structured around the variety of patrons visiting the historic town of St Andrews: May–June – small cast, middle-range work; July–August – popular entertainment; September – handsome, bigger-cast work; October – adventurous fare.' Recent productions: *September In The Rain; Blood And Ice; And A Nightingale Sang; Solomon And The Big Cat* (TIE). Hold general auditions as well as casting for each production – 'some cross casting is essential, but standards have risen through more specialized casting on shorter contracts.' Occasionally advertise in *SBS*. Welcome casting queries from actors. Send CV, photograph and SAE. The Byre has a strong and developing TIE policy and tours regularly throughout Scotland.

Comment:
This tiny theatre started life as a cow byre and was converted into an amateur theatre in 1933. During the war, it was taken over by a small professional company, and in 1969, the old Byre was demolished and the present purpose-built theatre was established, and operates year-round with a variety of productions.

Churchill Theatre Trust Ltd

Churchill Theatre, High Street,
Bromley, Kent BR1 1HA
Tel (081) 464 7131
Fax (081) 290 6968
Director Nick Salmon

Founded 1977. Seating capacity: 760.
Three seasons of approximately three
months each. Annually produce eight
to ten plays plus a pantomime with
occasional tours. Cast size ranges between four to 12 (more for musicals).
Recent productions: *High Flyers*
(directed by Keith Hack); *Intent to Kill*
(Kim Grant); *Beyond Reasonable Doubt*
and *As Time Goes By* (directed by David
Gilmore); *Wait Until Dark* (directed by
Chris Renshaw); *Rebecca* and *A Slight
Hangover* (directed by Clifford Williams); *Phantom of the Opera* (directed by
Ken Hill); *An Inspector Calls* (directed
by Mark Piper); *If You Knew Suzy*
(directed by Tony Britton). Sometimes
advertise in *The Stage* when producing
musicals. Hold general auditions and
also see people for individual productions.

Citizens Company

Citizens Theatre, Gorbals, Glasgow
G5 9DS
Tel (041) 429 5561
Artistic directors Giles Havergal,
Philip Prowse, Robert David
MacDonald

Founded 1945. Seating capacity: 657.
Three seasons – spring, summer,
autumn/winter – of approximately
three months each. Ten plays (British
and European classics) produced
annually with an average cast size of
ten. Recent productions: *Mrs. Warren's
Profession* (directed by Giles Havergal);

The Housekeeper (translated and
directed by Robert David MacDonald);
Jane Shore (directed and designed by
Philip Prowse). Cast for each production. Do not advertise for actors,
but welcome casting queries in the
form of a letter and photograph.

Theatre About Glasgow company (*see*
Young people's theatre companies).

Comment:
An internationally renowned theatre
with low seat prices and a good, hard-
hitting repertoire of unusual, high-
quality plays. Contemporary drama,
little-known classics and European
works make up the rich and varied
programme.

Civic Theatre

Fairfield Road, Chelmsford, Essex
CM1 1JH
Tel (Newpalm Productions)
(081) 349 0802
Artistic director John Newman

Fortnightly rep performed by
Newpalm Productions since 1970.
Season of ten plays (including pantomime and children's show) from
October to March, with an average
cast size of nine. Seating capacity: 512.
Recent productions: *Amadeus, Sweeney
Todd, Joseph and The Amazing Techni-
color Dreamcoat, The Forsyte Saga*. Do
not hold general auditions and do not
advertise for actors as most of the company taken from Newpalm touring
productions (*see* **Independent managements**). Will file details and photographs, but do not reply to query
letters due to pressure of work.

Contact Theatre Company

Oxford Road, Manchester M15 6JA
Tel (061) 274 3434
Artistic director Brigid Larmour

Founded 1972. Seating capacity: 300. Between six to nine plays produced between September and July, rehearsing for three weeks and playing for 3–4 weeks. Classics, plays with music and new works. Recent productions: *The Life of Galileo*, *Hot Fudge and Ice Cream*, *The Belle of Belfast City*, and *The Weirdstone of Brisingamen*. General auditions held in November and May. Try to cross cast as much as possible. Do not advertise for actors, but welcome casting queries. Write, enclosing CV, photograph and SAE. You will receive a reply and your information will be kept on file.
Studio theatre: seating capacity 60. Used by the company's youth theatre.

Comment:
Contact's brief is to produce exciting theatre for young people. However, its reputation extends far beyond that as a result of such productions of award-winning plays as Charlotte Keatley's *My Mother Said I Never Should* (George Devine award) and premières of plays by locally based writers. Also noted for its innovative classic productions – Brecht in particular – and its strong design values.

Crucible Theatre Trust Ltd

55 Norfolk Street, Sheffield S1 1DA
Tel (0742) 760621
Artistic director Mark Brickman

Founded 1971. Seating capacity: 1000. Two seasons: September to March and May to July; eight productions annually. Recent productions: *The Taming of The Shrew*; *A View From The Bridge*; *The Good Sisters*; *The Innocents*; *Billy Budd*. Do not advertise for actors, but welcome letter with full CV and photograph. Write to casting director. *Studio theatre* with seating capacity of 150–200, producing wide range of productions, favouring new plays and modern work. Four to six plays annually. Recent productions: *Whale* and *Joyriders*.

Education company (*see entry for 'Sheffield Crucible Education Company' in* **Theatre-in-Education companies**).

Comment:
The Crucible Main House produces a varied repertoire of epic and large-scale drama while the studio theatre continues to produce new and challenging work. With its two restaurants, wine bar, exhibitions and televized snooker, the theatre is an essential part of Sheffield life.

Derby Playhouse Company

Derby Playhouse, Theatre Walk, Eagle Centre, Derby DE1 2NF
Tel (0332) 363271
Executive director David Edwards
Contact Lyn Assman

Seating capacity: 500. No artistic director currently. Autumn, spring and summer seasons, with two Playhouse Company productions (with guest directors) per season. Recent directions include: *Teechers* (John Godber); *Tons of Money* (Alan Ayckbourn) *Rebecca* (Daphne du Maurier); and *Double Double* (Roger Rees).
Studio theatre with a seating capacity of 75+.

The Drum Theatre

See **Theatre Royal**

Duke's Playhouse

Moor Lane, Lancaster LA1 1QE
Tel (0524) 67461
Artistic director John Pope

Founded 1971. Seating capacity: 300.
One season from September to March,
with a season of open-air promenade
theatre from June to August. Five
plays (including pantomime) in the
main season, with an average cast size
of seven. Recent productions: *Rebecca,
Hansel and Gretel; Intimate Exchanges.*
Hold general auditions each summer.
Do not advertise, but welcome casting
queries from actors. Approach in writing in the first instance, enclosing CV,
photograph and SAE.
   Studio theatre: Theatre-in-the-round.
Seating capacity: 190. Productions
have included: *Trafford Tanzi; Not
About Heroes; Hell's Kitchen.*
   TIE company (*see* **Theatre-in-Education companies**).

Dundee Repertory Theatre

Tay Square, Dundee DD1 1PB
Tel (0382) 27684
Chief executive Stephen Lawrence
Artistic director Robert Robertson
Associate directors Cliff Burnett &
Neil Murray

Founded 1939 (new theatre opened
1982). Seating capacity: 450. Autumn
and spring seasons (August to April)
with four productions each season
plus a pantomime. Broad spectrum of
productions, including new plays.
Recent productions: *David Copperfield*
(directed by Neil Murray); *The Turn Of
The Screw* (directed by Robert

Robertson); *One For The Road* (directed
by Cliff Burnett). Hold general auditions in May/June (one week in
London and one week in Scotland).
Do not advertise, but welcome casting
queries from actors. Approach in writing in the first instance, enclosing, CV,
photograph and SAE. 'We keep details
on file, and the director looks through
them in May when compiling the
audition list. We also feel an entry in
Spotlight is essential to an actor.'

Everyman Theatre

Regent Street, Cheltenham, Glos.
GL50 1HQ
Tel (0242) 512515
Artistic director Martin Houghton

Re-opened in 1986 after a £2.5 million
refit. Seating capacity: 658. Autumn
and spring seasons, with approximately five productions each season.
Average cast size of eight to ten. Wide
range of productions including musicals and new drama. Recent productions: *The Provoked Wife; Noises
Off; A Little Hotel On The Side; Of Mice
And Men; Relatively Speaking.* Very
occasionally hold general auditions,
but usually specific casting. Sometimes advertise in *SBS* and Equity *Job
Grapevine.* Welcome casting queries
from actors. Write in the first instance,
enclosing CV, photograph and SAE.
   Studio theatre: The Richardson
Studio. Seating capacity of 50/60.
Emphasis on alternative drama.
Recent productions: *The Maids;
Auction.*
   Touring: community touring to a cir-
cuit, established 1990. Recent pro-
ductions include *Behind You Hill* and
Tales From Kite Hill.

Everyman Theatre

Hope Street, Liverpool L1 9BH
Tel (051) 708 0338
Artistic director John Doyle

Founded 1964. Seating capacity: 402.
Three seasons from October to
June/July; five or six plays with an
average cast size of 13. A wide range
of productions. Recent productions:
*The Trojan Women; 'Tis Pity She's A
Whore; Sarcophagus, As You Like It; Dr
Faustus; The Caucasian Chalk Circle.*
Mostly cast for each individual production. Rarely advertise for actors,
but welcome casting queries. Write in
the first instance, enclosing CV and
photograph, and SAE if reply required.

Comment:
The Everyman has established itself as
an important community theatre presenting new and challenging work.
Local writers and actors have always
been encouraged, and it was the starting point for the famous four – Alan
Bleasdale, Chris Bond, Bill Morrison
and Willy Russell – who then moved
down the road to liven up the
Liverpool Playhouse. John Doyle's
production policy for the Everyman
was not known at the time of writing.

Farnham Repertory Co. Ltd

Redgrave Theatre, Brightwells,
Farnham, Surrey GU9 7SB
Tel (0252) 727000
Artistic director Graham Watkins

Seating capacity: 362. Produce 13/14
plays throughout the year, with an
average cast size of eight to nine.
Recent productions: *The Devils Virtuoso*
by Ian Taylor (World Premiere); *The
Rivals; Blythe Spirit; Lady Chatterley's
Lover; The Entertainer.* Cast for each
production, and also hold general

auditions. Do not advertise for actors,
but will consider letters ('preferably
specific queries relating to productions
we are planning – i.e. suggest yourself
for a specific part . . . Enclose an SAE
or we cannot reply').

Studio theatre with a seating capacity
of 45. 'Rarely used due to financial
restrictions.'

TIE company: 'specifically formed
once or twice a year for schools tours.'

Gateway Theatre

Hamilton Place, Chester CH1 2BH
Tel (0244) 344238
Artistic director Peter Rowe

Founded 1968. Seating capacity: 440.
Autumn season of three plays plus a
tour; spring season of four plays;
Christmas show and summer show.
Produce classics, new writing and
populist contemporary work. Average
cast size of seven. Recent productions:
Our Day Out, Cabaret, and *Good*
(directed by Peter Rowe); *Uncle Vanya*
(directed by Stephen MacDonald); *The
Canterbury Tales* (directed by Martin
Jamieson); *A Midsummer Night's Dream*
(directed by Hettie Macdonald);
Mother Goose (directed by Ian Forrest)
and a touring production of *These
Things Do Happen* (directed by Valerie
Jenner). Advertise occasionally in *SBS.*
Welcome casting queries from actors.
'We prefer always to be contacted by
letter, and like many theatres, only
reply to an SAE, though it is usually a
printed note. We *do* consider *every* letter, and see actors if it's possible and
useful. We advise brief letters, small
photos and *clear* CVs.'

Studio theatre with a seating capacity
of 50, which takes incoming tours plus
productions by the main-house company. Ten plays annually with an
average cast size of four. Recent

productions: *The Stone Baby* (Full Theatre Company); *Skirmishes* (Theatre Unlimited); and *Routes to Freedom* (Strines Theatre Company).

No TIE company, but do co-productions with Action Transport Theatre Company.

Graham Players

Civic Theatre, Craigie Road, Ayr, Ayrshire KA8 0EZ
Tel (0292) 263755
Artistic director Victor Graham
Associate director Suzanne Jefferies

Founded 1956. Seating capacity: 350. Summer seasons of two-weekly rep; 14-week season of comedies and drama. Company of six to nine actors. Recent productions: *On Golden Pond, Duet for One, How's the World Treating You?, Educating Rita, Season's Greetings* and *Driving Miss Daisy* (all directed by Suzanne Jefferies). Do not advertise, but welcome casting queries from actors. Applications for the general auditions, held in London in May every year, should be made by letter in March.

Grand Theatre

Singleton Street, Swansea SA1 3QJ
Tel (0792) 475242
Fax (0792) 475379
General Manager Gary Iles

Seating capacity: 1021. In House productions periodically – usually four productions annually, plus eight-week pantomime season. Average cast size of eight. Recent productions: *Deadly Nightcap* and *Arsenic and Old Lace* (directed by Simon Whitfield); *The Man* and *Boeing Boeing* (Mark Woolgar); and *Grease* (directed by Bob

Tomson). Hold general auditions as well as casting for each production.

Greenwich Theatre

Crooms Hill, Greenwich, London SE10 8ES
Tel (081) 858 4447
Artistic director Matthew Francis

Founded 1969. Seating capacity: 423. Do not hold general auditions as they cast play by play. Do not advertise but will keep letters and actors' details on file. Enclose CV and photograph.

Hampstead Theatre

See **Fringe and Alternative Theatre**.

Harrogate Theatre Company

Harrogate Theatre, Oxford Street, Harrogate, N. Yorks. HG1 1QF
Tel (0423) 502710
Artistic director Andrew Manley

Founded 1900. Seating capacity: 476. Season of nine to ten plays from September to the end of April; from classical to modern plays, plus musicals. Average cast size of nine. Recent productions: *The Cherry Orchard* and *Uncle Vanya* (both British premieres adapted by David Mamet); *Hamlet; The Odd Couple* (female version); *Teechers; The Importance of Being Earnest; The Secret Rapture; Design for Living.* Most productions directed by Andrew Manley (Artistic Director). Recent Guest Directors – Ivor Benjamin, Ian

Forrest. 'Usually hold general auditions in June or July, and perhaps again in December. Best to write before these times. There is a high degree of permanency in the company, though there is some casting for each production.'

Studio theatre with a seating capacity of 50, which is used by visiting companies, local colleges and amateurs.

TIE company (*see* **Theatre-in-Education companies**).

Haymarket Theatre

Belgrave Gate, Leicester LE1 3YQ
Tel (0533) 530021
Artistic director Peter Lichtenfels
Associate director Chris Ellis

Founded 1972. Seating capacity: 752. Productions throughout the year. Recent productions: *M. Butterfly* (John Dexter); *Hamlet* (Yuri Lyubimov); *Little Shop of Horrors* (Tim Flavin); *Small Family Business* (Will Cohu). No general auditions; specific casting only. Sometimes advertise in *SBS*. Prefer to deal with agents, but will consider letters from actors (an SAE does *not* guarantee a reply).

Studio theatre: seating capacity 150. In-house and touring productions throughout the year. Recent productions: *Krapp's Last Tape/Catastrophe* (Antoni Liberia); *7 Lears* (co-production with The Wrestling School; Kenny Ireland); *The Naked* (Simon Usher); *The Mystery of Irma Vep* (Maria Aitken).

Outreach Dept: Jagdish Chouhan and Daniel Buckroyd. Workshops, productions and activities within the community. Responsible for Haymarket Young People's Theatre.

Horseshoe Theatre Company

The Shrubbery, Cliddesden Road, Basingstoke RG21 3ER
Tel (0256) 55844
Artistic director Adrian Reynolds

Founded 1974. Seating capacity: 420. Autumn and spring seasons at the Haymarket Theatre (September to May). An accessible programme of seven plays, some in co-production with commercial management, balanced by innovative work in the Central Studio. Mid-scale and major touring is now in progress. Recent productions: *A Christmas Truce* (directed by Ian Mullins); *The Forsyte Saga* (directed by Adrian Reynolds). Approach in writing (enclosing SAE) in the first instance.

Studio theatre: Central Studio, Queen Mary's 6th Form College, with Gareth Thomas as artistic director. Seating capacity: 100+. Two productions annually. Recent productions: *Master Harold and the Boys* (directed by Adrian Reynolds).

TIE work is integrated into the main programme, with play days and sessions in the schools on request.

Stephen Joseph Theatre-in-the-Round (Scarborough Theatre Trust Ltd)

Valley Bridge, Scarborough, N. Yorks. YO11 2PL
Tel (0723) 370540
Artistic director Alan Ayckbourn
Associate director Malcolm Hebden

Founded in 1955 by Stephen Joseph as the Studio Theatre Co. Seating capacity: 303. One season from May to January, sometimes followed by a tour. Approximately nine main house productions, plus four studio lunchtime shows. Average cast size of eight. Comedy, drama, farce; considerable output of new work; classics plus some European drama. Recent productions: *Othello*, *Taking Steps*, *Abiding Passions* (all directed by Alan Ayckbourn); *Alphabetical Order* (directed by Alan Strachan); *The Price* (directed by Caroline Smith); *Same Time Next Year* (directed by Malcolm Hebden); plus world premières of all new plays by Alan Ayckbourn directed by the author. Hold general and specific auditions; ideally like to cast through a season. Do not advertise for actors: 'We don't object to casting queries from actors, but we are inundated with applications and it is impossible to see everyone who contacts us.' Contact Michele Tidy (casting director) by letter with CV, photograph and SAE. 'We cannot afford to reply to people who do not enclose an SAE.'

Studio theatre situated in restaurant area, with a seating capacity of 100. Produce 4 in-house plays annually, with an average cast size of 2–5. Musical revues, full-length plays, one-act plays, one-man shows.

Comment:
Stephen Joseph first pioneered the American idea of 'theatre-in-the-round' in 1955 at the public library in Scarborough. The aim was to create a writers' theatre – a concept that was greeted with much suspicion by the diehards, who firmly believed that writers should be kept at a distance, but which yielded results, including the fledgling talent of Alan

Ayckbourn, now the theatre's Artistic Director.

In 1976, the company moved to the former Boys' High School in Scarborough, and is now engaged in fundraising for a new home in the town's former Odeon cinema.

Library Theatre Company

Library Theatre, St Peter's Square, Manchester M2 5PD
Tel (061) 234 1913
and Forum Theatre, Leningrad Square, Wythenshawe M22 5RT
Artistic director Christopher Honer
Associate director Roger Haines

Seating capacity: 308 (Library), 483 (Forum). Season at the Library: September to April (7 plays); Forum: October to June (5 plays). Wide range of productions including new plays, musicals, contemporary drama, some classics, plus pantomime and children's shows at Christmas. Recent productions: (*Library Theatre*) *Brother Eichmann*, *Fashion* (Christopher Honer); (*Forum Theatre*) *Baby* (Roger Haines). Only advertise if looking for actors with specialist skills. Welcome written casting queries. 'The directors try to see a number of actors every year for a general audition, but most of the casting is done play by play.'

Comment:
Housed in the basement of the Central Library, this was the first theatre in Britain to be funded from the public purse and opened in 1934. The Forum Theatre opened in the mid-1970s as a sister theatre to the Library Theatre. Both theatres offer a distinctive rep

programme with an emphasis on new and unusual plays.

Liverpool Playhouse

Williamson Square, Liverpool L1 1EL
Tel (051) 709 8478
Artistic director Ian Kellgren
Associate director Kate Willard

Founded 1911. Seating capacity: 758. Seasons include comedies, classics, musicals and new plays. Recent productions: *Sleuth*, *Around the World in 80 Days* (directed by Ian Kellgren), *The Little Sisters* (directed by Chris Bond), *A View From the Bridge* (directed by Ramin Gray), *Fences* (directed by Alby James). Audition for each show in London, plus general auditions in Liverpool in the summer. Occasionally advertise in *SBS*. Welcome casting queries from actors. Write in the first instance, enclosing CV, photograph and SAE.
Studio theatre: seating capacity 100. Production plans under review.

Comment:
This is the oldest surviving repertory theatre in the country. Having started life in 1866 as the Star Music Hall, it became a rep theatre in 1911. The original stucco exterior still survives, but in 1968, a drum-like extension – housing restaurant, bars and workshops – was added, offering a stark contrast to the Victorian elegance of the old music hall architecture. The auditorium was refurbished in June 1990. In January 1991, as a result of a financial crisis caused by constant underfunding, the theatre was granted an Administration Order by the High Court. At this point the future of the Liverpool Playhouse

is still uncertain but hopes remain that it will recommence its own productions in 1991.

Lyceum Company

Lyceum Theatre, 10 Heath Street, Crewe CW1 2BZ
Tel (0270) 258818

Founded 1911. Seating capacity: 750. One season (September to March) with 20 productions in weekly repertory. Popular drama and comedy plus some classics.
At time of going to press, the theatre was dark, and had no firm plans for the future. Do not welcome casting queries from actors.

Lyric Players' Theatre

55 Ridgeway Street, Stranmillis, Belfast BT9 5FB
Tel (0232) 669660

Founded 1969. Seating capacity: 305. One season (August to June/July) with usually 11 plays. Classics, comedies, new works, Belfast plays. Recent productions: *The Importance of Being Earnest*; *Cat On a Hot Tin Roof* and *Over The Bridge* (directed by Roland Jaquarello); *Ghosts* (directed by Kim Dambaek); *The Playboy of the Western World* (directed by Jonathan Holloway). Sometimes hold general auditions, but also cast for individual productions. Do not advertise, but welcome casting queries from actors. Approach in writing in the first instance, enclosing CV and photograph.

Lyric Theatre Hammersmith & Lyric Studio

King Street, London W6 0QL
Tel (081) 741 0824
Artistic director Peter James

The Lyric have an original and exciting programme of new work and international plays. Produce four to five plays in the main house annually, and the Studio plays host to many of the best Fringe groups. Recent productions: *The House of Bernarda Alba*, *Faust*, *The Infernal Machine*, *Thark* and *Morte d'Arthur*. Subsidized rep contracts. Do not advertise for actors, but keep CVs and photographs on file for reference.

Comment:
One of the best restored theatres in London (re-opened in 1979), having been originally built in 1895.

Mercury Theatre

Balkerne Gate, Colchester, Essex
CO1 1PT
Tel (0206) 577006
Artistic director/Chief Executive Michael Winter

Founded 1972. Seating capacity: 497. Spring and autumn seasons; five productions per season plus a pantomime. Recent productions: *Charley's Aunt*; *Little Shop of Horrors*; *Our Country's Good*; *The Rivals*; *Lettice and Lovage*; and *Aladdin* (directed by Michael Winter). Hold general auditions as well as casting for individual productions. Do not usually advertise, but welcome casting queries from actors. Write enclosing CV, photograph and SAE.

Studio theatre: seating capacity approximately 65. Occasionally take in touring productions but rarely used in-house.

The Mill at Sonning (Theatre) Ltd

Sonning Eye, Reading, Berks.
RG4 0TW
Tel (0734) 696039
Artistic director Sally Hughes

Founded 1982. Seating capacity: 215. Produce nine plays (both commercial theatre and new) throughout the year, with an average cast size of six. Recent productions: *Bedroom Farce* (Alan Ayckbourn); *The Unexpected Guest* (Agatha Christie); *There's A Girl In My Soup* (Terence Frisby); *Dangerous Obsession* (N.J. Crisp). Cast for each production; advertise for actors in *Rep Report* and *SBS*. Will consider casting queries from actors. Approach in writing in the first instance.

Kenneth More Theatre

Oakfield Road, Ilford, Essex IG1 1BT
Tel (081) 553 4464
Artistic director Vivyan Ellacott

Founded 1974. Plays, musicals, opera, pantomime and studio work. Recent productions include: *Pacific Overtures*, *Lucia di Lammermoor*, *Kiss of the Spider Woman*. Plans include a major Mozart festival (all directed by Vivyan Ellacott). Do not advertise for actors, but welcome casting queries – 'by letter only. As a repertory theatre, the director is almost always in rehearsal and phone calls cannot be dealt with.' Do not hold general auditions. 'Since this theatre specializes in providing opportunities for young actors, singers and dancers very early on in their careers, there is no shortage of available artistes. The standard required is a high one, but formal drama school training is not an absolute necessity. A recommendation from someone known to us can be helpful.'

National Theatre

See **Royal National Theatre**

New Victoria Theatre

Etruria Road, Newcastle-under-Lyme, Staffs. ST5 0JG
Tel (0782) 717954
Artistic director Peter Cheeseman
Associate director Chris Martin

The New Vic moved from Stoke-on-Trent to its new theatre-in-the-round in Newcastle-under-Lyme in 1986. Seating capacity: 605. Season from July to January, with a programme of six plays (three in repertoire). Average cast size of eight. Recent productions: *I Don't Want To Set The World On Fire* (directed by Bob Eaton); *Secret Rapture* (directed by Chris Martin); *Bouncers* (directed by Rob Swain). Do not hold general auditions. Actors are usually contracted for three or four productions. Do not advertise – 'a lot of our actors are people who have written in with their details.' Unlikely to be able to reply even if an SAE is enclosed due to pressure of work.

Stephen Joseph Studio Theatre: seating capacity 150. Not used on a regular basis for productions.

Comment:
The company was previously based at the Victoria Theatre in Stoke-on-Trent, which was opened in 1962 under the eagle eye of Stephen Joseph, the pioneer of British theatre-in-the-round.

The Vic quickly established itself as a dynamic centre with its roots firmly planted in the community. Under the direction of Peter Cheeseman, it is one of the few regional theatres that steers clear of recycled West End successes.

Northampton Repertory Players Ltd

Royal Theatre, Guildhall Road, Northampton NN1 1EA
Tel (0604) 38343
Artistic director Michael Napier Brown

Theatre built by C.J. Phipps 1884. Repertory Players founded 1927. Seating capacity 439 (plus 144 in the Gallery). Average cast size of 8. Recent productions include: *How Green Was My Valley* (World Premiere directed by Michael Napier Brown); *The Way Of The World* (Richard Cheshire); *Is This The Day?* (World Premiere directed by Michael Napier Brown); *Long Day's Journey Into Night* (Mark Clements); *Hay Fever* (Philip Grout). Hold general auditions. Occasionally advertise in *The Stage*. Welcome casting enquiries: please write legibly and to the point, enclosing an SAE if you would like a reply.

Studio Theatre: (downstairs at Derngate), situated next-door to the Royal, with a capacity of 120. Produce 3 or 4 plays per year, with average cast size of 3. Recent productions include: *Kiss Of The Spiderwoman*, *Crystal Clear* (Michael Napier Brown); *Happy Jack*, *Hard Times* (Mark Clements); *Hellow And Goodbye*, *Below The Belt* (Gavin Stride).

Theatre-In-Education / Community Touring Company. Operates TIE three productions per year to local schools via local education authority. Also twice-annual Community Tour to local village and town venues. Due to popularity, 1990 tour extended into neighbouring county.

The theatre also runs a cafe-bar – Royalties – and a small shop. Highly successful launch of first subscription season in 1990.

Comment:

The Royal Theatre opened in 1884, and has remained open continuously. It is a particularly fine example of late Victorian theatre architecture, being in the gothic style. The auditorium is resplendent with red plush seats, ornate boxes, and an elaborate ceiling. Another highlight is the beautifully-painted safety curtain (Henry Bird), depicting many famous historical theatrical figures, and theatre 'mythology'. The whole theatre has been splendidly preserved, and in 1990 the Victorian facade was completely renovated.

Northcott Theatre Company

Stocker Road, Exeter EX4 4QB
Tel (0392) 56182
Artistic director John Durnin
Associate director Martin Harvey

Founded 1967. Seating capacity: 433. Between nine and ten plays produced annually, from mid-April to end of January. Wide range of productions, from musicals and serious contemporary work to classics. Recent productions: *Thark*; *Witness for the Prosecution*; *Falling In Love Again* (World Premiere); *The Sleeping Beauty* (directed by Martin Harvey); *Serious Money* (directed by George Roman). Usually hold general auditions once a year. Do not advertise for actors but welcome casting queries – 'although there is a very limited number we can see.' Approach in writing in the first instance.

Studio theatre seating up to 100, producing mainly contemporary plays (two per year with a cast size of 2–6). Recent productions: *Gosforth's Fete/ Steinway Grand/The Anniversary* (triple bill directed by George Roman); *The Hypnos Hormone* (new chamber opera, directed by Martin Harvey); *The Ruffian On The Stair* and *Funeral Games* (directed by Martin Harvey).

Northern Stage

67a Westgate Road, Newcastle upon Tyne NE1 1SG
Tel (091) 232 3366
Fax (091) 261 9699

Founded 1989. The largest professional producing theatre company between York and Edinburgh. It is charged with providing high quality theatre for the north of England. It has no theatre building of its own, but utilizes a diverse range of different scale venues. Will generally audition for each production. Rarely advertise but will consider letters from actors, 'provided that the volume of applications is understood. It is not possible for us to acknowledge or reply to actors' letters without an SAE. We expect to receive a considerable number of letters each year, and it is unfortunately impossible for us to meet more than a small percentage of those who write.'

TIE company (*see* entry for 'Tynewear Theatre in Education' in **Theatre-in-Education companies**).

Nottingham Playhouse

Wellington Circus, Nottingham
NG1 5AF
Tel (0602) 474361
Fax (0602) 475759
Executive Director Ruth Mackenzie
Artistic director Pip Broughton
Administrative director Stuart Rogers

Founded 1948. Seating capacity: 685–766. Ten plays produced annually, playing for three weeks each. A wide range of productions with an international flavour and an average cast size of ten. Recent productions: The Market Theatre of Johannesburg's production of *My Children! My Africa!*; *The Importance of Being Earnest*, *Therese Raquin* and *Two-Way Mirror* (all directed by Pip Broughton); *Puss In Boots* (directed by Kenneth Alan Taylor). Rarely advertise for actors. Cast for each production, holding specific and general auditions in London and Nottingham. Will consider letters from actors: 'Always enclose photo, CV and SAE with first application.'

Do not have a studio theatre.

TIE company (*see* entry for 'Roundabout Theatre Company' in **Theatre-in-Education companies**).

Nuffield Theatre

University Road, Southampton
SO9 5NH
Tel (0703) 671871
Artistic director Patrick Sandford

Founded 1964. Seating capacity: 506. Autumn/spring season, with occasional late spring and early summer productions. Approximately seven plays, plus a Christmas show each year. Recent productions: *Exchanges*; *Around The World In 80 Days* (adapted by Patrick Sandford); *The Winter Wife*. Do not, as a rule, hold general auditions; occasionally advertise for actors. Welcome casting queries; write enclosing CV and photograph, and SAE if a reply is required.

TIE: hoping to start a company in the not-too-distant future.

Comment:
This lively rep company has a reputation for producing new plays, modern American classics and European plays not previously seen in the UK. A number of shows transfer to London's West End. *Daisy Pulls It Off* was a notable transfer.

Octagon Theatre

Howell Croft South, Bolton, Lancs.
BL1 1SB
Tel (0204) 29407
Artistic director Andrew Hay
Associate director Romy Baskerville

Founded 1967. Seating capacity: 350–420 (flexible). Two seasons – spring and autumn; four plays per season. Average cast size of 10/11. New plays, musicals. Recent productions include: *In the Midnight Hour* and *Road* (directed by Andrew Hay); *Blue Remembered Hills* and *No Worries* (Romy Baskerville). Do not usually hold general auditions; try to through cast. Occasionally advertise in *The Stage*. Welcome casting queries: approach in writing in the first instance. 'Although we get swamped with letters, we do try to reply to them all if an SAE is enclosed.'

Studio theatre: seating capacity 100. Takes in touring productions.

Youth theatre: Ian Hastings (director). For local children. Two groups: 11–13 and 14–18 years old. Two or three performances each year in the studio theatre.

Oldham Coliseum

Fairbottom Street, Oldham, Lancs.
OL1 3SW
Tel (061) 624 1731
Artistic director Paul Kerryson

Founded 1887 (theatre), 1978 (company). Seating capacity: 576. Season from September to June, comprising eight or more plays and one pantomime. Wide range of productions – new plays, classics, musicals. Average cast size of ten. Recent productions: *East; Richard III; Teechers;* and *Hot Stuff* (directed by Paul Kerryson). Cast for each production, but also hold general auditions. Do not advertise for actors but welcome casting queries. Approach in writing in the first instance. 'We receive thousands, but no theatre favours an initial approach by phone. Try to explain your particular interest in a specific company or play rather than "Dear Sir . . ." '

Palace Theatre

Clarendon Road, Watford WD1 1JZ
Tel (0923) 35455
Artistic director Lou Stein

Founded 1908. Seating capacity: 663. Autumn season: September to December. Spring season: January to May. Nine plays annually with average cast size of seven to eight. Produce new adaptations of classics, musicals, comedy and specially commissioned works. Recent productions: *Tartuffe; Period of Adjustment; The Marriage of Figaro; Widowers' Houses.* Cast for each production through Agents.

Comment:
This superb Edwardian theatre often takes on the West End at its own game and wins.

Palace Theatre

London Road, Westcliff-on-Sea, Essex
SS0 9LA
Tel (0702) 347816
Artistic director Christopher Dunham

Seating capacity: 612. Autumn/winter and spring seasons, and occasionally one in the summer. Recent productions: *Run For Your Wife; Dangerous Obsession; Mixed Blessings; M. Butterfly; Privates On Parade; Ladies Night.* Do not hold general auditions. Do not welcome query letters: 'we are inundated with them.'

Studio theatre and TIE company (*see* **Theatre-in-Education companies**).

Perth Repertory Theatre

185 High Street, Perth PH1 5UW
Tel (0738) 38123
Artistic director Joan Knight OBE

Founded 1935. Seating capacity: 470. Produce ten plays, plus a traditional pantomime, each year between August and May. Average cast size of ten. Recent productions: *Dangerous Obsession* (directed by Ken Alexander); *Who's Afraid of Virginia Woolf?* (directed by Clive Perry); *An Inspector Calls* (directed by Joan Knight); *The Steamie* (directed by John Buick); *Piaf* (directed by Terry Wale). General auditions usually held in June. Do not advertise, but welcome casting queries from actors. Approach in writing in the first instance. 'Perth Theatre has a policy of employing Scottish, or mainly Scottish-based, actors.'

Studio theatre with a seating capacity of 100. Produce two plays annually with an average cast size of four. Recent productions: *Macbeth* (adapted by John Clifford, directed by Ken Alexander); *The Scotch Play* (written by Ian Brown, directed by Joan Knight).

Pitlochry Festival Theatre

Port-na-Craig, Pitlochry, Perthshire
PH16 5DR
Tel (0796) 3054
Festival director Clive Perry

Founded 1951. Seating capacity: 544. Season (repertoire) of six plays, May–October. Average company of 22/25 actors. 1991 season: *What Every Woman Knows*; *How The Other Half Loves*; *The Ghost Train*; *Lettice and Lovage*; *The Hypochondriack* (translated by Victor Carin into Scots); *The Magistrate*. Auditions held each January in London, plus additional auditions in Edinburgh in mid-February. A lot of cross casting, and actors must be prepared to accept a seven-month contract (rehearsals begin early March). Do not advertise, but welcome letters with CVs and photographs at the end of the year.

Queen's Theatre

Billet Lane, Hornchurch, Essex
RM11 1QT
Tel (04024) 56118
Artistic director Bob Tomson

Founded 1952. Seating capacity: 506. Four/five weekly rep from September to June plus national tours, West End transfers and ten-week pantomime. Eight plays annually with an average cast size of ten. Recent productions: *Shakers*; *Catch Me If You Can*; *South Pacific*; *Sinbad – The Great Adventure*

(world premiere); *Tallulah Who* (world premiere – proposed West End transfer – February 1991). Do not hold general auditions. Cross cast, but 'not longer than two productions because of tax code laws'. Try to employ from within a 25-mile radius. Do not advertise but welcome casting queries from actors. Write in the first instance enclosing CV, photograph and SAE. Bob Tomson particularly looks for actors with varied skills, e.g. circus skills. 'Since the Arts Council withdrew funding four years ago, the company has to earn seventy per cent of its costs (thirty per cent coming from local government and Greater London Arts). Productions tend to be populist therefore and usually contemporary.'

Royal Exchange Theatre Company

Royal Exchange, St Ann's Square, Manchester M2 7DH
Tel (061) 833 9333
Artistic directors Gregory Hersov, James Maxwell, Braham Murray
Associate directors Phyllida Lloyd, Wyllie Longmore, Sophie Marshall

Opened 1976 (formerly 69 Theatre Co., founded 1968). Seating capacity: 750. Produce eight to ten plays annually between September and August, with runs of $2^1/_2$–$6^1/_2$ weeks. Plays range from Shakespeare, Shaw and Chekhov to modern playwrights such as Iain Heggie, Michael Wall and Wole Soyinka. Recent productions: *The Winter's Tale* (directed by Phyllida Lloyd); *The Crucible* (Gregory Hersov); *The School For Scandal* (Phyllida Lloyd); *The Tempest* (Braham Murray); *Donny Boy* (Caspar Wrede); and *The Beggar's*

Opera (Gregory Hersov). Do not advertise for actors, but season details are mailed to agents and *PCR*. Each production is cast separately. 'We only keep CVs and photos on file if they are likely to be relevant to our casting over subsequent months – otherwise, we would have thousands of out-of-date CVs and drawers too full to cope with. If actors send an SAE, we will reply eventually.' Letters should be addressed to the casting director: Sophie Marshall.

Comment:
This is one of the country's foremost producing theatres, featuring a mixture of classics, revivals and new work, in addition to which there is a varied programme of special events.

Royal Lyceum Theatre Company

Royal Lyceum Theatre, Grindlay Street, Edinburgh EH3 9AX
Tel (031) 229 7404 Fax (031) 228 3955
Artistic director Ian Wooldridge
Associate director Hugh Hodgart

Founded 1965. Seating capacity: 773. Three seasons – autumn, spring and summer. Four plays in each, plus Christmas show. Classics, new Scottish plays, translations and adaptations. Average cast size of 11. Recent productions: *The Country Wife*, *The Crucible*, *Hiawatha*, *Changed Days* (Alan Spence). Do not advertise, but welcome casting queries from actors. Approach in writing in the first instance. 'We cast for each production, but also hold auditions for Scottish-based actors when time allows.'

Royal National Theatre

Upper Ground, South Bank, London SE1 9PX
Tel (071) 928 2033 Telex 297306
Artistic director Richard Eyre
Executive director Genista McIntosh
Casting directors Serena Hill (head of casting), Alison Chard, John Cannon

Founded 1963. In 1976, the company moved from the Old Vic to its new home on the South Bank. The National houses three separate theatres: the Olivier (seating 1160), the Lyttelton (890) and the Cottesloe (400). The NT also has a Studio, based at the Old Vic Annexe, which is used as an experimental workshop for the company and to encourage new writing. Sir Peter Hall was succeeded by Richard Eyre as artistic director in September 1988.

Present a diverse repertoire embracing classics and new and neglected plays. Productions are cast from play to play with some cross casting. The casting directors occasionally hold interview sessions, but general auditions are not held. Performance notices are welcomed; the casting directors independently cover shows every night of the week. Letters and CVs from actors referring to a specific production are kept in the relevant production file for reference when casting. General letters enclosing CV and photographs are also kept on file for future reference. Actors must be full Equity members (although, on a few occasions, Equity has waived this ruling).

Royal Shakespeare Company

Barbican Theatre, Barbican Centre, London EC2Y 8DS
and Royal Shakespeare Theatre, Stratford-upon-Avon, Warwicks CV37 6BB
Tel (071) 628 3351 (Barbican Theatre) Fax (071) 374 0818
Artistic director Adrian Noble

The Royal Shakespeare Company has two centres. At Stratford is the Royal Shakespeare Theatre (seating 1500) and the Swan Theatre (400); the Other Place is currently closed for rebuilding until mid-1991. In London, there is the Barbican Theatre (seating 1162) and The Pit (200).

Apart from its Shakespeare productions, the RSC has a commitment to new plays and new writers. Only Shakespeare's plays are presented at the Royal Shakespeare Theatre, but at the Swan Theatre, recent productions have ranged from plays by contemporaries of Shakespeare to the work of Chekhov and Richard Nelson. In London, recent productions have ranged from works of Gorky to that of Peter Flannery. An actor's life within the company usually starts in Stratford and then transfers to London. A number of new plays are added to the London season which means that some additional actors join the company according to production requirements. Contracts are generally for two years (one year in Stratford and one year in London).

Do not hold general auditions. Actors are invited to audition after a casting director or director has seen their work. Welcome CVs, photographs and performance notices. Advise making contact around Christmas time when casting for the new season at Stratford commences. Correspondence should be addressed to Corrinne Rodriguez (casting director) at the Barbican Theatre.

Salisbury Playhouse

Malthouse Lane, Salisbury, Wilts. SP2 7RA
Tel (0722) 20117
Artistic director Deborah Paige

Founded 1975. Main House seating capacity: 516. One season August to June with 10–11 productions. Recent productions: *The Recruiting Officer* and *Jamaica Inn* (directed by David Horlock); *Sweeney Todd* and *Daisy Pulls It Off* (Graham Berown); *Uncle Vanya* (Annie Castledine), *Dick Whittington* (Graham Berown).

Do not hold general auditions. Try to cross cast as much as possible. Do not advertise for actors, but happy to receive enquiry letters enclosing CV, photograph and SAE. Details kept on file for a certain period of time.

Salberg Studio Theatre: seating capacity 100. In-house and touring companies. Approximately 12 productions from August to June. Recent productions: *Winter in Majorca* (David Horlock); *Moll Flanders* and *The Life and Adventures of Nicholas Nickleby* (Lynn Wyfe); *The Colony Comes A Cropper!* (Monstrous Regiment); *The Road To Mecca* (Millstream Touring).

TIE company (*see* **Theatre-in-Education companies**).

Sherman Theatre

Senghennydd Road, Off Park Place,
Cardiff CF2 4YE
Tel (0222) 396844
Artistic director Phil Clark

Main Theatre seating capacity: 472. Season: All year but closed August. Approximately seven to eight plays annually. Take in touring productions as well as touring own shows. Recent productions: *The Secret Diary of Adrian Mole* (directed by Phil Clark); *Up 'N' Under* (directed by Jamie Garven); *The Caretaker* (directed by Annie Castledine); *The Snow Spider* (Christmas show, directed by Phil Clark). Do not hold general auditions; cast per show. Sometimes advertise in *SBS* and Equity *Job Grapevine*. Welcome casting queries, send SAE if acknowledgement required. Casting Assistant Patti Wallis.

Arena Theatre – studio space seating 150/160. Touring and a number of in-house productions. Recent productions: *The Lost Child* (children's Christmas show for under 5s).
Hold workshops and summer schools for local youngsters.

Swan Theatre

The Moors, Worcester WR1 3EF
Tel (0905) 726969
Artistic director Pat Trueman
Assistant director vacant

Founded 1965. Seating capacity: 350. One season: August to March. Seven productions plus a Christmas show. Average cast size of ten. Broad range of productions, some with local appeal. Recent productions: *Our Country's Good* (Pat Trueman); *The Recruiting Officer* (Jenny Stephens); *The History of Tom Jones* (Pat Trueman). Sometimes hold general auditions. Do not advertise for actors. Welcome casting queries; write enclosing CV, photograph and SAE.
Studio theatre: not currently in use.

Theatr Clwyd

County Civic Centre, Mold, Clwyd
CH7 1YA
Tel (0352) 56331
Artistic director Toby Robertson
Casting Cheryl Nance

Founded 1978. Seating capacity: 530–570 (flexible staging). Spring, autumn and winter seasons. Approximately 10–12 productions (including Emlyn Williams studio theatre). Wide range of productions, including a percentage of new work. Recent productions: *Time and The Conways* (directed by Richard Olivier); *The Importance of Being Earnest* (direct by Toby Robertson); and *Swallows and Amazons* (directed by Marina Calderone). Do not hold general auditions. Very little cross casting. Casting details given to agents. Approach in writing, enclosing CV, photograph and SAE.

Emlyn Williams Theatre: flexible studio space with a seating capacity of 160–250. Recent productions: *The Constant Wife* (directed by Lucy Parker); *Daisy Pulls It Off* and *A Prayer for Wings* (Marina Calderone).

TIE company: Clwyd is served by Theatr Outreach Theatre Company (*see* **Theatre-in-Education companies**).

Theatre Royal

King Street, Bristol BS1 4ED
Tel (0272) 277466
Artistic director Paul Unwin

One of the country's oldest theatres, built in 1766. Seating capacity: 645. Autumn and spring seasons, with four plays per season. Production policy has been revised since Paul Unwin took over as artistic director in 1988. Recent productions: *Hamlet, Pal Joey, Lond Day's Journey Into Night, Uncle Vanya, The Clandestine Marriage, The Red Balloon.* Do not hold general auditions and do not advertise for actors: 'We cast from *Spotlight.*' Welcome casting queries; write in the first instance, enclosing CV, photograph and SAE.

Theatre Royal & The Drum Theatre

Royal Parade, Plymouth, Devon
PL1 2TR
Tel (0752) 668282
Artistic director Roger Redfarn

'We do not run a permanent company. The majority of main-house productions are done in conjunction with commercial managements (*see* **Non-producing theatres**). Drum Theatre Productions – the studio company – occasionally tour. We rarely hold general auditions because of the very nature of our work, and for large-scale musical productions, we always hold open auditions, which are advertised in *The Stage.* We are always anxious to hear of actors who live in the West Country or have a West Country background.'

Thorndike Theatre

Church Street, Leatherhead, Surrey
KT22 8DF
Tel (0372) 376211

Founded 1969. Seating capacity: 526. Own productions plus studio work,

YPT, TIE and occasional Sunday shows. A wide range of productions including West End transfers ('Regrettably, we are not able to build on our studio work record'). Average cast size of eight. Productions include: *Stepping Out* (première; directed by Julia McKenzie); *The Country Girl* (Robin Lefevre); *The Maintenance Man* (Roger Clissold). No general auditions. Normally cast show by show, with some cross casting. Do not advertise for actors.

The Casson Room studio theatre: seating capacity 60–100. Very little home-based work; mostly incoming tours, plus YPT activity.

TIE company (*see* **Theatre-in-Education companies**).

Torch Theatre Company Ltd

Torch Theatre, St Peter's Road, Milford Haven, Dyfed SA73 2BU
Tel (0646) 694192
Artistic director Kit Thacker

Founded 1977. Seating capacity: 297. One season of eight plays from June to February. Produce drama, comedy, classics, musicals and a Christmas show. Average cast size of nine. Recent productions: *Under Milk Wood* and *Mr. Polly* (directed by Mike James); *Cleudo, Lovers* and *Master Harold and the Boys* (directed by Kit Thacker); *Same Time, Next Year* (directed by Gareth Armstrong); *Merlin's Return* (Christopher Pilkington and Kit Thacker). Through casting with some one-offs; 2 tours per year in West Wales and beyond. Advertise in *SBS,* and welcome letters of enquiry from actors.

Comment:
This is very much a theatre for the community, with a good mixture of plays and musicals from the resident company.

Traverse Theatre

112 West Bow, Grassmarket,
Edinburgh EH1 2HH
Tel (031) 226 2633
Fax (031) 225 3308
Artistic director Ian Brown

Founded 1963. Seating capacity: 100. Usually have a season between April and December with an average cast size of four. Renowned for its policy of producing new plays by British and international writers previously unperformed in Britain. Recent productions: *Hardy and Baird* (James Kelman); *Hour of the Lynx* (Per Olav Enquist); *The Bench* (Alexander Gelman); *The Bondagers* (Sue Glover). Do not advertise for actors, but welcome casting queries. 'Replies and acknowledgements only sent if SAE has been enclosed. Do not bother to send more than one CV per year. Do not follow up a CV with a phone call asking for an audition. If you are Scottish, do mention it when writing to Scottish theatres – Scots are filed separately here. Put name and address on back of photo.'
Studio theatre: seating capacity 75.

Comment:
One of the mainstays of the annual Edinburgh Festival, the Traverse presents a programme of progressive new work with the emphasis on Scottish playwrights. It has long been hailed as one of the most original theatre companies in Britain. Once a warehouse, what the theatre lacks in luxury it makes up for in creativity.

Watermill Theatre

Bagnor, nr Newbury, Berks.
RG16 8AE
Tel (0635) 45834
Artistic director Jill Fraser

Founded 1967. Seating capacity: 185. Five plays in the main season (April–January) plus a Christmas show. Average cast size of six. Recent productions: *Moll Flanders; Toad of Toad Hall; An Inspector Calls; Cold Comfort Farm; Good Morning Bill* (P.G. Wodehouse); *My Wife Whatsername* (Christopher G. Sandford). Do not advertise for actors, but welcome letters of enquiry. Hold auditions for each production; no general auditions.

West Yorkshire Playhouse

Quarry Hill Mount, Leeds, W. Yorks.
LS9 8AW
Tel (0532) 442141
Artistic director Jude Kelly

Founded 1990. Twin auditoria: The Quarry (seating 750), and The Courtyard (seating 350). Repertory throughout the year. Varied range of productions – classics, comedies and new plays. Recent productions: *Ghosts; Sugar; Sunsets and Glories; Second From Last In The Sack Race; All My Sons; The Pope And The Witch.* Do nto advertise for actors, but welcome casting queries. Approach in writing in the first instance, enclosing CV, photograph and SAE.
TIE company (*see* **Leeds Theatre-in-Education**).

Windsor Theatre Company

Theatre Royal, Thames Street,
Windsor, Berks. SL4 1PS
Tel (0753) 863444
Artistic director Mark Piper

Founded 1938. Seating capacity: 633.
Produce 14 plays throughout the year,
with an average cast size of nine. A
programme of comedy, thrillers, classics and pantomime. Recent productions: *Otherwise Engaged*; *The
Philanthropist*; *Say Who You Are*; *Lettice
And Lovage*. Cast for each production.
Do not advertise for actors, and do not
welcome casting queries.

Wolsey Theatre Company

Civic Drive, Ipswich, Suffolk IP1 2AS
Tel (0473) 218911
Artistic director Antony Tuckey
Executive director Nick Jones

Founded 1979. Seating capacity: 410.
Produce 12–14 plays over a 46-week
period. Average cast size of 13. Recent
productions: *The Secret Rapture*, *The
Winter's Tale*, *Loot*, *Barefoot in The Park*,
Carousel. Cast for each production, but
also hold general auditions. Do not
generally advertise for actors, but welcome casting queries. Send a letter
with an SAE if a reply is required.

TIE company (*see* **Theatre-in-Education companies**).

York Theatre Royal

St Leonard's Place, York YO1 2HD
Tel (0904) 658162 Fax (0904) 611534
Artistic director Derek Nicholls

Founded 1934. Seating capacity: 899.
Produce ten shows annually, with five
incoming tours. Average cast size of
ten. Classics, new writing and pantomime. Recent productions: *West Side
Story*; *Wuthering Heights*; *Private Lives*;
One For The Road. Do not advertise for
actors, but welcome casting queries.

9 Producing Theatres and Independent Managements

The conditions and opportunities for actors in these companies is similar to those in repertory theatres and large- and mid-scale touring: touring is a normal activity for many companies. The main distinctions are that the variety of the repertory system will be absent, and contracts normally much longer. In high-profile shows in the West End or on the number one touring circuit, there will be less opportunities for unknowns in terms of casting. However, there are elaborate understudy arrangements which enable the young and inexperienced to learn, rehearse, and on occasion perform, major roles. For more established actors there is the chance of relative security in long and decently-paid contracts. There are many more opportunities for talented singers and dancers with the independent managements, given the current public taste for large-budget musicals.

Albemarle of London

74 Mortimer Street, London W1N 7DF
Tel (071) 631 0135
Contact Sulie Branscombe

Pantomimes and an occasional tour and Summer Season. Productions include: *Snow White* and *The Pied Piper*, both directed by Basil Chritchley. Occasionally advertise in *The Stage*. 'Don't mind casting queries, but usually deal through agents and our casting advisor, so keep a few actors' details on file. Telephone – followed, if requested, with photo and CV.' Hold both invited and general auditions.

Chichester Festival Theatre Productions Ltd

Oaklands Park, Chichester, W. Sussex PO19 4AP
Tel (0243) 784437 Fax (0243) 787288

Founded 1962. Festival season from April to September. 1990 productions: *The Merry Wives Of Windsor* (directed by Michael Rudman); *The Power and The Glory* (Tim Luscombe); *The Silver King* (Peter Wood); *Rumours* (Michael Rudman); *Born Again* (Peter Hall). New Minerva Theatre (1989) adds high-quality studio work to main-house repertoire. Do not advertise for actors, but welcome casting queries. Write, initially, in the new year, to Martin Harris, Administrator. Some-times hold general auditions. 'We have a policy of trying to help when-ever possible.'

Ron Coburn International Productions

Vaudevilla, Elliot Road, Dundee
DD2 1SY
Tel (0382) 69025
Contact Ron Coburn, Callum Coburn

Founded 1963. Scottish musical enter-tainments, pantomimes, world tours, Canadian/American tours, theatre revues, TV shows. Credits include: *A Breath of Scotland*, *The Waggle o' the Kilt*, *Shamrocks and Heather*, *The Royal Clansmen*. Do not advertise, but wel-come letters from actors, which 'will be entered on file and used if the occa-sion arises'. Do not hold general audi-tions. 'Only interested in actors in my own area. In this way, local actors, artistes and Equity members are not passed over by TV companies by buss-ing people in from the larger cities due to the lack of information on the avail-ability of people in the east of Scotland, north of the Forth.'

Michael Codron Ltd

Aldwych Theatre Offices, Aldwych,
London WC2B 4DF
Tel (071) 240 8291
Fax (071) 240 8467
Contact Joe Scott Parkinson

Manage the Aldwych and Adelphi Theatres and own the Vaudeville Theatre in the West End. Usually big-time fare like *Woman in Mind* with Julia McKenzie. Do not advertise for actors, although query letters from actors are welcome and will be acknowledged if an SAE is enclosed. Casting is usually up to individual directors of each play, in association with Mr Codron.

Compass Theatre Limited

Dean Clough, Halifax, W. Yorks.
HX3 5AX
Tel (0422) 345631
Fax (0422) 347256
Contact Pat Frederiksen (assistant director), Julian Forrester (general manager)

Founded 1984. Plays (mainly classical) on No. 1 tours and West End. Credits include: *The Tempest* (Anthony Quayle); *The Royal Hunt of the Sun* (Tim Piggott-Smith); *Julius Caesar* (Michael Joyce). Do not advertise, but welcome casting queries from actors. Approach in writing in the first instance. Cast for specific productions. Do not usually hold general auditions.

Mervyn Conn Organization

MC House, 14 Orange Street, London
WC2H 7ED
Tel (071) 930 7502

The *Annie* tour is the first piece of theatre the organization have pro-duced. Will advertise start of casting in

The Stage and other theatrical publications. Do hold general auditions, but do not welcome queries from actors, as there can be such long lapses between productions.

Ray Cooney Presentations Ltd

Duchess Theatre, Catherine Street,
London WC2B 5LA
Tel (071) 497 7701
Contact Mr H. S. Udwin

Founded 1965. Mainly comedies in the West End, Australia, United States and Canada. Credits include: *Rookery Nook*, *Run for Your Wife*, *Two into One*, *Pygmalion* and *Out Of Order* all directed by Ray Cooney. Do not advertise for actors, and do not welcome casting queries. Hold general auditions.

Co-Producers

161a Kennington Park Road, London
SE11 4JJ
Tel (071) 735 0769
Fax (071) 735 6273
Contact Joanna Hole, Eric Standidge
(joint artistic directors)

Founded 1986. Provincial touring on large and middle scale, straight plays, new plays and classical revivals. Productions include: *A Pin To See The Peepshow* (F. Tennyson-Jesse); *Totally Foxed* (Justin Greene and Steve Cooke); *Uncle Vanya; Loot* (Joe Orton). Advertise for actors in *SBS*. Welcome casting queries from actors, either by telephone or letter. Do not hold general auditions. 'We usually co-produce with subsidized repertory theatres and then tour.'

Cotes Logan Productions Ltd

Reg. office: Chancery House,
Chancery Lane, London WC2
Production office: 7 Hill Lawn Court,
Chipping Norton, Oxon
Tel (0608) 41208
Contact Peter Cotes, John Jevons

Founded 1947. West End and touring productions. Credits include: *The Children's Hour*, *A Pin to See the Peepshow*, *Home of the Brave*, *Candida*, *Land of the Living*, *The Long Mirror*, *For Services Rendered*, *Back to Methuselah*, *Miss Julie*, *Anna Christie*, *Rocket to the Moon*, *Pick Up Girl*, *John Gabriel Borkman*, *The Old Ladies*, *Janie Jackson*, *Staring At The Sun*, *Look No Hands*, *Caste*, *Happy And Glorious*, *The Rising Wind*, etc. (all directed by Peter Cotes). Do not advertise, but welcome casting queries from actors. Approach in writing in the first instance. Hold general auditions 'when the occasion arises'.

Cwmni Theatr Gwynedd

Theatr Gwynedd, Ffordd Deiniol,
Bangor, Gwynedd LL57 2TL
Tel (0248) 351707
Artistic director Graham Laker
Contact Graham Laker, J.O. Roberts,
John Ogwen, William R. Lewis.

Founded 1983. English musicals for summer seasons and, since 1986, a wide range of Welsh-language productions. Productions include: *Happy as a Sandbag, Relatively Speaking, Sleuth, Oliver* and *O Law I Law* (all directed by Graham Laker); *Cymerwch Chi Sigaret?* (William R. Lewis); *Lle Mynno'r Gwynt* (Grey Evans); *Plas Dafydd* (John Ogwen). Do not advertise for actors, but welcome casting queries; write in the first instance with photograph and

CV. Do not hold general auditions, but cast for each production with auditions as required. 'The company concentrates mainly on Welsh-language productions, touring within Wales, and always welcomes information from Welsh-speaking actors.'

Dramatis Personae Ltd

122 Kennington Road, London
SE11 6RE
Tel (071) 735 0831
Contact Maria Aitken, Nathan Silver

Founded 1983. Plays (West End and tours) and TV co-productions. Productions include: *Happy Family* by Giles Cooper and *Are You Sitting Comfortably?* by Sue Townsend (directed by Maria Aitken); *Sister Mary Ignatius Explains It All for You* by Christopher Durang (Richard Digby Day); *The Vortex* by Noël Coward (Philip Prowse). Do not advertise for actors. Do not especially welcome queries from actors as 'we prefer to make enquiries ourselves.' Write in the first instance – replies are not guaranteed due to staff limitations. To date, have not held general auditions. 'Our production work is sporadic and currently mainly in television.'

E & B Productions Ltd

Suite 3, Waldorf Chambers, 11 Aldwych, London WC2B 4DA
Tel (071) 836 2795
Fax (071) 379 4892
Contact Paul Elliott, Brian Hewitt-Jones

Previous productions include: *Run for Your Wife, Pirates of Penzance; Fifteen Streets*; and the hit musical *Buddy*; as well as up to 20 pantomimes each winter. Advertise in *The Stage* for dancers, and welcome query letters from actors for the Christmas shows. Hold general auditions.

Each World Productions

1 King's House, 396 King's Road, London SW10 0LL
and 43 Moormead Road, St. Margaret's, Twickenham TW1 1JS
Tel (081) 352 1852 and
(081) 892 0908
Contact David Adams, Mandie Joel

Founded 1984. Specialize in plays, musicals, TV drama, documentaries and feature films. Productions include: *Tales from a Long Room* (world première) and *Uncle Mort's North Country* at Lyric Hammersmith (directed by Peter James); *Cowboys No. 2* (British première) by Sam Shepard (David Adams); two West End productions of *Wren*, musical written and directed by David Adams. Advertise for actors in *PCR*, *SBS*. Welcome casting queries from actors; write in the first instance, unless it has been specified in casting publications that it is all right to telephone. Do not hold general auditions. 'It is always a bonus if an actor knows about the part he is going up for – reading the book or play is always a good idea.' Working on *The Cards of the Gambler*, a feature film to be shot in Dublin and Spain. Mainly Irish casting commencing no sooner than late 91/92.

English Shakespeare Company Ltd

369 St John Street, London EC1V 4LB
Tel (071) 278 7970
Fax (071) 278 7978
Contact Ludo Keston (general manager), Sue Evans (administrative assistant)

Founded 1986. Joint artistic directors: Michael Bogdanov and Michael Pennington. Recent productions: *Coriolanus*, *The Winter's Tale*, *The Merchant Of Venice*, *Volpone*. Two touring companies, plus an education company (not TIE) which recently presented *God Say Amen*. Do not advertise, but welcome casting queries from actors; approach in writing in the first instance. Do not hold general auditions.

Vanessa Ford Productions Ltd

Upper House Farm, Upper House Lane, Skarnley Green, Guildford GU5 0SX
Tel (0483) 268530
Contact Vanessa Ford

Founded 1979. Tours of plays – family entertainment and classics. Productions include: *One For The Road*, *A Man for All Seasons*, *Rosencrantz and Guildenstern Are Dead*, *The Importance of Being Earnest*, 15 productions of Shakespeare plays, *The Lion, the Witch and the Wardrobe* and other Narnia plays, *Winnie the Pooh*, *Noddy*, *Tales Of Toad Hall*, *A Christmas Carol*. Do not usually advertise, but welcome casting queries; send letter with CV and photograph. Sometimes hold general auditions.

Robert Fox Ltd

6 Beauchamp Place, London SW3 1HG
Tel (071) 584 6855
Fax (071) 225 1638
Contact Robert Hughes, Sally Champion, Kate Carter

Founded 1980. Plays and musicals in the West End. Credits include: *Anything Goes* (directed by Sally Zaks); *Burn This* (directed by Robert Ackerman); *Lettice and Lovage* (directed by Michael Blakemore); *Chess* (Trevor Nunn); *Another Country* (Stuart Burge). Occasionally advertise in *The Stage*. Prefer correspondence from actors when they are casting. Do not hold general auditions.

Freeshooter Productions Ltd

10 Clorane Gardens, London NW3 7PR
Tel (071) 794 0414

Founded 1979. Plays and musicals, West End and touring. Credits include: *The Petition* (directed by Sir Peter Hall); *Kipling* (Patrick Garland); *Godspell* (Paul Kerryson); *March of the Falsettos*; *Siegfried Sassoon*. Sometimes advertise in *SBS*, but do not welcome casting queries from actors. Do not hold general auditions.

Jill Freud & Company

22 Wimpole Street, London W1M 7AD
Tel (071) 580 2222
Contact Jill Freud

Founded 1980. Annual summer season at Southwold, plus an autumn tour of a classic such as *Under Milk Wood* and *Arms and the Man*. Credits also include: *Educating Rita* (directed by Knight Mantell); *A Man For All Seasons* (Richard Howard); *Stepping Out* (Kit Thacker); *Pack of Lies* (Nat Brenner). Casting takes place from February to April each year.

Mark Furness Ltd

10 Garrick Street, London WC2E 9BH
Tel (071) 836 7373

Recent productions include: *'Allo 'Allo* at the Palladium; *The Boys Next Door* at the Comedy; *Peter Pan* at the Cambridge; and *Dangerous Obsession* at the Apollo and the Fortune. Tours and Seasons include *A Murder Is Announced*, *Gypsy*, *Forsyte Saga*, and *Rumours*. Advertise in *PCR*, *SBS*, *The Stage*, and *Cast Call/Sneak Preview* telephone lines. Welcome query letters for specific productions, are usually unable to reply to all applicants, but CVs kept on file and used.

Trevor George Entertainments (UK) (Stairway Productions)

42 Marldon Road, Shiphay, Torquay, Devon TQ2 7EJ
Tel (0803) 613752 (3 lines)
Contact Trevor George or Billie George (director), Merle Knapman (secretary)

Founded 1959. Pantomime and summer shows in the provinces. Productions include various pantomimes directed by Billie George. Occasionally advertise for actors in *The Stage*. Welcome casting queries from

actors; write in the first instance. Do hold general auditions.

Francis Golightly Productions

7 Riverside Walk, Colchester, Essex CO1 1RD
Tel (0206) 765057
Fax (0206) 765057
Contact Francis Golightly

Founded 1973. Revue, pantomime and variety shows in provincial theatres. Occasionally advertise in *The Stage*, and welcome casting queries from actors. Telephone in the first instance. Do not hold general auditions.

Hiss & Boo Music Hall Company

24 West Grove, Waltham on Thames, Surrey KT12 5NX
Tel (0932) 248931
Contact Ian Liston

Founded 1976. West End and touring musicals, plays and children's shows. Credits include: *Novello: A Chance to Dream*; *Dear Ivor* and *Nunsense* (directed by Richard Digby Day); *Benefactors* (Stephen Barry); *Cluedo* (Hugh Goldie); *Corpse!* (Gerald Moon); *See How They Run* (Leslie Lawton); *Groucho: A Life in Revue* (with Triumph Theatre Productions; directed by Arthur Marx). Occasionally advertise in *The Stage*; do not hold general auditions. Will consider letters from actors: 'We will always reply to applicants who enclose an SAE. Actor's details are kept on file and frequently referred to during the course of the year.'

Bruce Hyman & Harvey Kass Ltd

5 Brewer Street, London W1R 3FN
Tel (071) 439 1984
Fax (071) 494 2570
Contact Bruce Hyman, Harvey Kass

Founded 1986. Plays and musicals – West End and tours. Credits include: *The Life of Napoleon*; *The Foreigner*; *The Mystery of Edwin Drood*; *A Life in the Theatre*; *Ladybird*; and *Stiff Options*. 'Rarely' advertise for actors. Welcome casting queries; approach in writing in the first instance. Do not hold general auditions.

Richard Jackson Personal Management Ltd

59 Knightsbridge, London SW1X 7RA
Tel (071) 235 3671
Contact Richard Jackson

Founded 1959. Plays and musicals on London's fringe, with the occasional West End transfer: 'Our policy is to produce new plays, mainly from France and Germany, but not to discount any English or American scripts of quality which come our way. They need to have small casts and be suitable for producing in fringe venues such as the Offstage, New End and Latchmere.' Credits include: *A Day in Hollywood, a Night in the Ukraine* (directed by Ian Davison); *The Singular Life of Albert Nobbs*, *Appearances*, *Portrait of Dora*, *The Revolt* and *The Human Voice* (directed by Simone Benmussa); *Flashpoint* (Anton Rodgers); *I Ought to Be in Pictures* and *Swimming Pools at War* (Robert Gillespie); *Tribute to Lili Lamont* (Jack Gold); *Better Days, Better Knights* (Max Stafford-Clark); *Pier Paolo Pasolini* (Tim Luscombe); *An Evening with Quentin*

Crisp. Do not advertise for actors. Do not really welcome casting queries: 'Nearly all the casting is done by invitation on consultation with the play's director. Although all casting enquiries by letter are considered, actors whose work is unknown to us are rarely used.'

Bill Kenwright Ltd

55–59 Shaftesbury Avenue, London W1V 7AA
Tel (071) 439 4466

Revivals and new shows for West End and touring theatres. West end Productions include: *Blood Brothers* and *Shirley Valentine* by Willy Russell, *Absurd Person Singular* and *How The Other Half Loves* by Alan Ayckbourn; *Fences* by August Wilson; *Stepping Out* and *The Business of Murder* by Richard Harris; *Having A Ball* and *Are You Lonesome Tonight?* by Alan Bleasdale, and Brecht's *Mother Courage* with Glenda Jackson.

Major Tours include: *Joseph* by Andrew Lloyd Webber and Tim Rice; *Shirley Valentine* and *Stepping Out*. In America he has recently presented a tour of *The Business Of Murder* and next year *Blood Brothers* will open in New York.

Bill Kenwright co-produced the film *Day After The Fair* starring Hannah Gordon and is executive producer on the film of *Stepping Out*, starring Liza Minelli, Julie Walters and Shelley Winters.

The Company occasionally advertise in *The Stage* for touring shows. Major parts in West End productions are usually cast by the producer and the individual directors. Directors who have worked with the company include Julie Mckenzie, Richard Olivier,

Bob Tomson, Alan Ayckbourn and Alan Strachan.

Bill Kenwright is also the Artistic Producer for the Thorndike Theatre, Leatherhead.

David Kirk Productions

12 Panmuir Road, London SW20 0PZ
Tel (081) 947 0130

Commercial management touring post-London revivals and some new plays to provincial and suburban theatres. Productions have included the post-London tours of *Master Class*, *Strippers*, *A Month of Sundays*, *The Old Country* (Alan Bennett), *The Man Most Likely To*, *Hindle Wakes*, and *Boeing-Boeing*. New plays have included: *Dead of Night* (Peter Whalley), *The Golf Umbrella* by William Douglas Home, *Local Murder* by Peter Whalley, *Mr Fothergill's Murder* by Peter O'Donnell, *Agenda for Murder* by Denis Cleary & Joseph Boyer. Most plays have small casts, and are cast from TV names and a pool of people already known to the management; other supporting roles are cast through agents.

Knightsbridge Theatrical Productions Ltd

15 Fetter Lane, London EC4A 1JJ
Tel (071) 583 2266
Fax (071) 583 0046

Musicals and straight plays suitable for production in the West End. Very occasional tours. Do not advertise for actors, and do not welcome query letters. Have not held auditions for several years.

Logan Theatres Ltd

Springvale, 73 East Princes Street, Helensburgh G84 7DG
Tel (0436) 71503   Fax (0436) 72124
Contact Jimmy Logan

Comedy and family shows, mostly starring Jimmy Logan. Past productions include: *Run for Your Wife*, *A Bedful of Foreigners*, *Not Now Darling* and *Lauder*. Do not advertise. Welcome casting queries from actors, especially Scottish-based actors or those with authentic Scottish accents. Although interested in new faces, there are limited casting opportunities, as sometimes the same company of actors will be employed for a year or more. Do hold auditions, usually in a theatre; also use agents and have contacts with Scottish drama schools.

Lyric Theatre Hammersmith

See **Repertory/Regional Theatres** section.

Cameron Mackintosh Ltd

1 Bedford Square, London WC1B 3RA
Tel (071) 637 8866
Contact The Casting Department

Founded 1980. Musicals. Credits include: *Cats*, *Les Miserables*, *Miss Saigon*, *Five Guys Named Moe* and *The Phantom of the Opera* (co-production with The Really Useful Theatre Company). Advertise for actors in *The Stage*. Welcome casting queries from actors, which should be addressed to the Casting Department. Hold general auditions, which are always advertised in *The Stage*.

Lee Menzies Ltd

20 Rupert Street, London W1V 7FN
Tel (071) 437 0127
Fax (071) 734 3495
Contact Lee Menzies

New commercial plays. Recent productions: Jeffrey Archer's *Beyond Reasonable Doubt*; *Dry Rot* with Sir Brian Rix. Do not advertise for actors. Do not welcome query letters from individual actors. Do not hold general auditions. Casting is usually the responsibility of the director working on each show.

National Theatre

See 'Royal National Theatre' in **Repertory/Regional Theatres** section.

Newgate Company & Air Play

P.O. Box 175, Bath BA1 2FX
Tel (0225) 318335/743782
Contact Glenys Gill, Jo Anderson, Alec Reid

Founded 1976 (Newgate), 1988 (Air Play). *Newgate Company* is principally involved in theatre production but often tied in with broadcasting media; ensemble-based, it re-assembles with specific projects. *Air Play*, an affiliated company, is based on audio-stereo drama tape recordings of new plays, screenplays and teleplays; has its own studio facilities. Projects initiated and developed by Newgate Company: *Ludwig* (directed at the Roundhouse in 1977 by Tony Craven; film version in association with Ken Russell); *Oldest Profession* (Globe Bankside Shakespeare Festival, 1987; BBC Radio 4 version directed by Ed Thomason; at

various theatres during the summer of 1988); *Hitler's Whistle* (in association with Orchard Theatre, 1989); *Solstice* (in association with Bristol Express Theatre Company; directed by Andy Jordan; Lyric Hammersmith showcase, 1987); and three projects with BBC in 1990. Sometimes advertise in *PCR* or *SBS*. 'We welcome introductions from *new*, graduating drama students, updates from working actors – i.e. we like to see actors in action. Always send a letter.' Do not hold general auditions. 'We prefer to cover actors we do not know when they are doing a showcase, have a "spot" on TV or radio, etc. Or invite them in for a "workout" session. Auditions prove little. Both Newgate Company and Air Play always have very specific requirements, so it is not all that worthwhile responding to our advertisements unless you really fit the bill.'

Newpalm Productions

26 Cavendish Avenue, Finchley, London N3 3QN
Tel (081) 349 0802
Contact Phil Compton

Usually produce national tours of such plays as *Noises Off*, *Seven Brides for Seven Brothers* and *Rebecca* at regional repertory theatres. Advertise for big productions in *The Stage* and *PCR*. Will accept casting queries from actors by letter. Details are kept on file and are consulted when audition lists for specific parts are being drawn up. Unless a suitable part is being cast, the chances of a reply are slim. Auditions for specific parts are sometimes held. There are no general auditions; use agents for casting.

The Niccol Centre

Brewery Court, Cirencester, Glos.
GL7 1SP
Tel (0285) 67181
Contact Paul Jamieson (director)

No 'in-house' theatre work. Only booking small-scale touring companies particularly interested in adaptations of classics. Artistic Director, Paul Jamieson, graduate of Performance Arts Degree at Middlesex Polytechnic.

Old Vic

Waterloo Road, London SE1 8NB
Tel (071) 928 2651
Producer David Mirvish
General Manager Andrew Leigh
Contact Pippa Ailion

Seating capacity: 1067. Opened 1818. 'The most famous playhouse in the world' was bought in 1983 by Canadian 'Honest Ed' Mirvish. Now controlled by his son David Mirvish, it produces limited runs of its own productions, or takes in co-productions with other producers.
Casting policy: no general auditions, no advertisements.

The Opera House

Gloucester Street, St Helier, Jersey, Channel Isles JE2 3QR
Tel (0534) 35348 Fax (0534) 34573
Contact Dick Ray

Founded 1900. Wide range of productions. Advertise in *The Stage*, and welcome casting queries from actors; approach in writing in the first instance. Hold general auditions.

Pola Jones Associates Ltd

5 Dean Street, London W1
Tel (071) 439 1165

Founded 1981. Credits include: touring and West End 1989/1990 *Evita*, *Show Boat*, *Lettice And Lovage*, and *Return To The Forbidden Planet*. Will accept CVs from actors and keep a file of details, although casting opportunities are limited and whoever is directing a show will usually make casting requests and decisions. Write in the first instance. Do not hold general auditions.

Prestige Plays Ltd

83 George Street, London W1H 5PL
Tel (071) 486 1732
Contact Jill Streatfield (personal assistant to Charles Vance)

Founded 1960. Tours, repertory, musicals and pantomimes. Productions 'too numerous to mention!' Advertise for actors through SBS and *The Stage*. Rarely hold general auditions. Welcome casting queries from actors, by letter only: 'Keep applications succinct, with clear CV and good photograph. A SAE is vital!'

Quill Theatre Productions

247 Norwood Road, London SE24 9AG
Tel (081) 674 1050
Contact Ann Parnell McGarry (artistic director)

Quill exist to produce new work, which may be serious plays, fast, witty comedies, musicals and childrens' plays. When decent new work cannot be found, as is often the case, there are huge gaps in the production schedule. Casting is therefore spasmodic, and opportunities for actors are limited. Casting queries from actors are not really welcomed, though details will be kept on file. Casting policy varies with the needs of each production. Occasionally advertise and audition for specialist parts. The artistic director is more interested in an actor with 'the ability to do it as much as having done it before'. Use casting directors and agents for West End productions.

Dick Ray Productions

See **The Opera House**.

Really Useful Theatre Company Limited

20 Greek Street, London W1V 5LF
Tel (071) 734 2114
Fax (071) 734 6230

Andrew Lloyd Webber's company, which produces West End musicals, plays and comedies. Credits include: *Cats, Starlight Express*; and *Aspects Of Love* (directed by Trevor Nunn); *Phantom of the Opera* (Hal Prince). Advertise in *The Stage*, and circulate casting requirements to agents. Hold general auditions. 'Do not attend auditions for jobs if your Equity status prevents you from taking the job simply in order to "be seen". Be honest and accurate about musical and dancing ability and vocal range.'

Michael Redington

10 Maunsel Street, London
SW1P 2QL
Tel (071) 834 5119

Plays, including *84 Charing Cross Road* (adapted and directed by James Roose-Evans) and *The Best of Friends* by Hugh Whitemore (directed by James Roose-

Evans); *Pack of Lies* and *Breaking the Code* by Hugh Whitemore (Clifford Williams); *Mr and Mrs Nobody* by Keith Waterhouse (Ned Sherrin). Do not advertise for actors. Do not welcome casting queries, and do not hold general auditions.

The Renaissance Theatre Company

Formed in April 1987 by Kenneth Branagh and David Parfitt. 'It was a natural development of the work that David Parfitt and I had been doing periodically on the London fringe, producing and appearing in lunchtime shows, new plays and finally a full scale production of *Romeo and Juliet*.' Productions include *Public Enemy, Life of Napoleon, Twelfth Night, Look Back In Anger, King Lear*, and *A Midsummer Night's Dream*. *Twelfth Night* and *Look Back In Anger* have been televised, and Kenneth Branagh directed and starred in an acclaimed film of *Henry V*. *Much Ado About Nothing* (directed by Judi Dench), *As You Like It* (Geraldine McEwan), *Hamlet* (Derek Jacobi).

Further information withheld by Renaissance to stem the flow of enquiries from actors.

Royal Court Theatre (English Stage Company Ltd)

Sloane Square, London SW1W 8AS
Tel (071) 730 5174
Artistic director Max Stafford-Clark
Associate director Lindsay Posner
Casting director Lisa Makin

The English Stage Company was founded by George Devine in 1956 to put on new plays. John Osborne, John Arden, Arnold Wesker, Edward Bond, Caryl Churchill, Howard Barker and Michael Hastings are among the writers this theatre has discovered. Recent productions: *The Recruiting Officer*; *My Country's Good*; *My Heart's A Suitcase*; *Seven Lears*; *Top Girls*; *Rafts and Dreams*. Cast from play to play; West End contracts. Do not hold general auditions, but Lisa Makin, the casting director, tries to cover actors' work and therefore likes information about what is going on. Actors' details are kept on file and referred to: 'It is not necessary to keep on sending in new photographs, etc.'

Theatre Upstairs: Seating capacity: 60. Cast from play to play. Rep contract. 'Equity cards can be issued with Theatre Upstairs contracts.'

Comment:
With its Young Writers' Festival and its ambitious Theatre Upstairs, the Royal Court is one of the few British theatres to hold out any hope to contemporary playwrights, actors and directors.

Royal National Theatre

See 'Royal National Theatre' in **Repertory/Regional Theatres** section.

Royal Shakespeare Company

See **Repertory/Regional Theatres** section.

RTC

Novello Theatre, High Street, Sunninghill, nr Ascot, Berks. Tel (0344) 20881
Contact June Rose (Executive director), Chris Grimwood (Artistic director)

Children's plays and musicals. Recent productions: *Annie, The Secret Garden, A Game Of Soldiers, Grease, Hard Times* and *Three Little Pigs*. Directors include: June Rose, Chris Grimwood, Sylvia Denning, Peter Lesley Wild, James Aidan.

St George's Theatre and Studio

Tufnell Park Road, London N7 0PS Tel (071) 607 7978
Artistic director George Murcell

Founded 1976, by George Murcell who was determined that Shakespeare should be presented without any frills or modern interpretations. The St George's Theatre (seating capacity: 600), presents Shakespeare only, always aiming to recreate the original Elizabethan stagings. Casting takes place each September. Company of 12 actors on Equity contracts for the season, with cross casting in at least two plays. Do not advertise, but welcome letters enclosing CV and photograph: 'We do not have the time to reply, unless interested in seeing an actor, so an SAE is not needed.' Require actors who have at least rep experience of performing Shakespeare (drama school Shakespeare is not sufficient). At present embarking on educational video production for the general reader.

Barrie Stacey Promotions (Barrie Stacey Productions/Sante Fe Productions Ltd)

3rd floor, 9 Denmark Street, London
WC2H 0LA
Tel (071) 836 6220/4128
Fax (071) 836 2949
Contact Barrie Stacey

Founded 1966. Children's musicals, pantomimes, the occasional straight play and many variety concerts. Productions include: *Snow White and the Seven Dwarfs* (directed by Barrie Stacey); *Pinocchio; Hans Christian Anderson*. Directors on file: Barrie Stacey, Keith Hopkins, Rosita Yardboy, David Marcus and Richard Franklin. Welcome casting enquiries in writing, with photograph and CV. Also supply Father Christmases, models, hostesses, muscle men, male strippers, etc.

Stagestruck Productions Ltd

57 Duke Street, Grosvenor Square,
London W1M 5DH
Tel (071) 629 2334
Fax (071) 493 3808   Telex 22713
Contact Simon Caplan (managing director), Theo Gobat (director)

Founded 1978. Plays and musicals; West End and tours. Credits include: *The Club* (directed by Tony Tanner); *Flashpoint* (Anton Rodgers); *Killing Jessica* (Bryan Forbes); *Separation* (Michael Attenborough). Advertise in *PCR*, and welcome casting queries from actors; send a letter enclosing biography/resumé only. Hold general auditions. 'Will consider new Equity members as well as experienced actors.'

Stoll Productions Ltd

Manor House, 21 Soho Square,
London W1V 5FD
Tel (071) 437 2274
Fax (071) 434 1217

One of the most influential theatre empires, with 12 theatres (including the Globe, Lyric, Apollo and Queen's in Shaftesbury Avenue) that tend to host straight plays; Her Majesty's and the Palladium are more often musical venues. Recent productions have included *Up on the Roof, The House of Bernarda Alba, Barnum* and *La Cage aux Folles*. Do not advertise, do not welcome query letters from actors and do not hold general auditions. All casting is handled by individual directors of shows.

T B A Music Ltd

361 Edgware Road, London W2 1BS
Tel (071) 723 5509
Fax (071) 724 4523/7287
Contact Peter Benda

Founded 1978. Plays, musicals and trade shows. Productions include national tours of *A Chorus Line, Two And Two Make Sex, Godspell* and *The Little Shop of Horrors*. Advertise for actors in *SBS*, and welcome query letters from actors, although 'we do not have time to reply and deal with casting letters unless we are looking for specific people for parts in a specific production.' Do not hold general auditions.

H. M. Tennent Ltd

Globe Theatre, Shaftesbury Avenue,
London W1V 7HD
Tel (071) 437 3647
Contact Sheila Formoy

London's oldest established theatre
production company. Recent productions have included: *A Month of
Sundays* (SWET Award); *Victor Spinetti
– A Very Private Diary; Garrison Keillor
In Person; A Little Night Music* (Chichester Festival Theatre). Do not
advertise for actors, but welcome
query letters. Actors' details are kept
on file for 18 months; individual directors of shows will consult the file if
they need to. Do not hold general
auditions.

Theatre of Comedy Company Ltd

Shaftesbury Theatre, 210 Shaftesbury
Avenue, London WC2H 8DP
Tel (071) 379 3345
Fax (071) 836 0466

Founded 1983. Comedies; West End
and tours. Credits include: *Run for
Your Wife* (directed by Ray Cooney);
When We Are Married (Ronald Eyre);
Out Of Order (directed by Ray
Cooney). Do not advertise, and wel-
come casting queries from actors.
Hold general auditions 'when
appropriate'.

Theatre Projects Consultants Ltd

3 Apollo Studios, Charlton Kings
Road, London NW5 2SU
Tel (071) 482 4224
Fax (071) 284 0636

West End and touring shows.
Productions include: *Edward II, Richard
III, She Stoops to Conquer, I'm Not
Rappaport, Cabaret, Fiddler on the Roof, A
Little Night Music.* Not currently in
production and do not know when
they will be. Do not welcome queries
from actors. Do not keep a file of details, as productions are infrequent
and each one is cast 'from scratch'.
Company's main activity is as theatre
and arts building planners and
consultants.

Theatre Royal, Margate Ltd

Addington Street, Margate, Thanet,
Kent CT9 1PV
Tel (0843) 221913
Contact Managing director

Theatre founded in 1786, and the company in 1988. The theatre re-opened in
late 1988 and now presents touring
productions, in-house productions
and co-productions.

Trafford & Parnell Productions

8 Jesmond Avenue, Blackpool, Lancs.
FY4 1EJ
Tel (0253) 48069/66928

Founded 1974. Plays, summer seasons, pantomimes. Productions include: summer seasons at the Spa
Theatres Scarborough, Whitby, Llan-
dudno and Hunstanton. Productions

directed by Ronnie Parnell and Keith Hopkins, choreographed by Adrienne Knight, Katie Milton, Arrianne May and Giancarla. Welcome casting queries. Telephone in the first instance, when photograph and CV may be requested. Do hold general auditions.

Triumph Proscenium Productions

Suite 4, Waldorf Chambers,
11 Aldwych, London WC2B 4DA
Tel (071) 836 0186
Chairman and Managing Director Duncan C. Weldon
Deputy Managing Director Peter Wilkins

A major producer of West End and touring shows, mostly revivals but with a regular output of new work. Recent West End productions have included *Richard II* and *Richard III*; *A Walk In The Woods*; *Another Time*; Pirandello's *Henry IV*; *Love Letters*; *Kean*; and the Peter Hall Company productions of *Orpheus Descending*; *The Merchant of Venice*; *The Wild Duck*; and *The Homecoming*. Do not hold general auditions; sometimes use freelance casting directors. Do not advertise for actors.

Viva Theatre Productions Ltd

42–46 St Lukes Mews, London W11
Tel (071) 221 5101
Fax (071) 221 3374
Telex 297314 ANSA HITTZ
Contact Christopher Malcolm (managing director)

Founded 1985. Productions include:

Metamorphosis; *Sink the Belgrano*; *Decadence*; *Greek*; *Salome*; *When I Was a Girl*; *Tuesday's Child*; *Single Spies*; *Frankie and Johnny*; *Rocky Horror Show*. Do not advertise for actors, but sometimes welcome query letters from them: 'Direct approaches only work if actors feel they are absolutely right for a project the producers are involved in. General sending out of information is usually a waste of time.' Do not hold general auditions; casting is usually done through casting directors: 'Actors should know and inform casting directors whenever they feel a change or improvement in their careers merits a communication.'

Michael Ward Theatre Productions

Radnors, 39 Thames Street, Windsor, Berks. SL4 1PR
Tel (0753) 863982
Contact Michael Ward

Founded 1980. Tours, West End try-outs, West End Investment. 'We tend to go out and about to view artists so no need to hold auditions. Any artists are welcome to send their CV but if they require an answer please enclose SAE. Also pleased to discuss the possibility of producing with artists who may be potential directors/authors.' Michael Ward is also Chairman of Millenium Productions Ltd.

Westminster Productions Ltd

12 Palace Street, London SW1E 5JB
Tel (071) 834 7882
Fax (071) 821 5819
Contact Hugh Steadman Williams

Founded 1986. West End shows and provincial tours. Productions and co-productions include: *An Inspector Calls* (directed by Peter Dews); *The Miracle Worker* (Adrian Reynolds); *The Lion, the Witch and the Wardrobe* and *The Voyage of the Dawn Treader* (Richard Williams); *Temptation* (James Roose-Evans). Do not hold general auditions.

Michael White

13 Duke Street, St James's, London
SW1Y 6DB
Tel (071) 839 3971
Fax (071) 839 3836
Contact Michael White

High-output company. Recent productions have included *On Your Toes* and *A Chorus Line*. Casting is done through casting directors, who will advertise auditions in *The Stage*. Do not welcome query letters, which are simply passed on to casting directors. See Michael White Productions in **Film and Video** section.

10 *Fringe and Alternative Theatre*

Fringe companies can be very prestigious. Some of the best-known attract actors of considerable stature and maintain a very high standard indeed. Like small-scale theatre companies, they frequently suffer from poverty. However, they very much tend towards adventurous and new work, and there is a chance of exceptionally good roles. There is a high possibility, especially in London, of being seen by potential employers, and many feel that fringe theatre is the best vehicle for an abrupt up-grading of status. But be warned: acclaimed fringe successes taken up by major production and film companies may well be re-cast, much to the chagrin of the original company.

Working conditions in fringe companies vary considerably. At best they are comparable to small-scale touring companies, with similar strictures about the available support. At less than best they can be operating in conditions which border on the surreal, unable to offer wages and requiring superhuman efforts from the participants. Startlingly good theatre nevertheless frequently springs from desperate beginnings. Theatre companies regularly trace their beginnings to roots in penury on the fringe.

Albany Empire

Douglas Way, London SE8 4AG
Tel (081) 691 8016
Artistic director Teddy Kiendl

The Albany moved to its new, purpose-built home in 1981. The base for the Combination Theatre Company, it is a lively community centre, and stages three or four in-house productions per year plus in-coming tours of theatre, dance, music and cabaret. Shows are targeted at the local community, which is predominantly Afro-Caribbean and white working-class. Recent productions: *Mass Carib*, *Romeo and Juliet* (set in Trinidad), *The Gut Girls* – all directed by Teddy Kiendl. Do not advertise for actors (tend to work through agents), but welcome casting queries, particularly from local actors. ITC/Equity small-scale contract of 8–9 weeks; cast from show to show.

The Albany is also the company base for IRIE, an Afro-Carib dance company (artistic director: Beverly Glean).

Almeida Theatre

See **Non-producing theatres**.

Artaud Theatre Company

See **Café Theatre Upstairs**.

Battersea Arts Centre

See **Non-producing theatres**.

Bush Theatre

Shepherds Bush Green, London
W12 8QD
Tel (071) 602 3703
Artistic directors Dominic Dromgoole

An exciting studio theatre, seating 105, producing new plays by British and foreign writers. Recent productions: *The Touch* by Peter Lloyd (directed by Brian Stirner); *The Evil Doers* by Chris Hannan (directed by Simon Usher); *Dancing Attendance* by Lucy Gannon (directed by Stuart Burge). Equity contracts. Do not advertise, and do not welcome casting queries from actors. 'Casting breakdowns are not given out, but a list of actors suitable for any part is drawn up. Their availabilities are checked so that casting proceeds from the theatre outwards rather than the reverse. The policy is to cast actors whose work we know. It is helpful, therefore, if actors keep us up to date with where their work can be seen.'

Café Theatre Upstairs

Bear & Staff, 37 Charing Cross Road, London WC2
Tel (071) 240 0794/9582
Fax (071) 831 1505
Artistic director Michael Almaz

The London base for the Artaud Theatre Company, founded as a touring company in 1973; have been in London since 1981. Produce at least 25 plays per year with the emphasis on adaptations. Productions include: *Intimacy* by Jean-Paul Sartre (directed by Michael Almaz); *Underground Man* by Feodor Dostoevsky (Israel Zohar).

All productions are profit-share. Occasionally advertise in *PCR* or *The Stage.* Hold general auditions, and welcome letters enclosing CV and photograph. Address them to: Michael Almaz, D41 Odhams Walk, Long Acre, London WC2H 9SB.

The Drill Hall

See **Non-producing theatres**.

Forkbeard Fantasy

See **Touring companies**.

Gate Theatre

11 Pembridge Road, London
W11 3HQ
Tel (071) 229 5387
Artistic director Stephen Daldry

Small venue, seating 60, which opened in 1979 above the Prince Albert Pub in Notting Hill. Recent productions: *Figaro Gets Divorced* (Stephen Daldry); *Punishment Without Revenge* (Laurence Boswell); *The Marquis of Keith* (Mark Dornford May); *Vassa Zheleznova* (Katie Mitchell). The only theatre in Britain dedicated to world drama, specialising in European classics in translation. 1990 winner of *Time Out/01 For London* and LWT *Plays On Stage* awards. Usually operate on a non-Equity basis. Advertise in *SBS*, and welcome CVs and photographs for files.

Hampstead Theatre

Swiss Cottage Centre, London
NW3 3EX
Tel (071) 722 9224
Fax (071) 722 3860
Artistic director Jenny Topper
Associate directors John Dove, Robin Lefevre, Matthew Lloyd

Founded 1959. Seating capacity: 174. Leading London company that produces five to six plays a year and concentrates on promoting new work by new and established writers, with the occasional revival of a modern classic. Recent productions: *Valued Friends* (Stephen Jeffreys); *Burn This* (Lanford Wilson); *The Day You'll Love Me* (Jose Ignacio Cabrujas); *Imagine Drowning* (Terry Johnson). Do not hold general auditions; cast separately for each production. Do not advertise for actors, but welcome letters with CV, photograph and SAE.

ICA Theatre

See **Non-producing theatres**.

King's Head Theatre Club

115 Upper Street, Islington, London
N1 1QN
Tel (071) 226 1916/8561
Artistic director Dan Crawford

Founded 1970. Seating capacity: 125. Leading fringe venue producing five in-house productions each year for six-week runs, plus in-coming companies. In 1988, two plays transferred to the West End. Productions include: *Easy Virtue, Artist Descending a Staircase* and *When She Danced* (all directed by Tim Luscombe). Non-Equity contracts (£100 per week). Advertise in *The Stage*, and welcome letters with CVs and photographs in response to these ads; do not, however, have the facilities to keep information on file.

There is also a lunch-time theatre (artistic director: Sid Golder); in-coming productions only.

Latchmere Theatre

503 Battersea Park Road, London
SW11 3BW
Tel (071) 223 3108
Artistic director Chris Fisher

Purpose-built studio theatre (seating 85) above the Latchmere Public House and base for the London Actors Theatre Company. Productions range from theatre for young people to new plays and revivals for the general public. Recent productions: *Franken-stein*, *Dr Jekyll and Mr Bumble* (London Actors Theatre Co, directed by Chris Fisher). Some productions are profit-share, some Equity contracts. Advertise for actors in *The Stage*, *SBS* and *PCR*. Do not welcome casting queries: 'Plays are cast on a production-to-production basis, and actors are advised to apply for auditions for specific productions, not general casting/unsolicited auditions, etc.'

London Actors Theatre Company

See **Latchmere Theatre**.

Man in the Moon Theatre Club

392 King's Road, Chelsea, London
SW3 5UZ
Tel (071) 351 2876
Contact Vivienne Cottrell, Kirstie Gulick

Small theatre (68 seats) above a pub, presenting new plays including adaptations of contemporary significance, with the accent on encouraging new writers at an early stage of their careers. In addition, they present revivals of rarely performed plays. Only 2–3 in-house productions per year; play host to in-coming plays. Recent in-house productions: *The False Court* (Aphra Benn); *Approaching Zanzibar* (Tim Howe); *Keely's Mother* (Berta Friestadt); as part of the 'Women in the Moon' season. Usually profit-share or an agreed fee. Sometimes advertise in *The Stage*, but do not welcome casting queries from actors.

Millfield Theatre

Silver Street, Edmonton, London
N18 1PJ
Tel (081) 807 6186
Theatre manager Graham Bennett
Contact Dave Sefton

Thriving, purpose-built theatre, seating 356–400, which opened in December 1988. Productions (both amateur and professional), tours, concerts, dance, alternative comedy, etc. Equity contracts. Advertise in *The Stage*, and do not welcome unsolicited casting queries from actors.

New End Theatre

27 New End, Hampstead, London
NW3 1JD
Tel (071) 794 0022

Seating capacity: 80. Recent in-house productions include *Sophie – the Last of the Red Hot Mamas*. Advertise in *SBS*. Please do not phone. Write with CV, photograph and SAE.

See **Non-producing theatres**.

Old Red Lion Theatre

St John Street, Islington, London
EC1V 4NJ
Tel (071) 833 3053
Director Richard Hansom

Founded 1979. Seating capacity: 60–80. Mainly a venue for visiting fringe companies such as Inner City and Empty Space, producing new plays. In 1983, the theatre had its first transfer to the West End with *Crystal Clear*. Most productions that visit the Old Red Lion are profit-share.

Orange Tree Theatre

45 Kew Road, Richmond, Surrey
TW9 2NQ
Tel (081) 940 0141/3633
Artistic director Sam Walters

Theatre-in-the-round seating 80. New plays, classics, musicals and revivals of neglected or overlooked work. Recent productions: *Les Parents Terribles* (Jean Cocteau); *Le Bourgeois Gentilhomme* (Molière); *Redevelopment* (Vaclav Havel). Equity contracts. Do not advertise, but welcome casting queries from actors; send letter with CV and photograph.

Comment
New theatre opened February 1991. Sam Walters won a *Time Out/01 for London* award in 1988 in recognition of an exceptional season of revivals of little-known works at the Orange Tree.

Oval House Theatre

See **Non-producing theatres**.

Pentameters Theatre

Three Horseshoes, 28 Heath Street, London NW3
Tel (071) 435 6757
Contact Leonie Scott-Matthews

Founded 1968 to promote poetry and new writing. Seating capacity: 100. Generally profit-share productions. Rarely advertise for actors, but welcome casting queries by telephone. Particularly interested in people who take an active interest in the theatre, which is run as a club. Leonie Scott-Matthews is always present on performance nights.

Pioneer Theatres Ltd

See **Theatre Royal Stratford East.**

Riverside Studios

Crisp Road, Hammersmith, London
W6 9RL
Tel (081) 741 2251
Director Jonathan Lamede

Founded in 1976 with Peter Gill as its first director, who established its reputation as an international theatre. Mainly hosts visiting companies – approximately 20–30 each year. Recent productions include: *Directions to*

Servants (Tokyo Globe); *Krapp's Last Tape* and *Catastrophe* (Leicester Haymarket); *The Furtive Nudist* (Ken Campbell); and *The Visit* (Théâtre de Complicité). Do not advertise for actors, and with no in-house productions, do not welcome casting queries.

Tabard Theatre

2 Bath Road, Turnham Green,
Chiswick, London W4 1LW
Tel (081) 995 6035
Literary manager Sam Dowling

Producing theatre with a policy of new writing. Established for 5 years. Seating capacity of 75. 6 in-house productions per year. Theatre also available for rental. In-house productions derive from self directing group of writers, actors, designers and other theatre workers working within a model (The Theatre of Praxis) which draws on a psychoanalytical approach to creativity and group dynamics. The ability to take personal responsibility for achieving high standards, and a willingness to extend the boundaries of experimentation, are essential. Some people find the method stressful. Recent productions include: *Mountain* and *A Season in Hell* by Sam Dowling which toured to Poland and USSR, *Infidelities* by Richard Zjadlic (winner of 1990 West London Playwriting Competition), *The Web* by Jill Truman (directed by Jilly Bond). Tours of Canada, America and Ireland are planned for 1991, along with return visits to Poland and USSR. All in-house productions are on a profit share basis. Advertise in *The Stage*, *PCR* and *CastCall* and welcome CVs

and photographs in response to these adverts. Please include SAE.

Talawa Theatre Company Ltd

38 King Street, Covent Garden,
London WC2E 8JT
Tel (071) 379 6509
Fax (071) 379 7579
Artistic director Yvonne Brewster

Founded in 1985 by Yvonne Brewster, Inigo Espejel, Mona Hammond and Carmen Munroe, Talawa has become one of the leading Afro-British theatre companies. Producing middle to large scale plays with a broad appeal. All productions to date have been directed by Yvonne Brewster and have included highly successful productions such as an all-black *Importance of Being Earnest*, and Ola Rotimi's Nigerian version of the Oedipus story: *The Gods Are Not to Blame*. Usually co-produce – past partners include Tyne Theatre Co., Liverpool Everyman, and Theatre Royal, Stratford East. Productions do an out of London season and then come into town to either the Bloomsbury Theatre or the Riverside Studios. All productions are cast individually. Equity contracts. Do not advertise but welcome casting queries from actors. Send photograph, CV and SAE – highly comprehensive files on Afro-British actors are kept for future reference.

Théâtre de Complicité

See **Touring companies**.

Theatre Royal Stratford East (Pioneer Theatres Ltd)

Gerry Raffles Square, Newham,
London E15 1BN
Tel (081) 534 7374
Artistic director Philip Hedley

A leading theatre, well known throughout the country, producing new work: Afro-Asian drama, family shows, melodramas, pantomimes, populist plays, variety and youth shows. A Victorian theatre built in 1884 with a seating capacity of 467. Recent productions: *Not Fade Away* and *Wild Justice* by Barrie Keeffe (directed by Philip Hedley); *The Dragon Can't Dance* by Earl Lovelace (Yvonne Brewster); Mike Leigh's *Greek Tragedy*; *Five Guys Named Moe* by Clarke Peters (Charles Augins); *Robin Hood – The Panto* by Patrick Prior and Dave Brown (Jeff Teare); *I thought I heard a Rustling* by Alan Plater (Philip Hedley). Equity Contracts. Sometimes advertise in *PCR*, but usually cast from their own files. Welcome letters with CV and photograph.

Comment
Joan Littlewood's Theatre Workshop moved to the Theatre Royal in 1953, but the high ideal of 'A British People's Theatre', which she had hitherto pursued with commendable single-mindedness, soon gave way to the many attractions – not least financial – of staging West End transfers. Popular and critical success followed with such productions as *The Hostage*, *A Taste of Honey*, *Fings Ain't Wot They Used to Be* and *Oh What a Lovely War!*.

Three Horseshoes

See **Pentameters Theatre** (above).

Trestle Theatre Company

See **Touring companies**.

Tricycle Theatre

269 Kilburn High Road, London
NW6 7JR
Tel (071) 372 6611
Artistic director Nicolas Kent

Founded in 1972 as a touring company and moved to its London base in 1980. The theatre was destroyed by fire in 1987, but re-opened in 1989 with a seating capacity of 225. Produce new plays; particularly interested in writing from ethnic minorities. Credits include: *The Great White Hope*, *Playboy of the West Indies*, *The Hostage*, *Joe Jurner's Come and Gone*, *Fashion*, and *Remembrance*. Also host visiting theatre companies. Equity contracts, normally six weeks long. Do not advertise for actors, but welcome casting queries. Approach in writing in the first instance; details are kept on file. No general auditions.

Tron Theatre Company

63 Trongate, Glasgow G1 5HB
Tel (041) 552 3748
Artistic director Michael Boyd

Formerly a church, the theatre opened in 1982 with a seating capacity of 225, having established a lively reputation with performances in its café/bar which opened in 1980. Produce major new plays from experienced Scottish writers, as well as new American and European writing. Also host Scottish touring companies such as Communicado, as well as such international companies as Pocket Opera, Lithuanian State Theatre, Moscow Pushkin Theatre, Moscow Studio

Theatre of the South-west, Shaliko and La Mamma from New York. Recent in-house productions include: *The Guid Sisters*, *Paddy's Market*, *Performance*, *Salvation*, *The Baby*, *The Witches of Pollok*. Equity contracts. Do not advertise, but will consider letters of enquiry from actors.

Warehouse Theatre Croydon

62 Dingwall Road, Croydon, Surrey
CRO 2NF
Tel (081) 681 1257
Artistic director Ted Craig

Major fringe theatre with a policy of producing new writing. A flexible performance space with seating of 100/120. According to the *Financial Times*, 'The auditorium has a genuine atmosphere under its splendid roof of beams and rafters.' The main aim of the theatre is to produce its own productions – usually six per year – running for 5–6 weeks each. Also promote touring companies who share this commitment to new work. Recent productions: *Sleeping Nightie* (co-production with Royal Court); *The Astronomer's Garden* (transferred to Royal Court); *Sugar Hill Blues* (transferred to Hampstead Theatre); *Conversations With George Sandburgh* (winner of the South London Playwriting Festival). Equity contracts. Occasionally advertise in *SBS* and *PCR* when special skills are required. Welcome casting queries from actors; send letter

with SAE: 'General letters can only be filed for further reference when casting. By far the most useful letter is one informing us of an appearance in a play or production which we are able to cover.'

The Young Vic

66 The Cut, Waterloo, London
SE1 8LZ
Tel (071) 633 0133
Artistic director David Thacker

Leading fringe venue with a main house theatre-in-the-round (seating 500) which can be adapted to thrust (seating 430), and a studio theatre seating 114. Produce classics, new plays, plays by contemporary writers, and plays for family audiences. Recent productions: *From the Mississippi Delta*, *Anna Christie*, *The Man Who Had All The Luck*, *TO*, *Timon of Athens*, *The Plough and the Stars*. Equity contracts. Do not advertise for actors, but welcome casting queries; approach in writing in the first instance.

Comment
The Young Vic was opened in 1970, under the direction of Frank Dunlop, as an offshoot of the National Theatre (at the time, based almost next door at the Old Vic). It went independent in 1974 and reaffirmed its reputation under Michael Bogdanov and, latterly, David Thacker.

11 *Touring Companies*

Working with a large- or mid-scale touring company is similar in many ways to being with a repertory company. It is unlikely that you will be contracted for more than one play, and you must learn to live out of a suitcase, but you can expect relatively sophisticated and experienced administrative and technical support. Many tours offer much longer contracts than repertory theatres, sometimes involving foreign travel.

As it is not common to tour more than one play, there will be no scope for a variety of roles. A lengthy tour certainly enables actors to develop an ensemble in performance, and to come to grips with individual parts. A lengthy tour may also ultimately dull the wits through endless repetition of the same role. Although you may be seen in many different locations, with an opportunity to be seen by many potential employers, some hard work – and a decent role – will be necessary for this to bear fruit. You may not be playing any one venue for very long, and it may be some time before you are actually available for work.

In small-scale touring, conditions vary widely. Most companies exist in a poverty which severely affects operations. They are unlikely to have wardrobe-mistresses, workshops, or even adequate lighting. Actors may well find rehearsals and performances suffer noticeably from the distractions of hand-to-mouth production standards, haphazard organisation and chronic under-staffing. Fitting-up sets before a show, and dismantling them afterwards may help to keep you fit, but it can eat into preparation-time, and it can certainly be very tiring.

On the other hand much small-scale touring is devoted to new writing and operates with great energy and imagination, frequently fuelled by idealism and/or desperation. As a result it can be a lot of fun. It can also offer relatively inexperienced actors exceptionally good roles and talented directors at the start of their careers.

All touring is tiring. Small-scale touring is frequently exhausting, particularly in winter. Accommodation on tour is always unpredictable and not always a pleasure. There is every possibility of seeing the whole of the country, and foreign parts as well. Substantial areas of rural Britain are very beautiful and can be wonderfully hospitable. Unfortunately rural Britain has very few potential employers, and you should be aware that an exceptional performance in a fine role may not lead to similar work in the future. Indeed, touring can render an actor 'invisible' for several months. It can be difficult (and sometimes impossible) to attend auditions for future work while on the road.

Actors Touring Company

Alford House, Aveline Street, London
SE11 5DQ
Tel (071) 735 8311
Artistic director Ceri Sherlock
General manager Joanna Reid

Founded 1978. Leading small-scale touring company which has established an excellent reputation for producing high quality productions of European Classic texts. Recent productions: *Tasso* (Goethe); *Phaedra* (Tsvetayeva); *Triumph of Love* (Marivaux); *The Illusion* (Corneille); *Princess Ivona* (Gombrowicz); *Faustus* (Marlowe). Perform in arts centres, studio theatres, and educational venues. ITC/ Equity contract of approximately four months. Perform single nights, two nights, split weeks, whole weeks, plus short season in London. Advertise in *SBS*, and *PCR*. No general enquiries please.

Age Exchange Theatre Trust

The Reminiscence Centre, 11 Blackheath Village, London SE3 9LA
Tel (081) 318 9105
Artistic director Pam Schweitzer

Founded 1983. Tour 'reminiscence' shows based on the memories of pensioners on a range of topics such as work and leisure in the 1920s and 1930s and life in general 50 years ago. Perform in old people's homes, sheltered housing units, community centres. Usually four tours annually. ITC/Equity small-scale touring contract of 7–13 weeks. Advertise in *The Stage*. Welcome casting queries; approach in writing in the first instance, enclosing CV, photograph and SAE. Most shows have a musical content, and it is important that actors can sing and, preferably, play a musical instrument. Also a youth theatre that holds workshops, etc. for local children aged 10–15 years; and training courses in the use of reminiscence, for professionals in community work.

Alarmist Theatre

Gazebo Studios, 17 Tichbourne
Street, Brighton BN1 1UR
Tel (0273) 208739
Artistic directors Stephen Plaice,
Helena Uren

The company's policy is to create a
theatre relevant to the New Europe.
Its roots lie in German Expressionism,
Russian Constructivism and Classical
Greek Theatre. The acting style owes
more to Meyerhold than to Stanislavsky. Productions include: Berkoff,
Churchill, Dorst, Aristophanes, Mayakovsky and Cocteau; and the company
has appeared in the First Avant Garde
Theatre Festival in Moscow. Please do
not phone, but write with CV, photograph and SAE.

Annexe Theatre Company Ltd

Block 4, Unit C3, Templeton Business
Centre, Templeton Street,
Glasgow G40 1DA
Tel (041) 551 0570
Administrator Doreen McArdle

Annexe is one of the leading small
touring companies in Scotland.
Productions include: *Boothies* by Peter
Murray; *Vodka and Daisies* by Lara Jane
Bunting; *The Surrogate* by Charles
Barren. Actors should write in the first
instance, with photograph and CV.
The company has a commitment to
new Scottish writers.

Bagatelle

Flat 7, 19–21 Egerton Crescent,
Withington, Manchester M20 9PN
Tel (061) 434 8400
Artistic director Boo Bennett

Founded 1984. Shows for 4–11 year-
olds, for every type of venue and
space, including outdoors. Original
physical comedies with environmental
themes – not T.I.E. Advertise in local
listings and regional arts association
magazines. Welcome casting queries
from actors – write first with CV, then
phone. Workshop auditions as
necessary.

Black Theatre Cooperative

8 Bradbury Street, London N16 8JN
Tel (071) 249 9150
Artistic director Malcolm Frederick

Founded 1980. Small-scale touring
company performing plays that touch
on the black experience universally.
Venues range from main houses to
community centres, including a main
London fringe venue. Recent productions: *Paper and Stone* (Zindika); *65
With a Bullet* (musical); and *Meetings*
(Mustapha Matura). Company of five
actors on Equity minimum contracts of
up to five months in length. Do not
advertise, but welcome casting queries
from actors; send letter with CV and
photograph.

Bootleg Theatre Company

Sherborne House, 20 Greyfriars
Close, Salisbury, Wilts. SP1 2LR
Tel (0722) 32687
Artistic director Colin Burden

Founded 1981. Tour new or rarely performed plays with socially relevant
subjects such as unemployment, drug

abuse, rape, etc. to art centres, studio venues, schools, colleges and youth clubs. Company of two actors. 'We negotiate performance contracts on number of performances.' Advertise in *The Stage* and welcome casting queries from actors; approach in writing in the first instance, enclosing CV. 'We formed the company through disillusionment with the type of plays on show. We wanted to stage good, new or obscure material that we believed was necessary, and although we have had several major setbacks (and this probably sounds very clichéd), we feel that sheer determination and belief in yourself is the only way to achieve any success at all.'

Borderline Theatre Company

North Harbour Street, Ayr KA8 8AA
Tel (0292) 281010
Artistic director John Murtagh

Founded 1974. Tour to main house theatres in city centres and small venues in outlying districts, plus the Edinburgh Festival, Mayfest and, occasionally, London. Mainly new and contemporary work, plus revivals. Productions include: *Can't Pay, Won't Pay*; *George's Marvellous Medicine*; *Mistero Buffo*; *Glasvegas*. Company of 6/8 actors on subsidized rep contracts of 8–15 weeks. Only advertise (in *SBS*) if seeking a specific type: 'We have a body of regular actors we use.' Welcome casting queries; details are kept on file and looked at when casting.

Bristol Express Theatre Company

20 Mocatta House, Brady Street, Whitechapel, London E1 5DL
Tel (071) 247 4156
Artistic director Andy Jordan

Founded 1978. Mainly produce new work by new writers, but the overall range is 'from the commercial to the difficult and challenging'. Usually seven productions annually. Recent credits: *Elsie and Norm's Macbeth* by John Christopher-Wood; *Winter Darkness* by Allan Cubitt; *Heaven* by Sarah Archer. Tour to a wide range of venues, from small-scale to No. 1 theatres. ITC/Equity contract of 20 weeks. Advertise in *The Stage*, and welcome casting queries from actors: approach in writing in the first instance – details are kept on file.

Bruvvers

Ouseburn Warehouse Workshops, 36 Lime Street, Stepney, Newcastle upon Tyne NE1 2FQ
Tel (091) 261 9230
Artistic director Michael Mould

Founded 1969. Tyneside Community tours for all age ranges. A policy of new writing, and fast, energetic musical plays. Productions have included: *See You Later Alligator* for juniors; *Whoppers* for adults; *The Gracie Fields Story* by Alan Plater. Bruvvers also tours to Europe. Michael Mould has worked in all areas of theatre, TV and films for over 25 years. He believes passionately in an actor's theatre and disadvantaged audiences. Tour to schools, hospitals, community centres, youth clubs, tenants huts, etc. Company of six actors on long-term contracts (musical ability necessary).

Rarely advertise, but welcome casting queries from actors.

Buster Theatre

35 Southborough Road, London E9
Tel (081) 986 5109
Artistic directors Sarah Harper, Sarah Cahn

Small-scale tours of devised work for an audience age range of 14 years upwards. Company of nine on 10–week contracts; pay Equity rates. Advertise in *The Stage*, and welcome casting queries from actors; approach in writing in the first instance. Auditions held twice a year.

Cambridge Theatre Company

8 Market Passage, Cambridge CB2 3PE
Tel (0223) 357134

Founded 1969. Classics, modern plays adaptations and new works. Tour nationwide and internationally performing in middle-scale theatres. Recent productions: *Mrs Warren's Profession*, *The Taming of The Shrew* and *Volpone*. Company of 6–11 actors on Esher contracts: 4–6 weeks rehearsal plus 6–10 weeks touring. Do not advertise for actors.

Artistic director (from 1991) Mike Alfreds, whose most recent work has been *The Miser* and *The Seagull* for the Oxford Stage Company and *The Wandering Jew*, *Countrymania* and *The Cherry Orchard* for the Royal National Theatre.

Carib Theatre Productions

Linburn House, 342 Kilburn High Road, London NW6 2QJ
Tel (071) 624 5860
Artistic director Anton Phillips

Founded 1981. Tours to middle-scale venues for approximately eight weeks in the spring, plus Theatre-in-Education (TIE) tour centred on London for the summer and autumn terms (8–15 weeks). Recent productions: *Remembrance* by Derek Walcott; *Breakthrough* by Norman Mattison, music by Alan Cooke; *Lights Out In Electric City* and *Bolt From The Blue*, by Errol Lloyd. Equity contracts. Sometimes advertise in *SBS*, and welcome casting queries from actors; approach in writing in the first instance. 'Carib Theatre was formed to give black actors, writers, designers, directors, technical staff and stage managers more opportunities to practise and develop their skills. Carib's work reflects the multi-cultural nature of British society and aims at the highest possible professional standards. Carib commissions new scripts for TIE work.'

Century Theatre

Lakeside, Keswick, Cumbria CA12 5DJ
Tel (07687) 72282 Fax (07687) 74698
Artistic director Han Duijvendak

Founded 1949. Commenced touring in 1950 in the unique mobile theatre known as the 'Blue Box' – a collection of trailers which, when assembled, comprised a 225–seat theatre. The Blue Box now hosts a separate Keswick Summer Season care of the same address.

Century Theatre tours nationally to conventional mid-scale venues throughout England, with some plans for overseas touring (*She Stoops to Conquer* was selected for a British Council tour of Pakistan in December 1990). The company is one of three main companies operating on the Arts Council middle-scale Matrix, with a policy of touring high-quality theatre to the regions. Century are noted for musicals and classic drama. Tour 4–5 shows annually for a total of around 30 weeks. Recent productions include *She Stoops to Conquer/The Playboy of the Western World* (tandem tour with same company of ten actors), *Irma la Douce*, Stephen Sondheim's musical *Company* (fourteen actor/musicians/singers each playing up to five instruments), and the two-hander thriller *Double Double* (Spring 1991 co-production with Chester Gateway Theatre). Tour length varies around 8–12 weeks. Advertise in *SBS* and *PCR*. Happy to accept letter with CVs and photographs. Do not hold general auditions. In working towards building an ensemble company for each project, Han Duijvendak does not require audition pieces; instead the actor reads from the play and takes part in a workshop: 'This enables both sides to see how well they can work together.'

Channel Theatre Company

Granville Theatre, Victoria Parade, Ramsgate, Kent CT11 8DG
Tel (0843) 588280
Artistic director Philip Dart

Founded 1980. Tour a wide range of productions to middle-scale venues. Recent credits: *Moll Flanders*; *Up On The Roof*; *The Woman in Black* (all directed by Philip Dart). Usually two tours annually of 10–12 weeks. Have a core of actors who are used regularly. Advertise in *Rep Report*. Prefer letters

to be in response to advertisements; always enclose SAE.

Charabanc Theatre Company

The Ulster Hall, Linenhall Street, Belfast BT2 7FF
Tel (0232) 234242
Joint directors Carol Scanlan, Eleanor Methven
Administrator Patricia McBride

Founded 1983. Tour throughout Ireland, UK, USA and Europe to small/middle scale venues. Perform new writing. Company of four to seven actors on 2 to 4-month contracts. Do not advertise for actors. Due to having only one administrator, they are unable to reply to queries from actors. 'We have never recruited from unsolicited applications from actors as we usually cast from people whose work we know.' ITC Approved Management.

Cheek by Jowl

Alford House, Aveline Street, London SE11 5DQ
Tel (071) 793 0153/4
Artistic directors Declan Donnellan, Nick Ormerod

Founded 1981. Award-winning touring company much lauded for its innovative productions of world classics. Middle- and small-scale tours annually, both national and worldwide. Recent productions: *The Doctor of Honor* by Calderon; *Lady Betty*, written and directed by Declan Donellan; *Sara* by G.E. Lessing; *Hamlet*. Company of 12–16 actors plus stage management of 3–4. Use TMA subsidized rep contracts (pay 30–40% above minimum rate); 5–10 months in length. Never advertise for actors, and do not welcome casting queries. 'We always use a casting director who produces an audition list for us. We regularly use people straight out of drama school who have been suggested in this way. We believe that a drama school training is essential for our style of work. We actively pursue an integrated casting policy.'

everyone's time. It should also be understood if the applicant is going to be asked to "do a piece" or "read". Applicants often turn up with nothing prepared or do not wish to read for a part, thinking it is merely an interview and not an audition. It is always wise for young artists to have something up their sleeves in case they are asked to do something. Choice of audition piece should be something that suits their talents and personality and, preferably, *not* the inevitable Hamlet or Juliet. Originality is a plus mark.'

The Cherub Company

13 St. Barnabas Road, Walthamstow, London E17 8JZ
Tel (081) 520 8498
Artistic director Andrew Visnevski

Founded 1978. Middle-scale tours of popular and neglected classics, new adaptations of world drama (e.g. Kafka, Calderon) and new plays that fit the company's policy. Average company size of 10–12 on Equity minimum contracts. Tour a minimum of three nights, plus 'tours abroad for the British Council, commercial managements and impresarios'. Recent productions: *Twelfth Night* and *The Duchess of Malfi*. Do not advertise, but welcome casting queries from actors; send letter with CV and SAE. 'It is important, when agents send clients for auditions, they understand exactly what they are auditioning for! Too often, agents send clients who are undoubtedly talented but totally unsuited to the job, which wastes

Clean Break Theatre Company

37–39 Kings Terrace, London NW1 0JR
Tel (071) 383 3786

Founded in 1979 by women prisoners. Small scale touring company that mainly employs women ex-offenders or women with experience of confinement (e.g. prison, mental institution, drug rehab. etc.). Productions are always based around issues of women in prison and include *Treading on my Tale* by Gilli Mebarek, *Open Secrets*, devised by the company and *Wicked*, by Bryony Lavery. Perform in a wide range of venues, including arts centres and theatres throughout Britain, prisons, drug rehabs., conferences for people involved in the criminal justice system etc. Annual company of up to five actors on 10–15 week Equity small-scale touring contracts. Advertise for cast in *The Stage*, *The Voice*, *City Limits* etc. Welcome casting enquiries from women with above experiences, writing only in the first instance. The company runs its own in-house training in the performing arts and creative writing.

Communicado

Royal Lyceum Theatre, Grindlay Street, Edinburgh EH3 9AX
Tel (031) 229 7404
Artistic director Gerard Mulgrew

Founded 1983. Small-scale touring company performing in anything from village halls to small- or medium-scale theatres. A wide range of productions, including new writing. Recent productions: *Jack Tamson's Bairns* (an epic commissioned to open the theatre season of Glasgow 1990 European City of Culture) and *Danton's Death* (Edinburgh International Festival and extensive tour from Orkney to Jersey). Company of 8–10 on ITC contracts of a minimum of six weeks (maximum 16 weeks). Occasionally advertise in *The Stage*. Welcome casting queries from actors; approach in writing in the first instance. 'We are an association of theatre artists working (mainly) in Scotland, interested in evolving an eclectic style of theatre which is at once popular and innovative, in which respect we mix text, live music, visual imagery and the physical resources of the performer as well as an awareness of our indigenous culture. The nature of our work is Scottish and international, specific but universal.' The company has won four Fringe Firsts for outstanding new work on the Edinburgh Festival Fringe and won the 1989 Prudential Award for Theatre.

Compass Theatre Company (Actors Cabal Ltd)

The Leadmill, 6–7 Leadmill Road, Sheffield S1 4SF
Tel (0742) 755328
Artistic director Neil Sissons

Founded 1981. Mainly tour classical works, with an occasional new play normally written by Neil Sissons and Nicholas Chadwin. Past productions have included: *The Alchemist*, *Volpone*, *Hamlet*, *The Tempest*, *A Higher Passion*, *Macbeth*, *Spartacus*, *The Odyssey*. Perform in a wide variety of venues – No. 1 theatres, small- and middle-scale venues, arts and community centres and schools. Currently tour 30 weeks a year, including internationally. The company operates as an ensemble employing six performers and aims to work with one company over a twelve month period. Compass is a member of ITC and operates ITC/Equity small scale contracts. The company is interested in working with performers with a strong interest in classical theatre and a commitment to the challenge of creating high impact theatre despite the rigours of touring.

Crummles Theatre Company

35 The Park, London W5 5NP
Tel (081) 567 8670 Fax (081) 567 0057
Contact Ellie Dickens (artistic director), Roger Bilder (administrator)

Founded 1983. Productions include: *Absurd Person Singular*, *Relatively Speaking* and *Absent Friends* (directed by Doug Fisher); *Othello* (Joseph Marcel); *My Dearest Kate* and *Mrs Worthington's Daughter* (John Dryden);

The Idiot Witness (Ellie Dickens); *George, Don't Do That*. Tours to small- and middle-scale venues, including annual visit to the Edinburgh Fringe. Occasionally profit-share. Advertise in *The Stage*, and welcome casting queries from actors; approach in writing in the first instance.

Cumbernauld Theatre Company

Cumbernauld Theatre, Kildrum,
Cumbernauld G67 2BN
Tel (0236) 737235
Director Liz Carruthers

Founded 1979. Produce popular theatre, new plays by Scottish writers, children's shows, educational drama and established plays. Tour to community centres, halls, schools and art centres, as well as performing at the Cumbernauld Theatre. Recent productions: *James And The Giant Peach*; *The Fitting* by Tom McGrath; *Videoscope* by Ann Marie di Mambro; and *If Elvis Lived In Meikle Earnock* by Peter Nardini. Company of 4–6 on Equity subsidized rep contracts of eight weeks. Occasionally advertise in *The Stage*, and welcome casting queries from actors; write in the first instance.

Dr Foster's Travelling Theatre

Makers, New Mills, Libby's Drive, Slad Road, Stroud GL5 1RN
Tel (0453) 751903

Founded 1980. Community and outdoor shows plus educational projects, all of which are suitable for mainly non-theatre going audiences in rural areas. Recent productions: *Out of It* (schools); *Deadlock* (murder mystery). 1991 productions: *Out of It*; outdoor

adaptation of *Robin Hood*; *Take It Away* (autumn national tour). Perform in village halls, community centres, schools, small arts centres and outdoors. Generally one-night stands in the South-west plus occasional weeks outside the region. Run by core company of professionals from theatre and theatre-related disciplines. Advertise in *The Stage* and prefer enquiries to specific job adverts, but will reply to query letters.

Dual Control Theatre Company Ltd

Woodlands Centre, Woodlands Road,
Gillingham, Kent ME7 2BX
Tel (0634) 281448
Artistic director Michael Bath

Founded 1985. New plays by writers from Southeast England and the Nord/Pas de Calais region of France, touring nationally and internationally. The first British producer to tour a European company on the British tour circuit with an Arts Council of Great Britain Touring Subsidy. Recent productions: *Black Nightingale*; *Plumes D'Amour*; *Bleu 'Ecailles*. Advertise in *PCR*, Equity *Jobgrapevine* and through agents. Welcome casting queries from bi-lingual actors; write in the first instance.

Durham Theatre Company

The Arts Centre, Vane Terrace,
Darlington, Co. Durham DL3 7AX
Tel (0325) 469861

Founded 1977. Autumn tour, junior schools' show and annual pantomime. Productions include: *Every Night Something Awful* by Denise Doogan;

The Mysteries (presented in Durham Cathedral); *The Beggar's Opera* and *Oh! What a Lovely War*. Perform in community centres, village halls, schools and small arts centres. One-night stands (returning to base each night), mainly in Co. Durham but also Cleveland and Tyne & Wear. Company of five actors and stage management of two on ITC/Equity contracts. Welcome letters from actors ('do not phone') with CVs and photographs.

Eastern Angles Theatre Company

Sir John Mills Theatre, Gatacre Road, Ipswich, Suffolk IP1 2LQ
Tel (0473) 218202 Fax (0473) 250954
Artistic director Ivan Cutting

Founded 1982. 'All productions use music and are original to the company. They often reflect some flavour of the region.' Tour a wide range of venues, from 'the smallest village hall to the largest theatre', mostly in the region, returning to base most nights. Performances are from Tuesday to Saturday. Recent productions: *Goodbye America* (new musical for larger venues); *Peddar's Way* (new play with music for village halls); *Waterland* (national tour and Shaw Theatre, London); *Sherlock Holmes And The Mystery Of The Missing Carol*. Company of 4–6 on ITC/Equity contracts ('Pay above minimum, but rarely pay overtime') of not less than ten weeks. Sometimes advertise in *The Stage*. Welcome casting queries, provided the actor is familiar with the company's work or has special skills such as ability to play an instrument.

Empty Space Theatre Company

59 Godolphin Road, London W12 8JF
Tel (081) 740 7115
Artistic director Andrew Holmes
Administrator Pauline Flannery

Founded 1985. Small scale touring runs at London fringe venues. Ensemble-based work with a strong emphasis on devised work and adaptations of literary originals. Productions include: *The Comfort of Strangers* by Ian McEwan, *The Rainbow* by D. H. Lawrence and *The Aspern Papers* by Henry James, *Dr. Jekyll and Mr. Hyde*, *Pilgrim's Progress*, and *Leaf Storm* by Gabriel Garcia Marquez. Company of 4/6 actors; non-Equity. Advertise in *PCR*, *SBS* and *The Stage*. Actors need to have experience of improvisational work.

Field Day Theatre Company

Foyle Arts Centre, Lawrence Hill, Derry BT48 7NJ
Tel (0504) 360196
Contact Gary McKeone

Founded 1980. Touring company committed to new Irish writing that is relevant to Ireland today. Tour in northern and southern Ireland to theatres, town halls, schools and community halls. Recent productions: *Translations*, by Brian Friel; *Boesman and Lena* by Athol Fugard; *Double Cross* by Thomas Kilroy; *Pentecost* by Stewart Parker; *St. Oscar*; and *The Cure at Troy*. Average company of 5/6 actors plus stage management of three on Equity contracts of 3–4 months. Do not advertise, but welcome casting queries from actors; telephone in the first instance.

Forest Forge Theatre Company

Ringwood Comprehensive School, Manor Road, Ringwood, Hants BH24 1RA
Tel (0425) 470188
Artistic director Karl Hibbert

Founded 1981. Small-scale touring company that performs projects for a specific audience (i.e. the elderly/TIE), traditional text and a Christmas family show. Also committed to organizing community projects involving local people. Shows generally devised by the company, music being an integral part of the productions. Annually tour three projects from September to March. A core of four actors, which is added to as required, on ITC/Equity small-scale touring contracts of six months. Advertise in *The Stage*, the ethnic minority press and through ITC's mailing. Prefer to receive letters only in response to specific advertisements. The company pursues an equal opportunities policy. 'Actors in the company must be very versatile – musical skills an advantage.'

Forkbeard Fantasy

Moor Cottage, Huntsham, Tiverton, Devon EX16 7NF
Tel (03986) 329

Founded 1974. Revenue client of Arts Council. Cooperative touring company performing devised comedy shows throughout the UK and Europe. Also tour to small cinemas and film clubs as the 'Brittonioni Brothers' with their 16mm films. Two tours annually plus educational residencies, working with schools and handicapped people (usually four sessions per year). Productions include: *Invasion of the Bloopies; The Brittonioni Bros. Across the Celluloid Divide; Desmond Fairybreath On Tour*. Do not advertise for actors or welcome casting queries as all performances are by the cooperative directors, Tim Britton and Chris Britton.

Foursight Theatre Company

Performing Arts Site, Dunkley Street, Wolverhampton WV1 4AN
Tel (0902) 714257

A women's theatre company re-assessing history through the eyes of women. Foursight tours to theatres, arts centres, colleges and schools, both nationally and internationally. Recent productions: *Hitler's Women, Mobs and Martyrs, Helen*, and *Pink Smoke at the Vatican – the Mystery of Pope Joan*. ITC contracts. Welcome queries from individual actors (female). Write with CV, photograph and SAE. Please do not phone.

Gay Sweatshop

Interchange Studios, 15 Wilkin Street, London NW5 3NG
Tel (071) 485 5799 Fax (071) 482 5292
Artistic directors David Benedict, Cordelia Ditton, Bryony Lavery

Founded 1975. Tours new work written by and for lesbians and gay men, ranging from text-based plays and company-devised pieces to the presentation of new plays as rehearsed readings during festivals. Usually present two productions annually, opening in London followed by small-scale touring of 3–5 weeks throughout England and Scotland. Performs in arts centres, studio theatres, civic theatres, university and college theatres. Productions have included: *Poppies* by Noel Grieg; *Telling Tales* by Philip Osment; *Raising The Wreck* by Sue Frumin; *Compromised Immunity* by Andy Kirby; *This Island's Mine* by Philip Osment; *Twice Over* by Jackie Kay; *Paradise Now And Then* by Noel Greig and Richard Coles; *Kitchen Matters* by Bryony Lavery. Company of up to seven on Equity contracts (minimum rate) of 10–11 weeks. Advertise in *The Stage*, lesbian and gay press (*Capital Gay*, *The Pink Paper*), black press (*The Voice*) and feminist press (*Spare Rib*). Welcome casting queries; send letter with CV and photograph. 'Gay Sweatshop is an equal opportunities employer, operating integrated casting, and it welcomes applications irrespective of gender, race, age or abilities. We actively encourage applications from lesbians and gay men, so if you do identify yourself as homosexual, please say so in your letter. Applicants should have have a commitment to challenging heterosexism and supporting the rights of lesbians and gay men, and should draw attention to any relevant work experience or areas of study. All casting information on file is consulted by directors for every production prior to advertising.'

Gloria

104 Haddo House, Haddo Street,
London SE10 9SE
Tel (081) 853 1243
Contact Simon Mellor

Gloria is a production company set up in 1988 to support and promote the work of four associated but independent artists: Neil Bartlett, Nicolas Bloomfield, Leah Hausman, and Simon Mellor. Productions include: *Lady Audley's Secret*, *A Vision of Love Revealed in Sleep part three*, *Ariadne*, and *Sarrasine*. All productions have a very strong music theatre element. The company advertises in *The Stage* when casting and does not welcome enquiries from individual actors.

Gog Theatre Company Ltd

'Ostia', Overleigh, Street, Somerset
BA16 0TJ
Tel (0458) 47353
Artistic directors Tom Clark, Caryne Clark

Annual Theatre-in-Education (TIE) production for Somerset primary schools. Recent International Theatre Exchange Programme with Rustavelli Theatre, in Tbilisi, Georgia USSR. Planned collaborative production touring Georgia and UK in Spring 1992. Creative video-making and teaching theatre workshops and communication skills sessions. Perform in schools, colleges, community venues and arts centres. Company of eight on three-month contracts; Equity. Occasionally advertise in *The Stage*, *ITC Newsletter* and local press. Always welcome casting queries, preferably by letter. 'We interview people by workshopping over a period of time – we don't audition as a company. Gog is a small-scale theatre company which is involved in innovative projects which differ in skills required usually in the "rep" theatre. For this reason, and for financial reasons, the company does not employ many new actors. However, we are always very interested in hearing from anyone.'

Good Company

46 Quebec Street, Brighton, E. Sussex
BN2 2UZ
Tel (0273) 606652 Fax (0273) 693560
Artistic director Sue Pomeroy

Founded 1986. Tour from small-
to large-scale theatres; particularly
concerned with new writing.
Approximately two tours each year.
Credits include: *Ear, Nose and Throat* by
Sue Townsend (No. 1 tour); *Crowned
with Fame* by Michael Ellis; *I, Bertolt
Brecht* (in collaboration with Bristol
Old Vic); *The Entertainer*; *The Pepys
Show*. Occasionally advertise in *SBS*.
Welcome casting queries from actors;
approach in writing in the first in-
stance, enclosing CV, photograph and
SAE. Musical skills an advantage.

Graeae Theatre Company

25 Bayham Street, London NW1 0EY
Tel (071) 383 7541 and 383 7492

Founded 1981, this year celebrating
its tenth anniversary. Graeae is
Britain's only professional company of
disabled performers touring London,
nationally and internationally. Graeae
produces a mixture of Theatre In
Education Programmes, small scale
touring productions, arts development workshops and disability awareness workshops. A company of four
actors, stage manager are employed
on Equity, ITC Contracts of approx. 14
weeks, (28 weeks TIE). Work over the
past year has included a national tour
of *Why* to arts centres, studio theatres.
Chances Are, TIE tour London and
Regions. Writers are commissioned to
write new work about aspects of disability culture. Advertise in *The Stage*,
The Voice, *Disability News*, *Dail
Magazine*, Newsletter and mailouts to
disability organisations. Particularly
welcome interest from disabled
performers.

Great Eastern Stage

William Park, Waterside South, Lincoln
LN5 7JN
Tel (0522) 534924
Artistic director Michael Fry

Founded 1977. Some new plays but
mainly 'classics'. Recent work includes: *Tess of the D'Urbevilles*; *Teaser*;
The Old Bachelor; *Richard III*; *La
Parisienne*; *Sarah's 'Emma' After Jane*.
ITC/Equity contracts, usually 8–10
weeks in length. Cast from tour to
tour. Advertise in *SBS* and welcome
casting queries from actors; approach
in writing in the first instance.

GW Theatre Company Ltd

Abraham Moss Centre Theatre,
Crescent Road, Crumpsall,
Manchester M8 6UF
Tel (061) 740 1491 ext 336
Administration: Dave Jones, Julie
Clays

Set up in September 1986 to take
theatre where it wouldn't normally be
seen. Seven nationally toured shows
to date, all of which have aimed for a
dramatic form that is accessible, witty,
humane, and doesn't pull punches.
Autumn 1991 – *Beauty and the Beasts* – a
black comedy that takes a beady-eyed
look at sex, class, violence and what
we call 'our civilisation'. Three core
members. Occasionally advertise in
The Stage and the local press, and welcome casting queries from actors;
approach in writing in the first
instance.

HAC Theatre Ltd

65a Kingsley Road, Hounslow, Middx.
TW3 1QB
Tel (081) 570 9681
Contact Preet Persaud (Co-ordinator)

Founded 1985. Small-scale tours of original work that specifically addresses contemporary social issues facing young British Asians, coupled with the wider issues facing the youth of today. Perform in arts centres and community venues. Two major productions a year (April/October); workshops (June–August); cabaret (all year). Recent productions: *Bad Company* and *Kings* by Parv Bancil. Equity contracts. Advertise in *The Stage*, and welcome casting queries from actors; send letter with CV. 'Although we are interested in all young talent, we particularly welcome CVs from young Asian actors. An essential part of HAC's policy is to promote and develop all young artistic talent; we are therefore always interested in potential playwrights, designers, etc.'

Hull Freetown Theatre

YPI Buildings, 83/93 George Street,
Hull HU1 3BN
Tel (0482) 5870082

Founded in 1990. Touring company that presents new and contemporary theatre in arts centres and theatres throughout the UK. Four productions per year, with eight-weeks tour on ITC contracts; drama workshops at schools and community centres. Company of five, operating as a co-operative. Recent productions include *Kiss of The Spider Woman*, and *Unveiling* (Havel). The company hopes to set up a foreign exchange tour in 1991/2. Welcome enquiries from individual actors. Write

in the first instance with CV, photograph and SAE. Please do not telephone. Advertise in *The Stage*. 'Our policy is to present work which breaks down barriers of prejudice and emotion, to increase awareness over issues which many tend to avoid. Performers must be fit, versatile, and willing to work as a member of a co-operative.'

Hull Truck Theatre Company

Spring Street Theatre, Spring Street,
Hull HU2 8RW
Tel (0482) 224800
Artistic director John Godber
Administrator Barry Nettleton
Associate directors Neil Sissons,
Richard Lewis, Robert Sian

Founded 1971 by Mike Bradwell. Barry Nettleton appointed as Administrator in 1975, and John Godber as Artistic Director in 1984. The company has grown into one of the leading small- to middle-scale touring companies, with shows transferring to London and regularly winning awards at the Edinburgh Festival. Until recently concentrated on new writing, but now including classics in their programming. Recent productions include: *Sweet Sorrow* by Alan Plater; *Romeo and Juliet*; *Treasure Island*; and a large-scale touring production of *On The Piste* by John Godber. Tour to small- middle- and large-scale venues. One major tour annually plus 2–4 smaller tours. Actors on contracts varying between five weeks and ten months; Equity/ ITC small-scale touring contract. Recruit from a pool of regular actors, but occasionally advertise in *SBS*. Keep details of actors on file. Recommend making contact a couple of months before their new season commences (at the Edinburgh Festival in August).

Impossible Theatre

38 Longley, Holmfirth, West Yorkshire HD7 1RS
Tel (0484) 681262
Artistic directors Charlott Diefenthal, Chris Squire

Founded 1983. Small-scale touring theatre to large outdoor spectaculars. Productions are 'intriguing visual and physical theatre with live music'. Number of company members varies from 2–5 up to 20 for some events; contracts vary according to project. Do not advertise for actors, and do not welcome casting queries unless acquainted with their work. 'Our group approach to working means we must be able to depend on good working relationships. We must see people at work or in workshops. We work mostly with musicians, dancers, sculptors, and artists, not actors.'

Inner City Theatre Company

The Print House, 18 Ashwin Street, Longon E8 3DL
Tel (071) 249 1711
Artistic director Les Miller

Founded 1982. Small- and mid-scale touring company committed to new plays. Recent productions: *Come And Make Eyes At Me*; *Here Comes The Candle*; *The Lambada Connection*. Perform in arts centres and colleges, with a touring pattern of two- to three-nighters, split weeks, one-night stands and three-week runs. Equity small-scale touring contracts. Advertise in *SBS*, and do not welcome casting queries from actors. Please do not phone.

Interim Theatre Productions Ltd

See **Theatre-in-Education companies**.

Interplay Community Theatre

Armley Ridge Road, Leeds LS12 3LE
Tel (0532) 638556 Fax (0532) 791347

Founded 1970. Community tours, residencies at the Interplay Community Theatre for groups and organizations, schools tours and summer outdoor touring shows. 'Our work is self-devised and specially designed for its particular audience and performing situations.' Recent productions: *Dr Swagger's Winter Cure-All*, *Scrooge's Yuletide Makemerry*. Perform in small-scale community venues – village halls, social clubs, leisure and community centres – plus festivals and galas. The company also has a very strong commitment to working with children with severe learning difficulties. Half of the touring is in Yorkshire, with 2–4 weeks per project in the regions. Six weeks touring the community show or special schools project, and 12 weeks touring the summer outdoor show. Company of four actors on ITC contracts of 3–5 months in length; gross weekly wage: £187.00. Advertise for actors in the *Guardian*, *The Stage* and the ITC noticeboard. Welcome casting queries; send letter enclosing CV. 'We are confirmed eclectics, ever open to a variety of forms, developing a style that includes music, humour, poetry, movement, visual imagery and audience participation, with a content that is anti-racist and anti-sexist.'

Joint Stock Theatre Group

40 Calthorpe Street, London WC1X 0JZ
Tel (071) 833 4684

Founded in 1974 by David Aukin, David Hare, and Max Stafford-Clark. This once lauded company has fallen on hard times. Productions include: *The Speakers; Light Shining in Buckinghamshire; Fanshen!; A Mad World, My Masters; Cloud Nine; Epsom Downs; The House; The Great Celestial Cow; Fire In the Lake; A Mouthful of Birds; Promised Land*. Without Arts Council subsidy it is unable currently to produce, but hopes to find financial backing for future work. Until that time Joint Stock does not welcome enquiries from individual actors.

Live Theatre Company

'The Live Theatre', Broad Chare, Quayside, Newcastle upon Tyne NE1 3DF
Tel (091) 261 2694
Artistic director Max Roberts

Founded 1973. Extensive touring, both regional and national, of in-house productions, collaborations with other theatre, film and TV companies, workshops and community projects. 'Our policy is to perform new work with a commitment to those writers, performers and technicians from the North-east whose work is innovative and challenging. These plays reflect experiences of working-class life, past and present, in a way that is neither exclusive nor parochial.' Recent productions: *Some Like It Cold* by Steve

Chambers; *Bandits* by CP Taylor; *Hair In The Gate* by Michael Chaplin; *Rocking the Cradle* by Pauline Hadaway, Anne Orwin and Karen Hope. Perform in a wide range of community venues and arts centres, small- and middle-scale theatres, as well as in their own 100-seat theatre. Spring tour – early February to April; autumn tour – September to November; small-scale Christmas tour; and other projects throughout the year, including building-based productions. Company of 4–5 actors plus stage management of two on ITC/Equity minimum contracts of 11 weeks in length. Advertise for actors in *The Stage* and the local press. Welcome casting queries; approach in writing in the first instance.

London Bubble Theatre Company

5 Elephant Court, London SE16 4JD
Tel (071) 237 4434 Fax (071) 231 2366
Artistic director Jonathan Petherbridge

Founded 1972. 'Popular theatre' company combining professional performance work, drama-based community projects and training courses for theatre practitioners. The Bubble theatre tent tours parks and open spaces around London during the summer, presenting upfront musical theatre and cabaret. Recent productions include: *The Gambler* by Peter Brewis/Bob Goody/Mel Smith, *The Threepenny Opera* by Bertolt Brecht/Kurt Weill and *Bugs and Slugs* by Kevin Dyer. Tent touring company of ten from June to September (12 weeks). ITC/Equity standard contract. Advertise in *The Stage*; do not welcome casting queries from actors. 'We work in a particular style and in a particular environment, quite often playing to a non theatre-going audience. It helps if you've seen the work.'

Lumiere & Son Theatre Company

70 Silverthorne Road, London SW8 3HE
Tel (071) 622 4865 Fax (071) 622 2053
Artistic director Hilary Westlake

Founded 1973. Perform new work only, either written by co-founder David Gale or devised and directed by Hilary Westlake. Tours plus large-scale site-specific shows using music, choreography, projection and text. Recent productions: *Panic*; *Deadwood* (Kew Gardens); *Paradise*; *Taboo*; *Circus Lumiere*; *Why Is Here There Everywhere Now?* at the Riverside Studios in association with the Soho Theatre Company. Perform in arts centres and small- to mid-scale theatres. Site-specific – e.g. Kew Gardens, Penzance Jubilee Bathing Pool, Singapore Zoo. Tour in autumn, spring and summer; outdoor work in summer. Touring company of 9–10; site-specific company of 50–150+. ITC/Equity contracts of 3–6 months. Advertise in *The Stage*, and welcome casting queries from actors; approach in writing in the first instance. 'Find out about the company *before* writing.'

M6 Theatre Company

Hamer CP School, Albert Royds Street, Rochdale OL16 2SU
Tel (0706) 355898
Resident director Eileen Murphy

Founded 1977. Tour one show per year to community venues in Greater Manchester and the North-west; three TIE productions to Rochdale schools; with some dates in Greater Manchester. Middle-scale Christmas Show in association with Rochdale CLS at Middleton Civic Hall. Company varies between 10 and 35. Advertise through *SBS* and occasionally in *The Stage* and *The Voice*. Casting enquiries to Eileen Murphy.

The Made-in-Wales Stage Company

Mount Stuart House, Mount Stuart Square, Cardiff CF1 6DQ
Tel (0222) 484017
Artistic director Gilly Adams
Associate Directors Gareth Armstrong, Jamie Garven

Founded 1982. Touring company committed to producing new work by Welsh or Wales based writers, writing in English. Recent productions include: *The Scam* by Peter Lloyd; *Branwen* by Tony Conran; *The Fourth World* by Dick Edwards; *The Best Years of Our Lives* by Laurence Allan. In addition to productions the Company mounts an annual Festival of New writing, *Write On*. Made In Wales performs mainly at the Sherman Theatre, Cardiff and at Theatr Clwyd, Mold with other venues in Wales and England as appropriate. On average a company of 6 on six/seven week Equity contracts (MRSL II). Advertise (if necessary) in *The Stage* and *SBS*. Welcome casting enquiries from actors, who should write in the first instance, but priority is given to Welsh and Wales based actors and graduates of the Welsh College of Music and Drama. The company offers actor training as part of the production process, where possible. Actors who enjoy the particular challenges of new work and who are prepared to take risks are welcomed.

The Magic Roundabout Theatre Company

Wyvern Theatre, Theatre Square, Swindon, Wilts. SN1 1QJ
Tel (0793) 614864
Artistic director Derek Hewitson

Community theatre, Theatre-in-Education (TIE) and small-scale touring productions in Wiltshire and surrounding area. Perform in village halls, community centres, schools, arts centres and mainstream theatres. Recent productions: *Frankie and Johnny in the Clair de Lune* (Terence McNally); *Night Mother* (Marsha Norman); *Sizwe Bansi is Dead* (Athol Fugard); *Hess* (Michael Burrell); *Stronger Than Superman* (Roy Kift). Company of 3–8 actors, depending on production, with tours of 3–6 weeks. Some through casting; standard Esher contract. Advertise in *The Stage*, *SBS* and *PCR*. Welcome casting queries from actors – 'strictly by letter'.

Major Road Theatre Company

29 Queens Road, Bradford, W. Yorks. BD8 7BS
Tel (0274) 480251 Fax (0274) 548528
Artistic director Graham Devlin

Founded 1973. Major Road's policy is to create and commission new work by new writers and to develop a highly visual style of theatre. The work involves a fusion of forms such as dance and music. Also run theatre residences in various settings, educational programmes and community work. Specialize in large-scale site specific productions. Tour to small-scale venues. Company of 4–8 actors on ITC/Equity contracts of 8–10 weeks. Welcome casting queries from actors; approach in writing in the first instance, enclosing CV, photograph and SAE (big enough for return of photograph). Details are kept on file. Major Road actively pursue an equal opportunities policy.

Manchester Actors Company

c/o Administration, 25 Holly Street, Tottington, Bury BL8 3EZ *or* c/o Arts Board, North West, 12 Harter Street, Manchester M1 6HY
Tel (0204) 884830
Artistic director Stephen Boyes
Administrator Brian Lavers

Founded 1980. Community theatre – small-scale touring to all branches of the community throughout Greater Manchester, plus some national touring. Recent productions: *Robocat* (children's show); *A Short History of the Female Detective* (adult show; pub tour); *Cries From The Heart* (musical); *Dracula* (promenade version); *Tales Never Told* (tour of libraries). 'We devise, or commission writers to produce, work tailor-made for specific areas in the community – i.e. youth clubs, elderly people, infant schools.' Perform in shopping precincts, schools, village halls, community centres, sports centres, mostly non-theatre venues, although 'we have played the Royal Exchange Theatre, Manchester.' Average of three shows per year. Company of four actors on six-week contracts. Paid slightly above Equity Minimum wages. Advertise for actors in *The Stage*, and welcome casting queries; send a letter enclosing CV and photograph. 'Our type of work provides a good, practical training ground for young actors with lots of stamina who are interested in taking theatre to non-theatre venues.'

Mikron Theatre Company Ltd

31 Warehouse Hill, Marsden, Huddersfield, W. Yorks. HD7 6AB
Tel (0484) 845264
Artistic director Mike Lucas

Founded 1972. Waterborne theatre company touring musical shows on a variety of topics, but all with a 'quality of life' theme. Productions include: *A Place To Stand* the story of the Yorkshire Luddites; and *Free For All* – 'an environmentally friendly musical'. Perform in canal and riverside pubs, museums, rallies and festivals. Generally a summer tour by narrowboat throughout the waterways of England, and in the autumn, a South Pennine tour. Company of four on 8–9-month contracts. Advertise in *The Stage*, and welcome casting queries from actors; approach in writing in the first instance.

Millstream Theatre Company

Yvonne Arnaud Theatre, Millbrook, Guildford, Surrey GU1 3UX
Tel (0483) 64571
Artistic director Christopher Masters

Founded 1982. Revivals and seldom-seen classics. Tour to theatres seating from 70 to 500. Recent productions: *Tom and Viv*; *The Sneeze*; and *Road to Mecca* (all directed by Christopher Masters). Two 9–10-week Millstream tours annually, plus a month-long tour of a new play. Company of five actors on subsidized rep contracts. Advertise in *SBS*, and do not welcome

casting queries from actors. *See also* entry for Yvonne Arnaud Theatre in Rep/Regional Theatres section.

Monstrous Regiment

190 Upper Street, London N1 1RQ
Tel (071) 359 9842 Fax (071) 359 5773

Founded 1975 by a group of professional actors who wanted to make 'exciting, political theatre based on women's experience; tired of seeing that experience marginalized or trivialized, we wanted to take it out of the wings and place it at the centre of the stage.' One of Britain's leading feminist theatre groups, managed by a collective of six women. Produce commissioned new plays (usually by women writers) and tour split and full weeks to studio theatres and arts centres. Recent productions: *The Colony Comes A Cropper* (Marivaux/Robyn Archer); *Love Story of the Century* (Marta Tikkanen); *More Than One Antoinette* (Debbie Shewell). Maximum cast size of four on Equity/ITC contracts of 12–16 weeks. Do not advertise, but welcome casting queries; approach in writing in the first instance. 'As a women's company, we normally encourage enquiries by women, but as we only do two productions a year with casts of no more than four, we cannot be too encouraging.'

Moving Being Ltd

St Stephen's Theatre Space, West Bute Street, Cardiff CF1 6EP
Tel (0222) 480961
Artistic director Geoff Moore

Founded 1968 in London; moved to Cardiff 1972. Used to tour extensively, but in 1982, bought St Stephen's Theatre Space and now perform there, although it is thought that touring may recommence in the future. Wide range of productions – classics plus new or devised work. Recent productions include *A Midsummer Night's Dream*; *The Duchess of Malfi*; and *The Castle*. Usually 2–3 productions annually. TMA subsidized rep contract, usually of 4–7 weeks. Very rarely advertise, but welcome casting queries from actors. Approach in writing in the first instance – details are kept on file.

Moving Theatre (Trust Ltd)

William IV School, Shepherdess Walk, London N1 7QE
Tel (071) 253 2590
Artistic director Jonathan Banatvala

Presents a wide range of theatre including national and international small- and mid-scale touring and new work on the London fringe. Moving Theatre is committed to full participation in Europe in 1992. Productions include: *This Geezer I Know*, *And The Mice Will Play*, *We Found Love and an Exquisite Set of Porcelain Figurines Aboard the S.S. Farndale Ave.* Offers ITC contracts, and welcomes enquiries from individual actors. Write in the first instance with CV, photograph and SAE.

National Student Theatre Company

20 Lansdowne Road, London N10 2AU
Tel (081) 883 4586
Artistic director Clive Wolfe

Since its debut in 1977, the NSTC, usually operating only in summer vacations, has presented 92 productions, mostly of new work, and helped 150 or more students to a career start in the entertainment world. Together with the annual National Student Drama Festival, the NSTC has also given birth to a professional offshoot, the Springboard Theatre Company. The leading fringe award winning company with ten 'Scotsman' Fringe Firsts, 1990 productions included 'Independent' Theatre Award winner *Can't Stand Up for Falling Down*, *The Hypochondriac* ('Guardian' Award runner-up) and the musical *West Side Story*. Auditions are advertised in *The Stage* and on college notice boards. Acting applications best sent third week of April for auditions May onward.

Natural Theatre Company

21 Union Passage, Bath BA1 1RD
Tel (0225) 469131 Fax (0225) 442555
Artistic director Ralph Oswick

The Naturals tour nationally (small and middle-scale) and internationally with street theatre and 'indoor' stage shows. Very heavy performing schedule (1,200 performances in 1990) involving up to four different companies at one time. 'All our work has strong visual comedy base and frequently includes audience participation!' Recent productions include *Scarlatti's Birthday Party* and *Scarlatti's Wedding*, *Spy Society* and *The British are Coming!*. 'Welcome enquiries from actors who have seen our work. Write in the first instance, with CV, photograph and details of improvisational skills/experience.' All 'interesting persons' will be kept on file and added to our computerised mailing list to receive regular bulletins on our activities. Street theatre training programmes are held approx. once a year and most performers are recruited from there.

colleges, on yachts, in bird sanctuaries and churches. Company of two. Have done Equity tours in the past but currently not advertising for actors.

New Perspectives Theatre Company

Mansfield Arts Centre, Leeming Street, Mansfield, Notts NG18 1NG
Tel (0623) 635225
Artistic director Helen White

New Perspectives is the professional touring company for the East Midlands area, revenue funded by East Midlands Arts. The company aims to provide a fully comprehensive theatre service to a variety of audiences and venues from community centres and theatre spaces. Productions include: *War Diaries of Hilda Mustard*, *Back Of The Bus*, *Mrs. Beeton's History Of The World*. Write in the first instance with CV, photograph and SAE.

Northern Lights Theatre Company

18 Armley Grove, Stamford, Lincs.
PE9 1DR
Tel (0780) 57055
Artistic directors Debbie Stroud, Bill Downing

Founded 1982. Produce Shakespeare with small casts, feminist comedies, classic tales and psychological drama, plus workshops for schools. Recent productions: *Pilgrim's Progress*, *Outcry*, *Female Parts*. Perform in arts centres, small theatres, festivals, schools and

Northumberland Theatre Company

The Playhouse, Bondgate Without, Alnwick, Northumberland NE66 1PQ
Tel (0665) 602586
Artistic director Gillian Hambleton

Company policy is to tour high quality theatre to predominantly rural areas: village halls and community centres that are a focal point for that particular community whose other access to professional theatre would be limited by geography and public transport. Plays are selected that are relevant to and resonate for those audiences but also contain resonances and questions of a universal nature. Productions 1990 include *Country Voices* by Stewart Howson, a new adaptation of *A Christmas Carol* and *Happy Jack* by John Godber. The company also follows an education policy of touring high quality extant YPT/TIE productions to schools for children of all ages; productions 1990 include *Dirty Rascals*, Leeds TIE and *Stamping, Shouting and Singing Home* by Lisa Evans. The company operates under ITC/Small Scale Touring Contract on a show to show basis but the intention is for a core of actors who will return on a regular basis. All local actors interested in casting with the company will be auditioned if they are interested in working with the company. Other auditions are held as required in Alnwick and London. All photos and CVs are kept on file and regularly referred to when auditioning.

Operating Theatre Company

53/55 Hoxton Square, London N1 6PB
Tel (071) 729 7915 and (071) 834 8631
Contacts Christine Hoodith, Kevin Squelch

Established in 1984, Operating Theatre Company produces a wide range of work, embracing innovative treatments of the classics and giving special attention to previously unperformed work. Recent productions include: *Medea* (directed by Richard Syms); *The Harlot's Curse* (written and directed by Rodney Archer and Powell Jones) winner of London Weekend Television's Plays on Stage Award 1989; *RUR* by the brothers Capek; *Blood Sports* by David Edgar; *Dance on You Pigs* (scenes from Kafka's diaries). Much of casting done in-house. When required, we advertise in *The Stage* and *PCR*. Please do not write.

Orchard Theatre

108 Newport Road, Barnstaple, Devon EX32 9BA
Tel (0271) 71475 Fax (0271) 71825
Artistic director Bill Buffery

One of Britain's longest established regional touring companies, serving the six counties of the South West. Produces a wide range of plays – new, classic, modern, childrens etc. – and promotes a variety of ancillary work associated with shows and with the company's youth and community programme. About four tours per year which play venues large and small with a mixture of week runs, split weeks and one-night stands. Actors are employed on TMA/Equity sub rep contracts and play a full part in all the company's activities. Occasionally advertise in *The Stage*, but welcome written enquiries and CVs at any time. Recent productions – *Fen* (Caryl Churchill), *Under the Earth* (devised), *The Singular Mystery of the Princess Caraboo* (Roger Stennett), *Beauty and the Beast* (Bill Buffery), *A Midsummer Night's Dream*.

Oxford Stage Company

15–19 George Street, Oxford OX1 2AU
Tel (0865) 723238 Fax (0865) 790625
Artistic director John Retallack

Founded 1974. Tour English and foreign classics, new plays and adaptations to middle-scale (300–1000-seat) theatres in towns without repertory theatres. Recent productions: *The Miser*; *Woza Albert*; *Measure For Measure*; *The Real Don Juan*; *As You Like It*; *The Princess and the Monkey Palace*. Company of 4–6 on Esher contracts of 11–15 weeks (September to May). Do not advertise for actors.

Oxfordshire Touring Theatre Company

Cricket Road Centre, Cricket Road, Oxford OX4 3DW
Tel (0865) 778119
Artistic director Mollie Guilfoyle

Founded 1982. Tour adaptations of classics and new writing to village halls, community centres, art centres, theatres and schools in Oxfordshire and other counties. Recent productions: *The Bus to Wanstock* by Sheila Dewey; *The Wind In The Willows* adapted by Mollie Guilfoyle; *Riot* by Mollie Guilfoyle; and *King Arthur* by Mollie Guilfoyle. Company of 2–4 actors on ITC Equity contracts (minimum rate) of 8–11 weeks. Advertise in *The Guardian*, *The Stage*, ITC and through agents.

Paines Plough – the writers' company

Interchange Studios, 15 Wilkin Street, London NW5 3NG
Tel (071) 284 4483 Fax (071) 284 4506
Artistic director Anna Furse

Founded 1974. Produce new works only, and support the development of writers at all stages. Recent productions include: *Thatcher's Women* by Kay Adshead; *Berlin Days, Hollywood Nights* by Nigel Gearing; *The Way to Go Home* by Rona Munro; *Germinal* by William Gaminara; *The Art of Success* by Nick Deas; *Crux* by April De Angelis; *The Clink* by Stephen Jeffreys. Tour to middle- and small-scale venues nationwide, both whole and split weeks. Company of eight actors on 12-week Equity contracts. Advertise for actors in *SBS* and Equity *Jobgrapevine*.

Pascal Theatre Company

35 Flaxman Court, Flaxman Terrace, London WC1H 9AR
Tel (071) 383 0920
Artistic director Julia Pascal

Founded 1983. Tour new plays on contemporary issues – e.g. Ireland, South Africa, Israel – and European writing to London venues such as Riverside Studios, Lyric Studio, Young Vic Studio, Drill Hall. Recent productions: *Salt River* by Yana Stajno; *Traitors* by Melanie Phillips; *The Murphy Girls*; *The German Connection*; *Soldiers* by Seamus Finnegan; *Theresa* by Julia Pascal.

Company of six on Equity minimum rates. Sometimes advertise in *The Stage*; do not welcome casting queries from actors as they have no full-time administrator.

Pentabus Arts

The Old School, Bromfield, Near Ludlow, Shropshire SY8 2JU
Tel (0584) 77564
Contact Robert Petty

Pentabus Arts is a theatre and community arts company touring the rural village halls, schools, community centres, etc. of Shropshire and Hereford & Worcester. It aims to bring live, professional theatre and other arts activities to isolated communities which do not have access to urban-based facilities. Pentabus produces at least four theatre productions every year; a winter show for family audiences, a playscheme show in the summer and shows in spring and autumn which have been drama/documentaries or based on work done by the community arts team. The winter show 1990/91 was a production of the Leon Garfield story, *Mr. Corbett's Ghost*, directed by Steve Johnstone. The Spring '91 show is a devised one-woman show, *Not Guilty* directed by Marian Lawrence. Production is about to begin on a pre-school show for nursery schools, mums and tots groups, libraries, etc. written by Guy Hutchins and directed by Frances Land. The autumn show will be about travellers based on community arts work and will be scripted by Peter Cann and directed by Steve Johnstone. Pentabus welcomes enquiries from individual actors. Please write including CV, a recent photograph and SAE.

Pit Prop Theatre

Railway Road, Leigh, Lancs. WN7
4AF
Tel (0942) 605258

Founded 1979. Community theatre
and Theatre-in-Education (TIE) tours
of new plays written or devised from
within the company, although writers
are sometimes commissioned. Productions include: *Bloodlines* (company
devised piece); *Sweet Banana Fruit Mix*
by Robert Holden; and *Angel* (company devised piece). Tour in the
Wigan borough of Greater Manchester, and sometimes to other
North-west boroughs. Collective of 11
people, mostly on open-ended contracts. ITC/Equity small-scale touring
contract. Advertise in *The Stage, The
Guardian, The Voice* and *Caribbean
Times.* Welcome casting queries; telephone in the first instance. 'Applicants
are advised to write showing some
understanding and interest in the particular forms of theatre we are involved in.'

Pocket Theatre Cumbria

Morley Street, Dentonholme, Carlisle,
Cumbria CA2 5HQ
Tel (0228) 512787
Artistic director Keiran Gillespie

Small to middle scale touring company. New writing, adaptations of
novels, modern and classical texts.
Primary function to tour professional
drama throughout Cumbria – national
touring also an important feature in
recent years. Recent productions include: *The Adventures of Tom Sawyer* by
Mark Twain, adapted and directed by
Brian Elsey, *Witchcraze* by Bryony
Lavery, director Joe Sumsion and
Northanger Abbey by Jane Austen,
adapted and directed by Keiran

Gillespie. Pocket Theatre Cumbria
welcomes enquiries from individual
actors for specific productions. Write
in the first instance, with CV, photograph and SAE, please do not
telephone.

Proteus Theatre Company

Fairfields Arts Centre, Council Road,
Basingstoke, Hampshire RG21 3DH
Tel (0256) 54541
Contact James Brining (Administrator)

Proteus Theatre Company are a small-
scale community touring theatre company. We are members of ITC and
tour Hampshire and Southern England with largely new plays. In
addition to established venues, the
company strives to take productions
into non-theatre venues and introduce
work to new audiences. Recent productions include: *Rights of Passage* by
Sarah Woods, (directed by Caroline
Eves); *The Rose and the Ring* adapted
from Thackeray by John Constable,
music by Fraser Skeoch, (directed by
Steve Addison) and *Gone With Hardy*
by David Allen, (directed by Steve
Addison). Welcome enquiries from
individual actors. Write in the first instance, with CV, photograph and SAE.

Rainbow Theatre Company

1 Ashurst Drive, Goring-by-Sea,
Worthing, W. Sussex BN12 4SN
Tel (0903) 502741
Artistic director Nicolas Young
Administrator Caroline Bean

Produce children's classics, Shakespeare workshops, 'Living History'
total participation shows, dramas,
cabaret, 'problem solving' for audiences of 5–20-year-olds and old
people in schools, colleges, old

people's homes and studio theatres. Company of four actors on contracts of term length. Advertise in *The Stage*, and welcome casting queries from actors 'with an ability to work happily and creatively in a small group, and an enjoyment in playing to and with children'. Approach in writing in the first instance. Teaching qualifications are not required, but song and dance skills an advantage. Auditions held each term. 'Hard work and cheerfulness early in the morning are essential requisites for Rainbow company members.'

Red Shift Theatre Company

Battersea Arts Centre, Lavender Hill, London SW11 5TF
Tel (071) 223 3256 Fax (071) 978 5207
Artistic director Jonathan Holloway
Associate director and designer Charlotte Humpson

Founded 1982. Adaptations of classic plays and novels and commissioned new plays performed in a highly visual sometimes physical ensemble style. Suits multi-skilled performers. Two tours each year – February to June and August to January – to small and middle scale venues. All productions directed by Jonathan Holloway. Past work includes three Edinburgh Fringe Firsts – *In the Image of the Beast* by Jonathan Holloway, *Le Misanthrope* in a new version by Neil Bartlett, *Frida and Diego* by Greg Cullen. Their 1989 *Timon of Athens* won a Charrington London Fringe Award. Company of 5–7 actors contracted project to project on Equity/ITC small-scale touring contracts. Sometimes advertise in *The Stage*; welcome letters

enclosing CV, photo and SAE. Details kept on file.

Remould Theatre Company

'The Greenhouse', Middleton Street, Spring Bank, Hull,
North Humberside HU3 1NB
Tel (0482) 226157
Contact Rupert Creed (Director) or Averil Coult (Administrator)

Touring nationally to theatres, arts centres, studio and non-theatre venues, with a special emphasis on village hall touring in Humberside and Lincolnshire. A 'new writing' company specialising in 'oral history' documentaries with specially commissioned live music. Based on a 5 month research process, the plays are authentic, entertaining and accessible. Past productions include *The Northern Trawl* (Rupert Creed and Jim Hawkins), *The Care Takers* (Rupert Creed), *Street Beat* (Rupert Creed and Peter Spafford). Advertise in *Stage* when casting, and do not maintain a file of unsolicited applications.

Riding Lights Theatre Company

4 College Street, York YO1 2JF
Tel (0904) 655317 Fax (0904) 651532
Artistic director Paul Burbridge

Founded 1977. Tour new full-length plays, classics, musicals, revues, adaptations of literature, children's shows and workshops, both locally and nationwide. Perform in major theatres, arts centres, schools and arts festival venues. Major tours in autumn/Christmas/spring; schools tour at Christmas; small-scale tours at other times of the year; international tour during January–March. Recent productions: *On Christmas Night* by Nigel Forde; *St John's Gospel*; *Three Men In A Boat*. Company of 6–8 on Equity small-scale touring contracts of about 8–12 weeks. Advertise in *The Stage*, and welcome casting queries from actors; write in the first instance. 'We often work with actors, devising the production in rehearsal, aiming for a strong actor-based style of ensemble playing. Singing abilities are often relevant, as well as other kinds of musical abilities.'

Rock Solid Theatre Company

165 Grove Road, Mitcham, Surrey CR4 1AF
Tel (081) 646 0310

Founded in 1988. Rock Solid is a Christian theatre company who tour a huge variety of small scale venues, but mainly schools and churches. Core artistic membership of four who jointly decide policy and plays. The company works to a high standard and therefore only take on actors committed to communicating the Christian message and those who have received training. Recent productions include: *Much Better Here* and *If It's Friday, It Must Be Canaan*. One to three company members, at present on non-equity contracts, from 6 weeks to 4 months. Welcome CVs and photographs with

SAE: details kept on file. Advertise in *PCR* and *The Stage*. No phone calls please.

7:84 Scottish People's Theatre

3rd floor, 2 Port Dundas Place, Glasgow G2 3LB
Tel (041) 331 2219
Artistic director David Hayman
Associate artistic director Gerard Kelly

Founded in 1973 by John McGrath, the policy under the artistic direction of David Hayman and Gerard Kelly makes a commitment to new writing. Recent productions include *The Sash*, *Road*, *Nae Problem*, *Govan Stories*, and *Bold Girls*. Tours throughout Scotland from community halls to No. 1 Theatres. Subsidised rep. contracts of variable lengths. Welcome letters from actors all of which are kept on file and those with SAE are acknowledged. 7:84 Scottish People's Theatre receives annual revenue funding from The Scottish Arts Council and Glasgow District Council.

Shared Experience Ltd

The Soho Laundry, 9 Doufour's Place, London W1V 1FE
Tel (071) 434 9248 Fax (071) 287 8763
Artistic director Nancy Meckler

Founded in 1976 by Mike Alfreds. Recent productions: *The Bacchae*, *True West*, *Heartbreak House*, *Abingdon Square*, and *The Birthday Party*. Tour to small- and middle-scale venues; 6–8-week tours with 4–5 weeks in London.

Equity contracts. Do not advertise, but welcome casting queries from actors; approach in writing in the first instance.

In 1988, an appeal for funds reached their target of £95,000, enabling the company to retain their premises in the Soho Laundry where rehearsals and workshops for actors are held.

Solent People's Theatre

The Heathfield Centre, Valentine Avenue, Sholing, Southampton, Hants SO2 8EQ
Tel (0703) 443943
Artistic director new appointment July 1991

Founded 1976. Community theatre company touring the Hampshire, Southampton and Southern Arts regions. Five or six projects per year; new writing, classics and some company devised pieces. Tour to old people's homes, special schools, community centres, village halls, arts centres, middle schools, hospitals and colleges; return to base each night. Several projects will be tours of three to four weeks: 1–2 shows per day for 5–6 days per week. Company of 4 actors on ITC/Equity small-scale touring contracts, usually open-ended, but expected to stay one to two years. Some freelance, esp. music, design. Advertise in *The Stage* for all posts. Actors need to be extremely versatile – a large playing range, good musical skills, movement and physical skills, plus experience and enjoyment of devised work and workshop activities. In addition to devising, performing workshop leading and skill sharing, performers need a co-operative attitude towards the work, and an interest in liaising with the local community.

Snarling Beasties

27 Grosvenor Road, Harborne, Birmingham B17 9AL
Tel (0203) 365650

Present stylized, controversial and dangerous theatre using all theatre skills including mime, movement, and improvisation, in all kinds of venues. Tour nationally. Productions include: *Bully Boys, Punch and Judy: The Real Story* (Independent Theatre Award 1989), *Valentino*. Welcome queries from individual actors. Write with CV, photograph and SAE. Please do not phone.

Springboard Theatre Company

20 Lansdowne Road, London N10 2AU
Tel (081) 883 4586
Executive director Clive Wolfe

Founded in 1987 to take accessible work into small scale venues, Springboard is the professional counterpart of the National Student Theatre Company using actors who have progressed from student drama to the professional stage. Productions have included: *Journeys Among the Dead* by Eugene Ionesco (British and English Language premiere); and *Handle with Care* by Jane Thornton. 'Anyone now at school or college who would like to work with Springboard later on can do no better than to start by attending the National Student

Drama Festival.' Currently unsponsored. There is no point without previous NSTC or NSDF experience.

Splash Theatre Company Ltd

Albermarle Centre, Ferensway, Hull, HU2 8LZ
Tel (0482) 24256

Founded 1985. Tour to schools, youth centres, residential homes and day centres for the elderly, as well as playschemes and outdoor venues in the local area. Recent productions: *Weaving Webs and Spinning Tales* (performance and workshops for 8–15-year-olds); *Chewing the Fat* (youth clubs show); *War Women*. Occasionally advertise in *The Stage*, and welcome casting queries from actors; write in the first instance. 'Our policy is to take professional live theatre into the community with an emphasis on the needs of young people.'

Strathcona Theatre Company

1 Heathfield Park, Willesden Green, London NW2 5JE
Tel (081) 451 7419
Artistic directors Joan Greening, Janet Bliss

Founded 1982. Dance and drama all written and created by the company. Perform in fringe theatres, community centres, schools and colleges. Constant company of 10 actors and two directors. The actors are all disabled.

TAG (Theatre About Glasgow) Theatre Company

See **Young People's Theatre**.

Tara Arts Group

356 Garratt Lane, London SW18 4ES
Tel (081) 871 1458
Artistic director Jatinder Verma

'Tara Arts began in 1976/7 as a community theatre group in South London. Tara Arts Group is Britain's leading Asian Theatre Company, revenue funded by the Arts Council of Great Britain, touring nationally and internationally with its own building base in London. Born of a need to express the Asian experience in Britain, Tara Arts' policy is to present each year plays ranging from the classic to the contemporary; all offering entertaining, informative and provocative insights into the Asian experience. Drawing upon Indian traditions of theatre-craft, Tara Arts aims to offer challenging alternatives to conventional theatre in Britain. The group's extensive touring, workshop and building-based programmes throughout the year seek actively to promote Asian creative work as widely as possible.' The *Tara Arts Group* has taken theatre shows and workshops to various venues both in London and throughout the UK. A total of 50 productions have been staged since the company was formed, each touring an average of nine weeks. Average company of six actors. Advertise in drama schools and *The Stage* and welcome casting queries from Asian actors; approach in writing in the first instance, enclosing CV and photograph.

Temba Theatre Company Ltd

Dominion House, 101 Southwark Street, London SE1 0JH
Tel (071) 261 0991
Artistic director Alby James

Founded 1972. Middle- and small-scale touring; seasons of small- and middle- scale work in London, community outreach and education workshops. Recent productions: *Black Sheep* by Derrick Cameron; *Romeo and Juliet* and *A Visitor to the Veldt* by Mfundi Vundla (directed by Alby James); *Black Love Song No. 1* by Kalamu ya Salaam (Heather Goodman). Currently developing mid-scale touring, contracts both ITC and TMA. Rarely advertise, but welcome casting queries from actors; send letter with CV and current photograph. Temba's policy is to: enable people to share in the artistic expression of black cultures and experience; to enable people in Britain to see black people in the wider context of the heritage and experience of black people around the world; to assist the development and representation of black writing in British theatre.

Theatr Bara Caws

Y Coleg Normal, Bangor, Gwynedd LL57 2DE
Tel (0248) 355579/355436
Co-operative company no directors

Founded 1977. From pub shows to chapel shows – all original productions. All work is through the medium of Welsh. 'The show must be of interest and relevance to the community.' Three new productions toured annually and 'New Authors Festival' held. Some productions tour nationally, others in Clwyd and Gwynedd only. Equity contracts of 3 months in length. 'Everyone on equal pay.' Advertise for actors in *The Stage*, *Y Cymro* and *Y Papurau Bro*. 'Greatly' welcome casting queries from actors. Send a letter enclosing CV and photograph. 'We should like all new faces to get in touch with us. We are always looking for new talent – actors, technicians and writers. We hold annual auditions. The company's policy is to promote original, Welsh artistic work.'

Sylfaenwyd 1977. O sioeau tafarn i berfformiadau capel – pob cynhyrchiad yn wreiddiol. 'Rhaid i'r sioe fod o ddiddordeb ac yn berthnasol i'r gymuned'. Teithio tair sioe newydd y flwyddyn a chynnal 'Gwyl Awduron Newydd'. Y mae rhai cynyrchiadau yn teithio'n genedlaethol ac eraill yng Nghlwyd a Gwynedd yn unig. Cytundeb Equity o dri mis, pawb ar gyflog cyfartal. Hysbysebu am actorion – *The Stage*, *Y Cymro*, *Y Papurau Bro*.

'Hoffem petai pob actor newydd yn cysylltu â ni, rydym wastad yn chwilio am dalent newydd – actorion, technegwyr a dramodwyr. Yr ydym yn cynnal cyfweliadau blynyddol. Polisi'r cwmni yw hybu gwaith artistig, gwreiddiol Cymraeg.'

Theatre Alibi

Northcott Studio Theatre, Emmanuel Road, Exeter EX4 1EJ
Tel (0392) 217315
Administrator Stephen Mole

Formed 1982, Theatre Alibi produces a wide range of work in a variety of venues, from arts centres and studio theatres to schools and community venues. The company presents its work locally, regionally and nationally. The majority of productions are new work, either commissioned or company devised. Recent productions include: *Dawn Chorus* (New song theatre); *Song Stories* (with Gardzienice Theatre Association, Poland); *A new Feast of Storytelling; The Goatsong*. The company welcomes enquiries from individual actors. Please write with CV, photograph and SAE. Advertises in *The Stage*. A familiarity with the company's work is an advantage.

Théâtre de Complicité

108 Upper Street, London N1 1QN
Tel (071) 226 7025

Founded 1983. Successful versatile company which specializes in physical theatre (most company members have trained at the Jacques Lecoq School in Paris). Tour to small and middle scale venues throughout the UK, including the Highlands and Islands; also Eire, Hong Kong, South America, USA, Italy, Belgium, Spain, Germany, Netherlands. In 1988 had a three and a half month residency at the Almeida Theatre in North London; touring four shows in 1989. Productions include: *Anything For a Quiet Life* and *The Phantom Violin* (directed by Simon McBurney); *The Visit* (Annabel Arden). Cast size ranges from 1 to 8; Equity contracts. Audition by workshop sessions. Actors who wish to be considered for these sessions should apply for inclusion on the workshop mailing list.

Theatre Foundry

The Multipurpose Centre, Victoria Road, Darlaston, W. Midlands WS10 8AP
Tel (021) 526 6947
Artistic director Jonathan Chadwick

Founded 1982. Community theatre company touring productions to community venues in the boroughs of Walsall, Dudley and Sandwell. Recent productions: *Macbeth; Babble; The Little Match Girl* (adapted by Rony Robinson). Also produce community plays including *Boomtown* (1990 Darlaston Community Play) and run a wide range of participatory projects. Company of 3–6 actors on Equity MRSL Scale 2 contracts of 8–10 weeks. Normally advertise for actors. Welcome casting query letters.

Theatre Nova

69 Highbury Road, Kings Heath, Birmingham B13 7QW
Tel (021) 443 4763
Joint artistic directors Nigel Stewart, Don McGovern

Founded 1984. Small- and middle-scale touring company working nationally and internationally whose concern is 'to create a theatre in which visual image, physical action, word and sound are given a new organic relation.' Productions include: *Cross Purposes* by Don McGovern; *Let Me Speak*; and *Pericles*. Company of 3–15; profit-share and occasional Equity minimum (depending on funding). Advertise in *The Stage*, and welcome casting queries from actors with particular training and experience in physical and music theatre; approach by letter in the first instance.

Theatre Rotto

Nanscawen Barn, Newmill, Penzance,
Cornwall TR20 8XN
Tel (0736) 65158
Artistic director Julia Mclean

Founded 1981. Children's shows for
schools and theatre venues, adult
mainstream productions, cabaret,
theatre training workshops. 'The emphasis is on imagination, comedy and
music and work with puppets. While
the group is mixed, women's ideas are
important.' Annual tour of schools in
the South-west with children's show;
one mainstream show every two
years. Nucleus of four actors with
others joining depending on the
show. Advertise in local publications,
and welcome casting queries from
actors resident in Cornwall; approach
in writing or by telephone.

Theatre Venture

Three Mills School, Abbey Lane,
Stratford, London E15 2RP
Tel (081) 519 6678/8769
Artistic director Jon Trevor
Associate director
(Outreach/Docklands) Steve Moffitt

Founded 1981. In the past few years,
the company has toured plays to community centres and for deaf children,
two short shows for OAPs and a large-
scale community play. Venues include
community centres, schools, hospitals
and fringe venues. Productions must
be accessible to 'an audience of people
who do not usually go to theatre. We
especially wish to prioritise those that
have, for cultural and/or economic
reasons or because of lack of physical

access, been unaccustomed or unable
to see or participate in theatre in the
past.' Recent productions: *Deluge*;
Storyworld; *Summer Safari*; *Beauty and
the Beast*; *Mother Goose*. Mainly one-
night stands. ITC/Equity contracts of
varying lengths.

Theatre Workshop Edinburgh

34 Hamilton Place, Edinburgh EH3
5AX
Tel (031) 225 7942
Artistic director Adrian Harris

Founded 1965. Major Scottish theatre
and arts centre providing productions
from our own companies and the best
in touring theatre, youth theatre,
theatre-in-education, special needs
drama, multicultural arts, classes, exhibitions, performance projects and
information and resources, both at our
Hamilton Place base and throughout
the communities of Edinburgh, the
Lothians and Scotland. Recent productions: *State of Confusion* by David
Kane, *Kiss of the Spiderwoman* by
Manuel Puig; *Rasho, Champion of the
Romany* by Simon Abbott; *The Other
Half* by Janet Fenton. Annual
Christmas production, one or two
national tours, T.I.E. annual tour and
other smaller-scale productions. Perform in schools, community centres,
village halls, theatres, studio theatres
and arts centres. Company of six
actors plus stage management of two
on nine-week Equity/ITC contracts.
Do not advertise for actors but welcome casting enquiries; approach in
writing in first instance. Casting policy
tends to favour actors in Scotland.

Theatr Powys

The Drama Centre, Tremont Road,
Llandrindod Wells, Powys LD1 5EB
Tel (0597) 824444
TIE director to be appointed
Community theatre director Guy
Roderick

Founded 1972. Theatre-in-Education
(TIE) to Powys schools and small- to
middle-scale theatre to community
centres, primarily in Powys, but also
to theatres throughout Wales. Usually
two TIE and two community tours
each year. Recent productions: *Bare
Necessities; Tarzanne; Jack and the Giant
Fib; Merch y Dewin; The Emperor's Book-
keepers.* 'Productions must have
relevance to our community as a part
of the world today, to empower,
educate, stimulate communication, re-
flection and action in society. To
demystify the arts and encourage participation in them.' Company of five
permanent actor/teachers. Company
house agreements on Equity subsidized rep long-term contracts, on
teachers' pay scale. Advertise in *The
Stage* and *Y Cymro.*

Trestle Theatre Company

47 Wood Street, Barnet, Herts. EN5
4BS
Tel (081) 441 0349 Fax (081) 449
7036
Administrator Penny Mayes

Founded 1981. Performs in small- and
middle-scale venues. The work is
company-devised mask theatre –
highly original and visual. The masks
are made by the company members.
Company operates ITC/Equity contracts. Incorporated a tour unit to tour
previous productions, therefore two
shows on tour most of the year.
Advertise in *The Stage*, ITC, the
Guardian, The Voice and *The Pink Paper.*
Welcome casting queries from actors;
approach in writing in the first instance – letters are kept on file. 'We
specialize in mask and mime, so it
helps to mention skills in any field on
your CV.'

Umbrella Theatre

The Basement, 46 Compton Avenue,
Brighton, E. Sussex BN1 3PS
Tel (0273) 775354
Joint artistic directors David
Lavender, Colin Granger

Founded 1979 to produce in English
unusual and exciting works from
abroad. Small-scale touring to venues
seating up to 500. Recent productions:
The World of the Café Waiters (original
French cabaret); *Joseph and Mary* by
Peter Turrini. Usually profit-share.
Advertise in *The Stage*, and welcome
casting queries from actors; approach
in writing in the first instance.

Umoja Theatre

59 Bethwin Road, Camberwell,
London SE5 0XY
Tel (071) 701 6396
Artistic director Gloria Hamilton

Founded 1983. Tour both adult and
children's productions on topics of relevance today, to community centres,
arts centres and schools – London only
in the case of the children's show and
nationwide for the adult show. Recent
productions: *One-Stop Driver; Playboy.*
Company of 15 on four-month Equity
contracts. Sometimes advertise in *The
Stage, The Voice, City Limits* and *Time
Out.* Welcome casting queries from
actors; telephone in the first instance.
Also run theatre training courses,

workshops and an employment agency.

Wildcat Stage Productions

The Clyde Theatre, Boquhanran Road, Clydebank, G81 3BE
Tel (041) 951 1444 Fax (041) 941 1508
Artistic director David Maclennan

Founded 1978. Tour new works of music theatre by writers working in Scotland to large- and medium-scale theatres, town and village halls and community centres. Four productions each year touring for 7–8 weeks each. Recent productions: *The Complete History of Rock 'n' Roll*; *Cleaning Up*; *The Riddle Of The Enchanted Bells*. Company of 8–10 actors on 12-week Esher standard contracts for subsidized repertory. In 1989 Wildcat obtained its own 850-seat theatre, The Clyde Theatre, where it performs its annual pantomime. The Clyde Theatre is also an independent producer. Do not advertise, but welcome casting queries from actors; write in the first instance, enclosing CV. 'We prefer to work with actors who are musicians and vice versa, and they should be good singers.'

Winged Horse Touring Productions

The Old Atheneum Building, 179 Buchanan Street, Glasgow G1 2JZ
Tel (041) 556 2494
Artistic director Hamish Glen

Founded 1979. Produce either specially commissioned work by Scottish-based authors or revivals of contemporary work from Scotland and abroad. Tour to theatres, community centres, studio theatres, village halls and art centres in Scotland and Northern England, in the spring and autumn. Recent productions: *Changed Days* by Alan Spence; *The Yellow On The Broom* by Anne Downie; *Glencoe – Three Faces Of A Crime* by Robin Munro; *Professional Pretenders* by John Clifford and Liz Lochhead; *Elizabeth Gordon Quinn* by Chris Hannan; *Bailegangaire* by Tom Murphy. Company of 1–7 on Equity/ITC contracts of approximately nine weeks. Do not advertise, but welcome casting queries from Scottish-based actors. Send letter with an SAE, 'otherwise we will not reply.'

The Women's Theatre Group

5 Leonard Street, London EC2A 4AQ
Tel (071) 251 0202

Founded 1974. National small- to middle-scale touring. The WTG commissions plays by women playwrights specifically for the company. Perform in arts centres, studio theatres, colleges and community centres from the autumn to spring/early summer. Recent productions: *Picture Palace* by Winsome Pinnock; *Lear's Daughters* by WTG & Elaine Feinstein; *Pinchdice and Co* by Julie Wilkinson; *Zerri's Choice* by Sandra Yaw; *Mortal* by Caroline Griffin and Maro Green; *Christmas Without Herods* by Lisa Evans and *Her Aching Heart* by Bryony Lavery. Average company of 4–5 on ITC/Equity contracts of varying lengths. Advertise in *The Stage*, *The Voice*, *Caribbean Times* and *Outwrite*. Welcome casting queries; approach in writing in the first instance. 'We present new work which is intended to record and expand the real experiences of women and, ultimately, change the way women are perceived in society. It is the aim of the company to make the work innovative, accessible, meaningful and entertaining.' Enquiries to Su Parrish, Artistic Director.

Yorkshire Theatre Company

LCVS, 229 Woodhouse Lane, Leeds
LS2 9LF
Tel (0532) 444053

Founded 1982. 'YTC is committed to encouraging new plays dealing with crucial cultural and social issues.' Tour to arts centres, studio theatres, universities, colleges, schools, prisons and community centres nationwide. Company of 5–6 on Equity contracts of approximately 20 weeks. Advertise in *The Stage* and local press. Welcome casting queries from actors; send letter with CV and photograph. 'The company is committed to producing easily accessible theatre which broadens its audience beyond the accustomed theatre-goer by virtue of its subject matter and/or form. Recent production, *State of Play*, *State of Mind* and *State of the Nation* (a trilogy) by Ian Hartley and Toby Swift, was a highly stylized, physical and, above all, comic examination of the male ego.'

Zip Theatre

Dunkley Street, Wolverhampton WV1 4AN
Tel (0902) 712251

Take accessible theatre to all kinds of venues throughout the West Midlands and beyond. Productions include: *The Tipton Slasher*; *Macbethe: Wolves – The Musical*. Welcome queries from individual actors. Write with CV, photograph and SAE. Details kept on file. Please do not phone.

12 Non-producing Theatres

Non-producing theatres do not mount productions. They are available for rent to production companies. The telephone numbers noted below are for the administrative offices, not the box-office.

London

Adelphi Theatre

Strand, London WC2E 7NA
Tel (071) 836 1166

Seating capacity: 1554. Dates back to 1806; it was the home of melodrama in the last half of the 19th century, and had its own real-life drama in 1897, when the leading actor, William Terriss, was stabbed to death outside the Royal Entrance in Maiden Lane. Legend has it that his ghost still haunts the theatre. The present theatre, the fourth on the site, opened in 1930. Today it is the musicals that bring in audiences, including most recently *Me and My Girl*. Part of the James Nederlander Theatres group. *Funding*: self-financing.

Albery Theatre

St Martin's Lane, London WC2
Tel (071) 867 1125

Seating capacity: 900. Plays, musicals. Renowned for the Olivier/Richardson seasons of the 1940s. Other successes include *Blood Brothers, Oliver!* (which ran for five years from 1960, returning to sweep the board again in 1977), and a number of transfers from the subsidized section – including *Children of a Lesser God* from the Mermaid. Part of the Maybox Theatres group (Chesterfield Properties). *Funding*: self-financing.

Aldwych Theatre

Aldwych, London WC2B 4DF
Tel (071) 379 6736

Seating capacity: 1057. Designed to pair the Strand Theatre, it opened seven months after its twin in December 1905. Between the wars, the theatre was renowned for the famous 'Aldwych' farces, many by Ben Travers. The Aldwych also housed the World Theatre seasons that Peter Daubeny presented from 1964 to 1975. The theatre was bought by James Nederlander, the Broadway producer, in 1982, when he outbid Andrew Lloyd Webber. The English Stage Company's *Coriolanus* and *The Winter's Tale* are among its recent productions. *Funding*: self-financing.

Almeida Theatre

Almeida Street, London N1 1TA
Tel (071) 226 7432
Artistic director Ian McDiarmid

Seating capacity: 300. Full range of performance arts, with an excellent balance of contemporary British and international works. A London platform for innovative work from regional repertory theatres, plus seasons by a semi-resident theatre company, and an international festival of contemporary music. Mainly funded by Greater London Arts; additional funding from London Borough Grants Scheme (LBGS), the London Borough of Islington and the Arts Council.

Ambassadors Theatre

West Street, London WC2H 9ND
Tel (071) 836 4797

Seating capacity: 450. Opened in 1913, the theatre initially made its name with the London debuts of Vivien Leigh and Ivor Novello. But it is chiefly remembered as the home of London's longest-running play, *The Mousetrap*, which was here for 22 years before transferring to St Martin's

Theatre next door. Recent productions include the Royal Shakespeare Company's *Les Liaisons Dangereuses*. *Funding*: self-financing.

Apollo Theatre

Shaftesbury Avenue, London
W1V 7HD
Tel (071) 437 3435

Seating capacity: 756. A turn-of-the-century theatre, the Apollo specialized in musicals in its early days. However, its most famous production was the comedy, *Boeing Boeing*, which ran for $3^1/_2$ years from 1962. Alfred Uhry's *Driving Miss Daisy* was among its recent productions. *Funding*: self-financing.

Apollo Victoria

17 Wilton Road, London SW1
Tel (071) 834 6318

Seating capacity: 2170. Hosts major musicals and international artists. Currently showing Andrew Lloyd Webber's *Starlight Express*. *Funding*: self-financing.

Battersea Arts Centre

Old Town Hall, Lavender Hill, London
SW11 5TF
Tel (071) 223 2223

Seating capacity: 100–120. The Arts Centre was originally opened by the local authority, but closed in 1980 because of local government cuts. An independent trust reopened the Centre in January 1981. It hosts small-scale touring companies, fringe companies, cabaret and jazz. *Funding*: Greater London Arts and Wandsworth Council.

Bloomsbury Theatre

15 Gordon Street, London WC1H 0AH
Tel (071) 383 5976
Fax (071) 383 4080

Seating capacity: 560. Opened in 1968 and operated by University College, London as a student theatre until 1974 when, to help finances, visiting professional companies were encouraged to present shows. Now runs an all-year programme of visiting theatre, opera, dance and concerts, plus in-house and student productions. *Funding*: University College, London.

Cambridge Theatre

Earlham Street, London WC2H 9HU
Tel (071) 240 7664

Seating capacity: approximately 1000. Reopened in 1987 with American musical version of *Peter Pan* and in 1988 staged the musical *Budgie* starring Adam Faith and Anita Dobson. Currently presenting the run-away success *Return to the Forbidden Planet*. Contact Stoll Moss Theatres, Cranbourn Mansions, Cranbourn Street, London WC2H 7AG. Tel (071) 437 2274.

Comedy Theatre

Panton Street, London SW1Y 4DN
Tel (071) 839 5522

Seating capacity: 820. Opened in 1881, the Comedy had – until its refurbishment in 1954 – the oldest surviving auditorium in London. In the mid-1950s, the theatre was an important centre for strong contemporary drama and became the base for the New Watergate Club which presented American works banned by the Lord Chamberlain. With plays by Arthur Miller and Tennessee Williams on offer, the Club's membership rocketed to 68,000, making it an important force in weakening the power of the censor. The Comedy went traditional with the long-running *There's a Girl in My Soup*, then was again associated with new and innovative work when Nell Dunn's *Steaming* transferred from the Theatre Royal, Stratford East. *Funding*: self-financing.

The Drill Hall

16 Chenies Street, London WC1E 7ET
Tel (071) 637 8270 (box office)

Seating capacity: 280. Opened in 1976 as the base for Action Space, the Drill Hall is now used by touring companies with a committed political programme. Sexual politics are high on the list, with regular visits from Monstrous Regiment and Gay Sweatshop. *Funding*: Camden Council, London Boroughs Arts Scheme and Greater London Arts.

Duchess Theatre

Catherine Street, London WC2B 5LA
Tel (071) 839 1134

Seating capacity: 484. One of the smallest West End theatres, the Duchess was built to an original design by the architect Ewen Barr in 1929. The theatre is on two different levels; the circle is narrower than the stalls and is supported by steel girders from the roof, giving it some of the best sight lines of any London theatre. J.B. Priestley began a long association with the theatre in 1933, and a number of his plays were seen here. Coward's *Blithe Spirit* had a triumphant opening in 1942 and ran for 1997 performances. *Oh Calcutta!* occasioned some raised eyebrows in 1974, even though it had already run for four years at the Royalty. *Funding*: self-financing.

Duke of York's Theatre

St Martin's Lane, London WC2H 0HD
Tel (071) 836 6260

Seating capacity: 640. An unassuming but attractive theatre, owned by Capital Radio. The first theatre to open in St Martin's Lane, it was unusual in that the auditorium was heated by three roaring fires. Legend has it that the building is haunted by Violette Melnotte, one half of the acting team that founded the theatre in 1892. *Funding*: self-financing.

Fortune Theatre

Russell Street, London WC2B 5HH
Tel (071) 240 1514

Seating capacity: 435. This tiny theatre, opened in 1924, was the first to be built after World War I. Standing in the shadow of the famous colonnade of the Theatre Royal, Drury Lane, its history has been chequered. In the 1950s and 1960s, revues proved popular, *Beyond the Fringe* being the best-remembered. *The Promise* and David Storey's *The Contractor* brought a return to drama, though thrillers proved the success of the 1970s. *The Woman In Black* is among recent productions. *Funding*: self-financing.

Garrick Theatre

Charing Cross Road, London
WC2H 0HH
Tel (071) 836 8271

Seating capacity: 710. The Garrick opened in 1889 with Pinero's play *The*

Profligate. Among its successes were *Love on the Dole* in 1935, which introduced Wendy Hiller to the West End, Theatre Workshop's *Fing's Ain't Wot They Used to Be*, *No Sex Please*, *We're British*, Coward's *Easy Virtue*, and Anouilh's *The Rehearsal*. *Funding*: self-financing.

Globe Theatre

Shaftesbury Avenue, London
W1V 8AR
Tel (071) 437 6003

Seating capacity: 897. Designed in Louis XVI style and built in 1906 as a pair to the Queen's Theatre, the Globe has seen successful productions by Maugham, Coward, Novello, Rattigan, Fry, Bolt and, more recently, Ayckbourn and Frayn. *Funding*: self-financing.

Hackney Empire

291 Mare Street, Hackney, London
E8 1EJ
Tel (081) 986 0171

Seating capacity: 1000. Built 1901, with a large but friendly auditorium and splendid Edwardian decor. All facilities are constantly being improved, as the theatre was used as a bingo hall until its conversion and reopening in 1986. Management intend to create a national theatre of entertainment, comedy and music, with some in-house events and outside promoters and companies suitable for the wide appeal of the theatre. Will not accept racist or sexist material. *Funding*: self-financing.

Her Majesty's Theatre

Haymarket, London SW1Y 4QR
Tel (071) 930 5337

Seating capacity: 1210. The history of Her Majesty's is long and illustrious. The original theatre – designed by the architect and playwright, Sir John Vanbrugh – opened in 1705. Two further theatres, both with established reputations for fashionable opera, occupied the site until the present theatre opened in 1897. One of the larger London theatres, this final version was built by the famous actor/manager, Max Beerbohm Tree. In his day, there were spectacular revivals of Shakespeare, the first production of Shaw's *Pygmalion* and the musical *Chu Chin Chow*. Musicals have proved popular fare in recent years: *West Side Story*, *Fiddler on the Roof*, *Ain't Misbehavin'* and currently *Phantom of the Opera*. Owned by Stoll Moss group.

ICA Theatre

Nash House, Carlton Terrace, The Mall, London SW1
Tel (071) 930 0493

Seating capacity: 220. The theatre opened in 1973. It has a large acting space that lends itself well to free-ranging experimental drama. No in-house productions; this is a centre for British and foreign touring companies offering highly visual new works. *Funding*: Westminster Council, the British Council and Greater London Arts.

London Coliseum

St Martin's Lane, London WC2N 4ES
Tel (071) 836 0111

Seating capacity: 2358. The Coliseum is London's largest theatre. It was built on a grand scale in 1904 by Oswald Stoll, and had a special escalator to take royal parties to their boxes, lifts to conduct patrons to the upper levels and foyer facilities for typing and sending telegrams. Moreover, the theatre was equipped with the first revolving stage in Britain. The exterior was equally impressive with columns, arches, chariots, lions and a globe designed to revolve. When this was declared illegal, Stoll resorted to simulating movement with flashing lights. In the early days, spectaculars of all kinds were staged here. Musicals took over in the 1930s, and the English National Opera moved here from Sadler's Wells in 1968. *Funding*: Arts Council of Great Britain, City of Westminster.

London Palladium

Argyll Street, London W1A 3AB
Tel (071) 437 6166

Seating capacity: 2317. Although now heavily dependent on TV to provide it with star turns, this last refuge of variety is probably the best-known London venue for those in search of a good night out. The Palladium started life in the 1880s as the home of Hengler's Circus, so it is entirely fitting that *Barnum*, the story of the 19th-century circus impresario, should have had a run of several years here. After Hengler's death in 1887, a skating rink replaced the circus, until the new music hall opened in 1900. One of its unique features was a box-to-box telephone system that enabled patrons to talk to their friends! The Palladium can still be relied upon to provide spectacular entertainment, albeit of a transatlantic flavour. Owned by Stoll Moss group. *Funding*: self-financing.

Lyric Theatre

Shaftesbury Avenue, London
W1V 8ES
Tel (071) 437 1231

Seating capacity: 967. Opened in 1888 with a long-forgotten, but then highly popular, operetta. It was the second theatre in the Victorian grand design for Shaftesbury Avenue. Completely redecorated in 1933, it still retains its 1930s style. *Funding*: self-financing.

New End Theatre

27 New End, Hampstead, London
NW3 1JD
Tel (071) 794 0022

Seating capacity: 80. Housed in a building that was once a mortuary, the theatre first opened in 1974. Some in-house productions and visited by fringe theatre companies.

New London Theatre

Drury Lane/Parker Street, London
WC2B 5PW
Tel (071) 242 9802

Seating capacity: 900. Opened in 1973. A highly versatile theatre: stage, seats and even walls move at the flick of a

switch. *Cats* has been a sensational hit here.

The Old Vic

Waterloo Road, London SE1 8NB
Tel (071) 928 2651

Seating capacity: 1000. Opened as the Royal Coburg in 1818 and renamed as the Royal Victoria Theatre in 1833. In 1912 Lilian Baylis became theatre manager and founded The Old Vic Shakespeare Company in 1914. The legendary productions starring actors such as Sybil Thorndike, Edith Evans, Peggy Ashcroft, John Gielgud, Laurence Olivier, and Ralph Richardson carried on until 1941 (Tyrone Guthrie took over from Lilian Baylis in 1937), when the war forced the theatre to close. It reopened in 1950 and The Old Vic Company played 49 seasons until the advent of the National Theatre in 1963. The Prospect Theatre Company made the Old Vic its London base until 1981 and in 1982 the theatre was bought by Canadian businessman Ed Mirvish. A nine-month £2 million face-lift followed and the theatre reopened in 1983 with a new Tim Rice musical, *Blondel*.

See *also* **Producing Theatres and Independent Managements.**

Oval House Theatre

52–54 Kennington Oval, London SE11
Tel (071) 735 2786

Seating capacity: 100 (downstairs studio) and 50 (upstairs studio). Visited by 50 fringe companies each year such as Intimate Strangers, Random Pact and Red Rag Theatre Company. Experimental new work workshops plus Youth Theatre.

Palace Theatre

Shaftesbury Avenue, London
W1V 8AY
Tel (071) 434 0088

Seating capacity: 1394. This extraordinary red brick and terracotta theatre took two years to build, and was opened by Richard D'Oyly Carte in 1891 as the Royal English Opera House. His hopes for English grand opera were short-lived, however, for a year later, it became a variety theatre, changing its name to the Palace. Its greatest successes have been musicals: *The Sound of Music* played here for six years and *Jesus Christ Superstar* played for eight. *Les Miserables*, the Royal Shakespeare Company production (and British première) of the musical by Alain Boblil and Claude-Michel Shonberg, is currently playing. *Funding*: self-financing.

Phoenix Theatre

110 Charing Cross Road, London
WC2H 0JP
Tel (071) 836 7431

Seating capacity: 1012. The Phoenix opened in 1930 with Noel Coward's *Private Lives*. Post-war, *The Canterbury Tales* opened in 1968 and ran for over 2000 performances. Recently hosted a season by Kenneth Branagh's Renaissance Theatre Company. Now owned by Roger Wingate's Chesterfield Properties. *Funding*: self-financing.

Piccadilly Theatre

Denman Street, London W1V 8DY
Tel (071) 437 2397

Seating capacity: 1232. Built in 1928 and then taken over by Warner Bros to become a screening venue for the country's first talkies. Live entertainment returned in the 1930s when Noel Coward scored a hit with *Blithe Spirit*. Gielgud's *Macbeth* and the musical *Panama Hattie* played to wartime audiences until the theatre was damaged by flying bombs in 1944. Donald Albery took over in 1960, and under his management, links were formed between commercial and subsidized theatre. A number of transfers, mainly from the Royal Shakespeare Company, have been housed here: *Wild Oats*, *Privates on Parade*, *Piaf*, *Once in a Lifetime* and *Educating Rita*. Currently presenting *The Rocky Horror Show*. Part of the Maybox Theatres group (Chesterfield Properties). *Funding*: self-financing.

Playhouse Theatre

Northumberland Avenue, London
WC2N 5DE
Tel (071) 839 4292

Seating capacity: 786. First opened as the Royal Avenue Theatre in 1882 and extensively rebuilt in 1907 after part of Charing Cross Station collapsed on top of it in 1905. Used by the BBC as a radio studio for *The Goons*, *Tony Hancock* and other productions from 1951. Reopened in 1988 with the musical *Girlfriends* by Howard Goodall (directed by John Retallack). Jeffrey Archer now a 60 per cent owner.

Prince Edward Theatre

Old Compton Street, London
W1V 6HS
Tel (071) 437 2024

Seating capacity: 1647. The theatre has had a chequered career since it was opened in 1930. Designed as a musical and revue venue, it was converted into a cabaret restaurant in 1936 and renamed the London Casino. In 1954, it housed the spectacular Cinerama, and in 1974, it became a dual-purpose theatre offering both films and shows. In 1977, live entertainment had its revenge when the musical *Evita* moved in. Currently houses *Children of Eden*. *Funding*: self-financing.

Prince of Wales Theatre

31 Coventry Street, London W1V 8AS
Tel (071) 930 1867

Seating capacity: 1133. Actor/manager Edward Bruce opened the first theatre on this site in 1884. Gracie Fields laid the foundation stone of the present theatre which was redesigned and rebuilt in 1937. An ideal venue for musicals, it currently houses *Aspects of Love*. *Funding*: self-financing.

Queen's Theatre

Shaftesbury Avenue, London
W1V 8BA
Tel (071) 734 1348

Seating capacity: 979. The Queen's was originally built in 1907 as the twin to the Globe. After bomb damage, it was almost completely restored in 1958, when Hugh Casson and Bryan Westwood designed the present glass frontage (preserving the Edwardian interior). In recent years, the theatre has been associated with a string of prestigious productions – *Otherwise Engaged*; *Saturday, Sunday, Monday*; *Another Country*; and *Beyond Reasonable Doubt* by Jeffrey Archer. *Funding*: self-financing.

Royalty Theatre

Portugal Street, off Kingsway, London
WC2A 2HT
Tel (071) 242 9136

Seating capacity: 1000. Musicals, pop concerts, drama. Opened with *The Visit*, directed by Peter Brook, and has since seen service as a cinema, and as the home for Paul Raymond's risqué revue *Birds of a Feather* as well as the American musical *Bubbling Brown Sugar*. *Funding*: self-financing.

Sadler's Wells Theatre

Rosebery Avenue, London EC1R 4TN
Tel (071) 278 6563

Seating capacity: 1499. Home of New Sadler's Wells Opera and Sadler's Wells Royal Ballet. Also attracts top British and international opera, ballet, dance and mime companies. *Funding*: London Boroughs Grants Scheme, London Borough of Islington.

St Martin's Theatre

West Street, London WC2H 9NH
Tel (071) 836 1086

Seating capacity: 554. Since 1974, home of Agatha Christie's *The Mousetrap*, which has now been running in London for 35 years. *Funding*: self-financing.

Savoy Theatre

Savoy Court, Strand, London
WC2R OET
Tel (071) 836 8117

Seating capacity: 1122. Opened in 1881 by Richard D'Oyly Carte as the home for Gilbert & Sullivan operettas, the Savoy was the first theatre to have electric light. In 1902, it became a general West End venue, and the entrance was switched from the Embankment to its present position in the front courtyard of the Savoy Hotel. Complete rebuilding took place in 1929 when the interior was swept away to be replaced by the present striking art deco design. *Funding*: self-financing. After considerable damage by fire, it hopes to re-open in 1992.

Shaftesbury Theatre

Shaftesbury Avenue, London
WC2H 8DP
Tel (071) 379 3345

Seating capacity: 1327. This theatre has always been slightly disadvantaged by its position – at least a quarter of a mile from its nearest rival. It opened in 1911, and was forced to close in 1973 when the roof collapsed during the run of the musical *Hair*. A campaign by Paul Scofield and Alec Guinness saved the theatre from threatened redevelopment. *Funding*: self-financing.

Strand Theatre

Aldwych, London WC2B 5LD
Tel (071) 836 4144

Seating capacity: 923. Opened May 1905, the theatre was designed, like its twin the Aldwych, by W.G.R. Sprague. It has had a history of long-running comedies: *Arsenic and Old Lace* played 1337 performances to wartime audiences, while *No Sex Please, We're British* played here for over a decade before moving to the Garrick.

Theatre Royal, Drury Lane

Catherine Street, London WC2B 5JF
Tel (071) 836 3687

Seating capacity: 2237. This theatre – now a Grade I listed building – has the longest continuous theatrical tradition in the UK. The first theatre on the site was built in 1663, and was rebuilt in 1774 and 1812. Garrick acquired the patent to the theatre in 1747, and was replaced on his retirement by Sheridan, who presented *School for Scandal* in 1777. The 1880s were famous for Augustus Harris's great spectaculars – sea battles and chariot races were re-enacted with no expense spared. Then followed a move towards romantic musicals, which reached their peak in the 1930s with a series of Ivor Novello successes. ENSA made the theatre their wartime headquarters; the post-war period has been devoted almost entirely to musicals. Owned by Stoll Moss group. *Funding*: self-financing.

Theatre Royal Haymarket

Haymarket, London SW1Y 4HT
Tel (071) 930 8890

Seating capacity: 905. Although this theatre dates back to 1720, it was not granted the essential 'Royal' patent until 1766. Even then, it was only allowed to open in the summer months when the two grand houses – Drury Lane and Covent Garden – were closed. The present Grade I-listed theatre, with its splendid portico, was designed by John Nash and opened in 1821. It has a long and distinguished history as an upmarket venue. It is currently presenting *Miss Saigon*. *Funding*: self-financing.

Vaudeville Theatre

Strand, London WC2R ONH
Tel (071) 836 3191

Seating capacity: 690. This small theatre was built in 1870 and remodelled in 1891. The next change occurred only in 1969, when its new owner, Sir Peter Saunders, gave it a complete decorative overhaul; now owned by Michael Codron. Its most memorable productions include: *Salad Days*, which ran for over 2000 performances from 1954; *The Man Most Likely To*; *Move Over, Mrs Markham*; and *Present Laughter*. *Funding*: self-financing.

Victoria Palace

Victoria Street, London SW1 5EA
Tel (071) 834 2781

Seating capacity: 1564. Designed as a music hall, the Victoria Palace has been associated with variety and musical productions throughout its history. The Crazy Gang installed themselves here in 1949 and remained until 1962, when *The Black & White Minstrel Show* began its eight-year run. *Annie*, *The Sound of Music*, and *Buddy* have proved lucrative in recent years. Owned by Stoll Moss group. *Funding*: self-financing.

Westminster Theatre

Palace Street, Buckingham Palace Road, London SW1E 5JB
Tel (071) 834 7882

Seating capacity: 585. The theatre stands on the site of a chapel built in 1776 by an off-beat clergyman who used his wife's lottery winnings to finance the building! In 1931, Anmer Hall transformed this former chapel-of-ease into a theatre (naming it after his former school), and a bold policy of presenting Pirandello, Shaw, Ibsen and O'Neill put the theatre in the forefront of its contemporaries. In 1946, Moral Rearmament took over, and the theatre opened for 'worthy' shows and the profitable Christmas season.

Whitehall Theatre

14 Whitehall, London SW1A 2DY
Tel (071) 867 1129

Seating capacity: 680. The Whitehall was one of a rash of theatres to open in 1930 and is best known as the post-war home of British farce. Paul Raymond took it over in the 1970s for his sex revues, but there was a return to the good old days in 1981 when the political farce *Anyone for Denis?* swept in. Now part of the Maybox Theatres group (Chesterfield Properties). *Funding*: self-financing.

Wimbledon Theatre

The Broadway, Wimbledon, London SW19 1QG
Tel (081) 543 4549

Seating capacity: 1600. The theatre offers a wide range of entertainment. It is on the circuit for big touring opera and ballet companies, and stages the occasional pre-West End run. There is an annual pantomime. *Funding*: self-financing.

Wyndham's Theatre

Charing Cross Road, London
WC2H 0DA
Tel (071) 867 1125

Seating capacity: 800. One of London's most romantic theatres, Wyndham's was built in 1899 by the actor/manager Charles Wyndham. The auditorium is decorated in cream, gold and blue, and the bust above the proscenium is said to be of Mary Moore, Wyndham's leading lady and later his wife. The theatre has had a long and close association with the fringe, and its successful transfers include *A Taste of Honey*, *Oh What a Lovely War!*, *No Man's Land* (with John Gielgud and Ralph Richardson), *Once a Catholic*, *Piaf*, *Accidental Death of an Anarchist*, *Crystal Clear*, *Serious Money*, *The Secret of Sherlock Holmes*, and *What The Butler Saw*. Now part of the Maybox Theatres group (Chesterfield Properties). *Funding*: self-financing.

England (excluding London)

Alexandra Theatre

Station Street, Birmingham B5 4DS
Tel (021) 643 5536

Seating capacity: 1367. This top touring venue attracts star TV names in musicals, light comedies and pantomime, and hosts many pre- and post-West End shows. *Funding*: City of Birmingham.

Alhambra Theatre

Morley Street, Bradford, W. Yorks.
BD7 1AJ
Tel (0274) 753623

Seating capacity: 1482. The theatre is the venue of touring opera, ballet, plays, musicals, variety and concerts. In 1986, it underwent a £6 million refurbishment by well-known theatre architects RHWL. The exterior, with towers and cupolas, was completely restored, with the addition of some ultra-modern design features, including a glass-fronted staircase inside the main rotunda which unites all the interior levels. The National Theatre is planning to make the studio at the rear of the theatre into its northern home. *Funding*: Bradford Metropolitan District Council.

Apollo Theatre

Ardwick Green, Manchester M12 6AP
Tel (061) 273 6921

Seating capacity: 2641. Although opera, ballet and drama are seen here, the theatre is mostly used for rock concerts. *Funding*: self-financing.

Ashcroft Theatre

Park Lane, Croydon, Surrey CR9 1DG
Tel (081) 681 0821

Seating capacity: 763. The theatre houses touring companies, producing mostly comedies and thrillers. There is an annual pantomime. *Funding*: London Borough of Croydon.

Babbacombe Theatre

Babbacombe Downs, Torquay
TQ1 3LU
Tel (0803) 528693

Seating capacity: 600. Summer season only; amateurs. *Funding*: self-financing.

The Beck Theatre

Grange Road, Hayes, Middlesex
Tel (081) 561 8371

Seating capacity: 598 (flexible). The Beck Theatre, named after a local worthy, was opened in 1977. Offers a mixed programme of touring drama, mostly light comedies and thrillers.

Birmingham Hippodrome

Hurst Street, Birmingham B5 4TB
Tel (021) 622 7437

Seating capacity: 1367. Blockbuster tours of plays, musicals, operas, ballet; an annual panto; and some variety. Many pre- and post-West End plays. *Funding*: City of Birmingham.

Bournemouth Pier Theatre

Bournemouth, Dorset BH1 5AD
Tel (0202) 290250

Seating capacity: 850. Open May to October only. Summer seasons, concerts. *Funding*: self-financing.

Buxton Opera House

Water Street, Buxton, Derbys.
SK17 6XN
Tel (0298) 71573

Seating capacity: 946. Varied programme of professional and amateur productions, one-night stands and a festival in July and August (*see* Festivals). *Funding*: North Western Arts, High Peak Borough Council, Derbyshire County Council.

Cambridge Arts Theatre

PO Box 17, Cambridge CB2 3PW
Tel (0223) 355246

Seating capacity: 650. A traditional theatre built in 1936, that offers standard comedies and thrillers as well as new work from such touring companies as the Cambridge Theatre Company and the Oxford Playhouse Company. Also ballet, films and panto. *Funding*: University of Cambridge.

Chatham Central Hall Theatre

170 High Street, Chatham, Kent
ME4 4AS
Tel (0634) 48584

Seating capacity: 945. One-night stands and weekly productions: music, plays. *Funding*: self-financing.

City Varieties Music Hall

The Headrow, Leeds LS1 6LW
Tel (0532) 450366

Seating capacity: 586. A traditional music hall over 200 years old. Variety, revue, pantomime, drama and music. *Funding*: self-financing.

Connaught Theatre

Union Place, Worthing, W. Sussex
BN11 1LG
Tel (0903) 31799

Seating capacity: 514. Mixed programme of amateur and professional shows; some films. *Funding*: Worthing Borough Council.

Corby Civic Theatre

George Street, Corby, Northants.
N17 1QB
Tel (0536) 402551

Seating capacity: 530. Part of Corby civic centre, built in 1966. Ballet, opera, rock and classical concerts. *Funding*: Corby District Council.

Gordon Craig Theatre

Stevenage Leisure Centre, Lytton
Way, Stevenage SG11 1LZ
Tel (0438) 317956

Seating capacity: 507. This venue provides a wide programme of light touring drama, music, films, children's shows and an annual panto, aiming to suit all tastes and ages. *Funding*: Stevenage Borough Council, Eastern Arts.

Daneside Theatre

Park Road, Congleton, Cheshire
Tel (0260) 278481

Seating capacity: 300. Mostly amateur productions, but available for professional bookings. *Funding*: self-financing.

Darlington Civic Theatre

Parkgate, Darlington DL1 1RR
Tel (0325) 468006

Seating capacity: 599. An Edwardian theatre, built in 1907, it houses major tours of plays, ballet, opera, recitals, concerts and a pantomime season. Director Brian Goddard claims the highest average attendance of any provincial theatre, by booking popular shows and then marketing them so that people know what is on. *Funding*: Darlington Borough Council.

Devonshire Park Theatre

8 Compton Street, Eastbourne,
E. Sussex
Tel (0323) 412424

Seating capacity: 936. Major touring productions, pre- and post-West End; some classical plays. *Funding*: self-financing.

The Drum

See **Theatre Royal**.

Doncaster Civic Theatre

Waterdale, Doncaster, S. Yorks.
DN1 3ET
Tel (0302) 22817

Seating capacity: 511. Used mostly by amateur companies; available for bookings at other times. *Funding*: Doncaster Metropolitan Borough Council.

Empire Theatre

Lime Street, Liverpool 1
Tel (051) 709 3514

Seating capacity: 2348. One of the major touring houses in the North-west, attracting top drama, opera and ballet companies. *Funding*: self-financing.

Forum Theatre

Town Centre, Billingham, Cleveland
TS23 2LJ
Tel (0642) 551389

Seating capacity: 631. Part of a large, multi-purpose centre comprising a swimming pool and other leisure facilities, the theatre offers a mixed programme of good-quality touring drama, children's shows, one-night stands, music and an annual panto. *Funding*: Stockton Borough Council.

Georgian Theatre Royal

Victoria Road, Richmond, N. Yorks.
DL10 4DW
Tel (0748) 3021

Seating capacity: 231. This remarkable theatre, originally built in 1788, re-opened in 1963 after being used as a wine store and an auction house: everything from the paybox to the pro-scenium arch doors is authentic. It offers an interesting programme of touring drama, music and one-night stands, as well as hosting the local amateur dramatic society. *Funding*: self-financing.

Grand Theatre

Church Street, Blackpool FY1 1HT
Tel (0253) 28309

Seating capacity: 1238. Originally built in 1894, designed by the great theatre architect Frank Matcham, the Grand reopened as a touring venue in 1981: top drama; musicals; concerts; ballet; the usual comedy acts and one-night stands on offer during the summer; annual panto. *Funding*: local authority.

Grand Theatre

Lichfield Street, Wolverhampton,
W. Midlands WV1 1DE
Tel (0902) 28165

Seating capacity: 1200. Drama, opera, pantomime, light entertainment, children's shows, amateur musicals, concerts. *Funding*: Wolverhampton City Council.

Grand Theatre & Opera House

New Briggate, Leeds LS1 6NZ
Tel (0532) 456014

Seating capacity: 1550. One of Britain's finest examples of a Victorian theatre and opera house, and the home of Opera North. It offers a varied programme of opera, one-night stands, touring ballet and major touring drama productions. *Funding*: Leeds City Council.

Harlequin

Warwick Quadrant, Redhill, Surrey
RH1 1NN
Tel (0737) 765547

Seating capacity: 494. Middle-scale touring productions; pantomime season. *Funding*: Reigate & Banstead Borough Council.

Harrogate Theatre

Oxford Street, Harrogate, N. Yorks.
HG1 1QF
Tel (0423) 502710

Seating capacity: 476. Victorian theatre with many outstanding features. There is a repertory company resident from late August to the end of April (*see* Rep/Regional Theatres), but from

May to August, there is a touring season with a full range of performing arts: drama, dance, music, mime, children's shows. Bookings range from whole weeks to one-night stands. *Funding*: Yorkshire Arts, Harrogate Borough Council, N. Yorks. County Council.

Hull New Theatre

Kingston Square, Hull, N. Humberside HU1 3HF
Tel (0482) 20244

Seating capacity: 1200. Large touring productions, opera, ballet and concerts. Produces a large annual panto. *Funding*: Hull County Council, Beverley Borough Council, Hull Leisure Services.

Key Theatre

Embankment Road, Peterborough, Cambs. PE1 1EF
Tel (0733) 52437

Seating capacity: 399. Plays, musicals, jazz, amateur shows – entertainment of all kinds. *Funding*: Peterborough County Council.

King's Theatre

Albert Road, Southsea, Hants PO5 2QT
Tel (0705) 811394

Seating capacity: 1750. Drama, opera, musical, ballet – covering a wide range of tastes. *Funding*: self-financing, Southern Arts grid/circuit funding.

Limelight Theatre

Queens Park Centre, Queens Park, Aylesbury HP21 7RT
Tel (0296) 431272

Seating capacity: 150. Visiting small-scale theatre and dance companies. *Funding*: Buckinghamshire Arts Association.

Malthouse Theatre

Malthouse Lane, nr Hurstpierpoint College, Hassocks, W. Sussex
Tel (04446) 41047
Artistic director Sandra Scriven

Seating capacity: 100. Medieval barn with adjoining restaurant and bar. Visiting companies ranging from opera and music hall to drama and one-man shows. *Funding*: self-financing.

Marina Theatre

Marina, Lowestoft, Suffolk NR32 1HH
Tel (0502) 569646

Seating capacity: 751. Variety, dance, music, opera, star names one-night stands and weekly bookings. Cinema. *Funding*: Waveney District Council.

Marlowe Theatre

The Friars, Canterbury, Kent CT1 2AS
Tel (0227) 767246

Seating capacity: 986. Touring, concerts, pantomime, one-night stands. *Funding*: Canterbury City Council.

Mayflower Theatre

Commercial Road, Southampton
SO1 0GE
Tel (0703) 330083

Seating capacity: 2299. The largest regional theatre in the South, it presents opera, ballet, pantomime, rock and pop concerts, drama and musicals (pre- and post-West End). *Funding*: self-financing.

Mountbatten Theatre

East Park Terrace, Southampton
SO9 4WW
Tel (0703) 221991

Seating capacity: 515. Amateur and professional musicals, comedies, occasional drama, concerts and films. *Funding*: Hampshire County Council.

The Music Hall

The Square, Shrewsbury, Salop
SY1 1LH
Tel (0743) 50761

Seating capacity: 410. Drama, musicals, dance, pop and classical concerts; one-night stands and weekly shows. *Funding*: Shrewsbury & Atcham Borough Council.

Neptune Theatre

Hanover Street, Liverpool 1
Tel (051) 709 7844

Seating capacity: 445. Available for hire by professional and amateur companies. *Funding*: Liverpool City Council.

New Theatre Royal

Guildhall Walk, Portsmouth PO1 2DD
Tel (0705) 864611

Seating capacity: currently 250. The theatre is undergoing restoration and rebuilding, and facilities are very limited. At present, performances and events can take place only in the auditorium. *Funding*: Hampshire County Council, Portsmouth City Council.

North Pier Theatre

Westover Road, Bournemouth, Dorset
BH2 5BH
Tel (0202) 20980

Seating capacity: 1518. Opera, ballet, musicals, summer shows, one-night stands, pantomime. *Funding*: self-financing.

Opera House

Quay Street, Manchester M3 3HP
Tel (061) 834 1787

Seating capacity: 2000. Presents extended runs of major musicals. *Funding*: self-financing.

The Orchard

Home Gardens, Dartford, Kent
DA1 1ED
Tel (0322) 343222

Seating capacity: 900. Can be used in the round or with proscenium arch. A top touring venue with mixed programme of drama, music, dance, opera and films. *Funding*: Dartford Borough Council.

Palace Theatre

Oxford Street, Manchester M1 6FT
Tel (061) 228 6255

Seating capacity: 2000. A leading touring venue, it houses drama, ballet,
music and visits from the Royal
Opera. *Funding*: self-financing.

Palace Theatre

Alcester Street, Redditch, Worcs.
B98 8EA
Tel (0527) 61544

Seating capacity: 399. Professional and
amateur productions; bought-in one/
two-night stand music, theatre, dance.
Also exhibitions, films, youth theatre,
holiday activities for young people.
Policy of community involvement and
access to the arts. *Funding*: Redditch
Borough Council.

Pavilion Theatre

North Pier, The Promenade, Blackpool
FY1 1NE
Tel (0253) 21452

Seating capacity: 1564. Summer season
only. *Funding*: self-financing.

Pavilion Theatre

The Esplanade, Weymouth, Dorset
DT4 8ED
Tel (0305) 786732

Seating capacity: 1000. Summer season,
pantomime, one-night stands, concerts; some amateur use. *Funding*:
Weymouth & Portland Borough
Council.

Pavilion Theatre

Marine Parade, Worthing, W. Sussex
BN12 4ET
Tel (0903) 39999 ext. 129

Seating capacity: 850. Wide range of
shows – concerts, children's entertainment, dance. *Funding*: Worthing
Borough Council.

Phoenix Theatre

6 Newarke Street, Leicester LE1 5TA
Tel (0533) 554854 (box office)

Reopened in 1988, after extensive
refurbishment, as an arts centre run in
conjunction with Leicester Polytechnic. Visiting companies plus films.

The Playhouse

The High, Harlow, Essex CM20 1LS
Tel (0279) 24391

Seating capacity: auditorium 435, studio
110. Wide programme of touring
drama, dance and music. Amateur
work mainly in the studio. *Funding*:
Harlow District Council, Eastern Arts.

Pomegranate Theatre

Corporation Street, Chesterfield,
Derbys. S41 7TX
Tel (0246) 234633

Seating capacity: 549. Touring, plays,
pantomimes, musicals, variety, Sunday concerts; some one-night stands
and amateur shows. *Funding*: Chesterfield Borough Council, Derbyshire
County Council.

Princess Theatre

Torbay Road, Torquay TQ2 5EZ
Tel (0803) 528693

Seating capacity: 1514. Summer shows, pantomime, touring plays, ballet, opera; weekly or one-night stands. *Funding*: self-financing.

Richmond Theatre

The Green, Richmond-upon-Thames, Surrey TW9 1QJ
Tel (081) 940 0220

Seating capacity: 920. Mostly light drama, much of it pre-West End. *Funding*: self-financing.

Ritz Theatre

High Street, Lincoln LN5 7PJ
Tel (0522) 537127

Seating capacity: 1400. Drama, films, one-night stands, concerts. *Funding*: self-financing.

Royal Hippodrome Theatre

Seaside Road, Eastbourne, E. Sussex
Tel (0323) 411818

Seating capacity: 643. Summer season, variety, musicals, concerts. *Funding*: self-financing.

Spa Terrace

South Marine Drive, Bridlington, Yorks.
Tel (0262) 678255

Seating capacity: 1031. Summer shows, professional tours and amateur shows. *Funding*: East Yorks. Borough Council.

Sunderland Empire Theatre

High Street West, Sunderland
SR1 3EX
Tel (091) 514 2517

Seating capacity: main auditorium 1550, studio 150. Pantomime, variety, opera, plays and concerts. *Funding*: Sunderland Borough Council, Grid/circuit funding (No. 1 circuit).

Tameside Theatre

Oldham Road, Ashton-under-Lyne, Greater Manchester OL6 7SE
Tel (061) 330 2095

Seating capacity: 1262. Tours, plays, music, pantomime, one-night stands, children's shows, TV transmissions. *Funding*: Tameside Municipal Borough Council.

Theatre Royal

Sawclose, Bath, Avon BA1 1ET
Tel (0225) 65074

Seating capacity: 950. One of the oldest theatres in the country, superbly restored. Often premières shows, and has close links with the National Theatre, who preview a number of their productions here in advance of the South Bank. Caters for all tastes, with opera, drama and comedy. *Funding*: self-financing.

Theatre Royal

New Road, Brighton BN1 1SD
Tel (0273) 27480

Seating capacity: 951. A venue for top touring companies, with a traditional programme of comedies and thrillers, many of them pre-West End. *Funding*: self-financing.

Theatre Royal

Westgate Street, Bury St Edmunds, Suffolk IP33 1QR
Tel (0284) 755127

Seating capacity: 350. A charming period theatre that for many years served as a brewer's warehouse; now owned by the National Trust. Plays, dance, opera, music, films and pantomime; one-night stands, weekly and half-weekly bookings. *Funding*: Suffolk County Council, St Edmundsbury Borough Council.

Theatre Royal

Grey Street, Newcastle upon Tyne
NE1 6BR
Tel (091) 232 0997

Seating capacity: 1350. Recently refurbished at a cost of £8 million, the bars and foyers have been expanded and backstage facilities completely modernized, while the superb Matchem interior has been faithfully restored. It houses top touring productions, usually thrillers and comedies, and also opera and ballet. *Funding*: Newcastle City Council.

Theatre Royal

Theatre Street, Norwich NR2 1RL
Tel (0603) 623562

Seating capacity: 1275. This claims to be the most profitable civic theatre in Europe. Revues, variety acts and musicals share the stage with opera, ballet and top drama; there is an annual pantomime. *Funding*: self-financing.

Theatre Royal

Theatre Square, Nottingham
NG1 5ND
Tel (0602) 483505

Seating capacity: 1188. Large-scale touring opera, ballet, variety, concerts, pantomime and light drama. *Funding*: Nottingham City Council.

Theatre Royal

Corporation Street, St Helens, Lancs.
WA10 1LQ
Tel (0744) 28467

Seating capacity: 703. Touring venue for dance, music and limited drama. Also has films, lectures, children's shows, amateur events and pantomime. *Funding*: Theatre Royal (St Helens) Trust.

Theatre Royal

7 Pall Mall, Hanley, Stoke-on-Trent
ST1 1EE
Tel (0782) 266343

Seating capacity: 1424. All types of productions; week, split week and one-night stands. *Funding*: self-financing.

Theatre Royal

Jewry Street, Winchester SO23 8SB
Tel (0962) 842122

Seating capacity: 409. Touring drama, music and one-night stands – a varied but light programme. *Funding*: Winchester City Council, Hampshire County Council.

Theatre Royal & The Drum

Royal Parade, Plymouth PL1 2TR
Tel (0752) 668282

Seating capacity: Theatre Royal 1296, Drum 205. In-house productions; also touring opera and ballet, children's shows and concerts. Visiting fringe groups and experimental drama in The Drum. *Funding*: Arts Council and Local Authorities. (*See also* **Rep/ Regional Theatres.**)

Theatre Royal & Opera House

Drury Lane, Wakefield, W. Yorks.
WF1 2TE
Tel (0924) 373757

Seating capacity: 530. All forms of music, dance and drama. *Funding*: Wakefield Municipal District Council, Yorkshire Arts.

Towngate Theatre

Towngate, Basildon, Essex
Tel (0268) 531343

Seating capacity: main house 550, studio 200. Built by architects RHWL and opened in April 1988, the theatre has a traditional Georgian horseshoe format, but can be transformed into a flat floor space using the latest air castor technology. It houses touring dance, music and drama, the latter ranging from new and alternative work to popular comedies; also films. *Funding*: local authority.

Watermans Arts Centre

40 High Street, Brentford, Middx.
TW8 0DS
Tel (081) 847 5651

Seating capacity: 240. Opened 1983. Touring theatre companies, dance and music. *Funding*: Greater London Arts, the London Borough Grants Scheme and Hounslow Council.

West Cliff Theatre

Tower Road, Clacton-on-Sea, Essex
Tel (0255) 426526

Seating capacity: 598. Summer season; also bookings by professional and amateur companies. Closed four months of the year. *Funding*: District Council grant.

Isle of Man

Gaiety Theatre

Harris Promenade, Douglas, Isle of Man
Tel (0624) 25001

Seating capacity: 1168. Opened in 1900, this has a splendid opulent auditorium, recently restored to the original specification. Musicals, plays, opera, ballet and rock, jazz and classical concerts. *Funding*: Isle of Man Government.

Northern Ireland

Ardhowen: The Theatre by the Lakes

Dublin Road, Enniskillen, Co. Fermanagh
Tel (0365) 23233

Seating capacity: 300. Mainly touring professional theatre and music, but some community theatre, folk, traditional and jazz music, dance, opera and light entertainment. *Funding*: local authority, Arts Council of Northern Ireland.

Belfast Civic Arts Theatre

41 Botanic Avenue, Belfast BT7 1JG
Tel (0232) 242819
Administrator Mr W.E. Brown

Seating capacity: 500. Having been closed for some years, the theatre reopened in 1977 with the Ulster Actors Company in residence. Variety and children's shows, drama, dance, plus the occasional in-house production with guest directors. *Funding*: Arts Council of Northern Ireland and Belfast City Council.

Grand Opera House

Great Victoria Street, Belfast BT2 7HR
Tel (0232) 667687

Seating capacity: 1001. A splendid Victorian theatre, and Northern Ireland's only large venue for touring opera, drama and ballet. Light comedies and shows with TV names are most popular. *Funding*: Arts Council of Northern Ireland.

Scotland

Ayr Civic Theatre

Craigie Road, Ayr, Ayrshire KA8 OE7
Tel (0292) 263755

Seating capacity: 350. A small theatre linked to the Gaiety Theatre (*see below*), it is housed in an old converted church. It offers a summer repertory season and a modest programme of plays and concerts. *Funding*: Kyle & Carrick District Council.

Eden Court Theatre

Bishop's Road, Inverness IV3 5SA
Tel (0463) 239841

Seating capacity: 791. Mixed programme: music, films, some drama. *Funding*: Scottish Arts Council, Inverness District Council.

Gaiety Theatre

Carrick Street, Ayr
Tel (0292) 264630

Seating capacity: 570.. Broad policy – touring plays, musicals, ballet. Resident season. *Funding*: Kyle & Carrick District Council. (*See also* **Ayr Civic Theatre**.)

His Majesty's Theatre

Rosemount Viaduct, Aberdeen
Tel (0224) 637788

Seating capacity: 1456. Opened in 1906, and designed to give a sense of luxury and (despite the large capacity of the auditorium) a feeling of intimacy, this is a premier theatre for large touring companies presenting opera, ballet, concerts and quality mainstream drama. *Funding*: local authority and self-financing.

King's Theatre

2 Leven Street, Edinburgh EH3 9LQ
Tel (031) 229 4840

Seating capacity: 1336. All types of large-scale touring productions: ballet, opera, mainstream drama, comedy. *Funding*: Edinburgh District Council, Scottish Arts Council grid/circuit funding.

King's Theatre

Bath Street, Glasgow G2 4JN
Tel (041) 248 5332

Seating capacity: 1785. Top touring venue offering drama, comedy, musicals, pantomimes, opera, ballet and one-night stands. Occasional Sunday concerts. *Funding*: Glasgow City Council, Scottish Arts Council grid/circuit funding.

Mitchell Theatre

Granville Street, Glasgow G3 7DR
Tel (041) 227 5033

Seating capacity: 418. Opened in 1981, this acts as an overspill venue for top touring drama, ballet and music companies. *Funding*: Glasgow City Council.

Orkney Arts Theatre

Mill Street, Kirkwall, Orkney KW5
Tel (0856) 2131 (day) and
(0856) 4803 (evenings)

Seating capacity: 324. Modern facilities for local and touring companies. *Funding*: Orkney Islands Council.

Palace Theatre

9 Green Street, Kilmarnock KA1 3BN
Tel (0563) 37710

Seating capacity: 503. Dance, opera, local dramatics – broad variety. *Funding*: Kilmarnock District Council, Scottish Arts Council grid/circuit funding.

Pavilion Theatre

121 Renfrew Street, Glasgow G2 3AX
Tel (041) 332 7579

Seating capacity: 1449. Plays, variety, pantomime; rock and pop concerts. *Funding*: self-financing.

Adam Smith Theatre

Bennochy Road, Kirkcaldy, Fife KY1 1ET
Tel (0592) 202855

Seating capacity: 475. Touring plays, variety, children's theatre; occasional one-night stands. Some in-house productions including pantomime. *Funding*: Kirkcaldy District Council.

Theatre Royal

Hope Street, Glasgow G2 3QA
Tel (041) 332 3321

Seating capacity: 1547. Home of Scottish Opera from October to June, and of Scottish Ballet for seven weeks. It takes in top touring companies for the remainder of the year. *Funding*: Scottish Arts Council, Glasgow District Council, Strathclyde Regional Council.

Whitehall Theatre

Bellfield Street, Dundee DD1 5JA
Tel (0382) 22684

Seating capacity: 750. Open 20–25 weeks of the year. Touring shows, one-night stands, local opera and music societies. *Funding*: self-financing.

Wales

New Theatre

Park Place, Cardiff CF1 3LN
Tel (0222) 394232

Seating capacity: 1168. An Empire-style Edwardian theatre, completely refurbished by theatre architects RHWL, who have expanded the inadequate bar and foyer space. The home base of Welsh National Opera who perform here for 15–20 weeks a year. Top-quality touring theatre, housing the Royal Shakespeare Company, National Theatre and other major companies. Dance (classical and modern), musicals, children's shows, six-week pantomime. *Funding*: Cardiff City Council.

Theatre Hafren

Llanidloes Road, Newtown, Powys
SY16 2EN
Tel (0686) 25447

Seating capacity: 448. Dance, opera, classical music and celebrities. *Funding*: Powys County Council, grid/circuit funding – North Wales Arts touring scheme and Mid Wales Entertainment.

13 *Festivals*

Festivals can be great fun, especially if you are part of a company specially invited to perform. You can bask in fame, however temporary, and meet performers from other companies, eat, drink and be merry. If you appear on a festival 'fringe', hoping to be discovered, you are likely to be disappointed and you will be certain to spend a lot of money in the process. The most famous fringe of all, in Edinburgh, is now mostly the preserve of comic solos and double-acts. New drama is rare and greatly overshadowed by cabaret. It remains great fun nonetheless.

Bath International Festival

Festival office: Linley House, 1 Pierrepont Place, Bath BA1 1JY
Tel (0225) 462231/466411

Annual festival; 1991 dates: 24 May–9 June. Concentration on music and visual arts.

Belfast Festival at Queen's

Festival House, 25 College Gardens, Belfast BT9 6BS
Tel (0232) 667687

Founded 1963. Annual festival held at and near Queen's University. 1991 dates: 4–23 November. Opera, theatre, music, dance, cinema, exhibitions, jazz as well as literary, children's and fringe events. Regular visitors include: The National Theatre; RSC; Shared Experience; and 7:84 Scotland.

Brighton Festival

Festival office: Marlborough House, 54 Old Steine, Brighton,
E. Sussex BN1 1EQ
Tel (0273) 29801

Founded 1967. Annual international festival held in May. Theatre, music, dance, opera, visual arts and literature. 1991 festival – 3–26 May. 1991 drama highlights included: *Trackers of Oxyrhynchus* (National Theatre); *Onigata* (Lindsay Kemp Co); *The Rose Tattoo* (Sir Peter Hall Co); *The Cherry Orchard* (Theatre Clwyd); plus a theatre showcase weekend featuring 14 innovative new works by British small-scale companies.

Buxton Festival

Festival office: 1 Crescent View, Hall Bank, Buxton, Derbys. SK17 6EN
Tel (0298) 70395 Fax (0298) 72289

Founded 1979. Three-week summer festival of opera, drama, music and films. 1990 drama included: *Hard Times* performed by the 'Not The National Theatre' Company and *Phaedra* performed by ATC. 1991 dates: 20 July to 11 August.

Cambridge Festival

Festival office: Mandela House, 4 Regent Street, Cambridge CB2 1BY
Tel (0223) 358977 ext 3834

Founded 1962. Annual two-week summer festival with a theme – in 1991, this will be Shakespearian. Music, theatre, jazz, film, community arts, visual arts and dance. 1991 Programme includes: Cambridge Theatre Company's *Twelfth Night*, Judy Dench and Michael Williams, Henry Goodman and Co.

Canterbury Festival

Festival office: 59 Ivy Lane, Canterbury, Kent CT1 1TU
Tel (0227) 452853

Founded 1984. Annual festival of music, drama, dance, film, master classes, opera, exhibitions and talks. 1991 festival dates: 12–26 October. Theme: *A Matter of Time*. Drama at the Canterbury Festival has included productions from the National Theatre, Birmingham Repertory Theatre,

Cheek by Jowl, Patricia Routledge, Shared Experience and Oxford Stage Company.

Chichester Festival Theatre

Dumfries & Galloway Arts Festival

Festival office: Gracefield Arts Centre, 28 Edinburgh Road, Dumfries DG1 1JQ
Tel (0387) 60447

Annual ten-day festival held in May/June. The 1991 festival will include the Singapore Symphony Orchestra, London Lewis Ballet, and Peter Donohoe.

Edinburgh Festival

Festival office: 21 Market Street, Edinburgh EH1 1BW
Tel (031) 226 4001

Founded 1947. Leading annual international festival of music, theatre, film, jazz, dance and tattoo, as well as a fringe consisting of some 500 events. 1991 dates: 11 August to 1 September. 1991 Festival continues the Japanese theatre season begun in 1990. There will also be a major celebration of theatre, opera, music and dance from Czechoslovakia.

Exeter Festival

Festival office: Civic Centre, Dix's Field, Exeter, Devon EX1 1JN
Tel (0392) 265200

Founded 1974 as a community festival and expanded into its current professional status in 1980. The magnificent Gothic Cathedral is the setting for all major concerts featuring international artists and orchestras. Other venues include The Northcott Theatre, The University Great Hall, and Killerton House. Programme published mid-March.

Greenwich Festival

Festival office: 151 Powis Street, Woolwich, London SE18 6JL
Tel (081) 317 8687

Founded 1970. Annual festival held in June. 1991 dates: 7–16 June (21st Birthday) with a theme of Censorship. Theatre, dance, music, and visual arts. 1990 included: Frankie Howerd, Dame Peggy Ashcroft and Julian Bream.

Harrogate International Festival

Festival office: Royal Baths, Harrogate, N. Yorks. HG1 2RR
Tel (0423) 562303
Fax (0423) 521264

Founded 1966. Annual two-week summer festival. Mainly music with some cabaret, dance, drama and exhibitions.

Henley Festival

Festival Yard, 42 Bell Street, Henley-on-Thames, Oxon, RG9 2BG
Tel (0491) 410414
Fax (0491) 410482

Four evenings in July, the week following Henley Royal Regatta, using Riverside site. Orchestral concerts on a Floating Stage, internationally famous soloists, with art and sculpture exhibitions, recitals by promising young artists, jazz bands, magicians, dancers, a marching band and fireworks. Various restaurants. Black tie only.

London International Festival of Theatre (LIFT)

Festival office: 23 Neal Street, London WC2H 9PU
Tel (071) 836 7186

Biennial festival bringing the best of international contemporary performance to London for a three-week season every other summer. Performances take place in large and small venues and outdoor locations all over London. Next festival – the sixth – begins on 1 July 1991. In the past, festivals have included companies from the USSR, US, China, Latin America, Europe, Africa and India. The directors, Lucy Neal and Rose de Wend Fenton, won the International Theatre Institute's 'Award for Excellence in International Theatre' in 1988.

Ludlow Festival

Festival office: Castle Square, Ludlow, Salop SY8 1AY
Tel (0584) 872150

Annual summer festival – 1991 will be its 32nd year. Drama, music, lectures, exhibitions. During the two weeks of the festival, a Shakespeare play is performed in the grounds of Ludlow Castle: in 1991, Alan Cohen will direct *Macbeth*.

Mayfest (Glasgow's International Festival)

Festival office: 18 Albion Street, Glasgow G1 1LH
Tel (041) 221 4911 Fax (041) 552 6612
Director Robert Robson

Founded 1983. Three-week festival each May – the second largest in the UK. Opera, visual arts and community events. Theatre productions include: Peter Brook's production of *The Mahabharata*, Glasgow Citizens Company in *Lady Windermere's Fan*, the Maly Drama Theatre of Leningrad in *Stars in the Morning Sky*, Wildcat Stage Productions in *The Celtic Story* and Joint Stock's production of *A Child in the Heart*.

National Student Drama Festival

Festival office: 20 Lansdowne Road, Muswell Hill, London N10 2AU
Tel (081) 883 4586

36th festival 4–11 April 1991, sponsored by The Sunday Times, ITV and Scarborough Borough Council. 37th festival 9–16 April 1992. The only regular focus and forum for British student drama, it includes fourteen or so performances of new and old works, post performance discussions, talks, a remarkable range of workshops, and a daily festival newspaper, produced by all and sundry, plus a student drama critic award. Leaders, judges and speakers who have taken part in the past include Alan Ayckbourn, John Guilgud, John Hurt, Ian McKellen, Warren Mitchell, Michael Palin, Joan Plowright, Prunella Scales, Timothy West, Susannah York. The scores of well known past participants as students include Brian Blessed, Ian Charleson, Caryl Churchill, Ben Elton, Stephen Fry, John Godber, Terry Hands, Bernard Hill, Rik Mayall, John Nettles, Dennis Potter, Antony Sher . . . The Festival also 'discovered' Harold Pinter and helped launch David Edgar's playwriting career. Productions can be entered for adjudication – details from the above address.

Newbury Spring Festival

Festival office: Suite 4, Town Hall, Newbury, Berks. RG14 5AA
Tel (0635) 32421

Founded 1979. Annual festival of music and visual arts held in May.

Nottingham Festival

Festival office: City of Nottingham Arts Department, 51 Castle Gate, Nottingham NG1 6AF
Tel (0602) 483504

Founded over 20 years ago but only recently developed into the large-scale annual event it now is. Theatre, music, opera and jazz.

Perth Festival of the Arts

Festival office: Perth Theatre Box Office, High Street, Perth
Tel (0738) 21031

Founded 1971. Annual 11-day festival. Music, theatre, opera, dance and visual arts.

Pitlochry Festival Theatre

See **Rep/Regional Theatres.**

Polesden Lacey Open Air Theatre

National Trust, Polesden Lacey, Dorking, Surrey RH5 6BD
Tel (0372) 457223

Annual three-week season of open-air amateur drama and music. 1991 dates: 19 June–7 July. Productions: *A Midsummer Night's Dream; South Pacific.*

Reading Arts Festival

Festival office: 21 South Street, Reading RG1 4QR

One-week general arts festival (October).

Salisbury Festival

Festival office: The King's House, 65 The Close, Salisbury, Wilts. SP1 2EN
Tel and Fax (0722) 323883

Annual music-led festival for two weeks every September, incorporating some drama – both fringe and mainstream, usually at Salisbury Arts Centre and Salisbury Playhouse – as well as film, dance, talks, celebrity lectures, literary events.

Wallington Festival

Adminstrator, Wallington, Cambo, Morpeth, Northumb. NE61 4AR
Tel (067 074) 283

Founded 1986. Annual festival held in and around this National Trust House. Festival varies in length depending on how many events are booked. In 1991 Theatre Set Up perform *Measure For Measure* from 25 to 29 June.

Warwick Festival

Festival office: Northgate, Warwick CV34 4JL
Tel (0926) 410747

Founded 1980. Annual summer festival. 1991 dates: 3–14 July. Music, theatre, dance and visual arts. 1990 drama included a performance of *Much Ado About Nothing* in Warwick Castle.

York Festival & Mystery Plays

Festival office: 1 Newgate, York YO1 2LA
Tel (0904) 610266

Quadrennial summer festival – the next one is in 1992. Four weeks of drama, dance, music, film, opera, lectures and many fringe events. 1988 drama productions included: *The Wars of the Roses* (English Shakespeare Company); *Trumpets and Drums* (York Theatre Company); *A Hard Day's Night* (Hull Truck). The York Mystery Plays are performed by local amateurs, with the role of Christ being taken by a professional actor.

14 Children's and Young People's Theatre

It is vital to understand that this is a specialist and very demanding area of the acting profession. It often requires not only a range of performing skills, but a high degree of creativity in the non-performing skills of devising and writing. In T.I.E. (Theatre in Education) an understanding of educational processes is also necessary.

Children's and Young People's Theatre should not be mistaken for the starting point on the road to gaining starring roles at the RSC or the National. It is definitely not a training agency for the inexperienced but enthusiastic. There is very little cross-over between other areas of the profession and T.I.E., which frequently requires recognised teaching qualifications in addition to the talents noted above.

Young audiences can be very tough. They do not have the inhibitions and politeness which might prevent adults from indicating boredom or dislike – and it's not unknown for a favourable response to turn from enthusiasm into uncontrollable anarchy. Many experienced practitioners consider it more challenging than any other form of theatre. It is certainly not a soft option. Unless the company is one of the few which produces classic plays for young audiences, it is unlikely to offer the chance of a substantial role. Your work will not receive much attention from critics or prove particularly attractive to future employers. It does tend to involve relatively civilized hours of work, but in the commercial sector it can mean extended touring.

T.I.E. starts with education as its aim, and uses theatrical means principally to raise questions. It will normally involve pre- and post-show work as part of an educational package. Clarity of purpose is paramount, rather than purely theatrical values. T.I.E. therefore requires performers with experience of young people, of touring, and of the educational system. It also places considerable emphasis on acting companies who can devise their own material related to specific projects. There is little dependence on existing texts, although a small number of devised pieces such as *Flags and Bandages* and *Dirty Rascals* have become established standards.

Some T.I.E. companies attached to regional repertory companies have a commitment to provide classic plays for schools. In this case the non-specialist might reasonably approach them; it is always best to check the company's policy.

The existence of many T.I.E companies is now seriously threatened. Those attached to repertory theatres may be closed down to help solve the financial problems of the parent company. The pressures on centralised education authorities, and the financial constraints on individual schools have created an atmosphere of uncertainty and cut-back. The introduction of a national curriculum has encouraged schools to request exclusively curriculum-based material. T.I.E. companies normally thrive upon the freedom to create plays and programmes which involve cross-curricular issues and topics.

Age Exchange Theatre Trust

See **Touring companies.**

Bagatelle

See **Touring companies.**

Bolton Octagon Youth Theatre

See **Repertory and regional theatres.**

Cannon Hill Puppet Theatre

MAC, Cannon Hill Park, Birmingham B12 9QH
Tel (021) 440 4221
Artistic director John Blundall

Founded 1968. Britain's largest residential professional puppet theatre company, it has played to over half a million children at its home base at the Midlands Arts Centre and many more on tour in the UK and Europe in over 54 productions. These feature all kinds of puppet figures, from small hand-held ones to large elaborate rod puppets and masks, all of which are designed and constructed in the theatre's own workshops. Material includes original scripts written specially for the company as well as adaptations based on music, folk literature and classical children's literature. Do not hold general auditions. Advertise for actors in *The Stage*, and welcome casting queries from actors/puppeteers who can sing. Write with CV and photograph in the first instance.

Carib Theatre Productions

See **Touring companies**.

Contact Theatre Company

See **Repertory and regional theatres**.

DAC

See **Touring companies**.

Forest Forge Theatre Company

See **Touring companies**.

Globe Players Theatre Company

36 St James Avenue, Hampton Hill, Middx TW12 1HH
Tel (081) 979 5497

Shakespeare and fairy stories only, for touring to schools throughout the London area. Welcome queries from actors in October, when they are casting for the busy Christmas season which runs from November through December, with seven companies of 5–6 actors on the road. Write or phone in the first instance. Queries at any other time of year will be referred to October.

Gog Theatre Company Ltd

See **Touring companies**.

Graeae

See **Touring companies**.

Greenwich Young People's Theatre Ltd

Burrage Road, Plumstead, London SE18 7JZ
Tel (081) 854 1316 and 855 4911
Artistic director Chris Vine

Theatre-in-Education (TIE) programmes for primary, secondary and further education audiences; youth theatre and arts workshops for an age range of 7–25 years. Perform in the Greenwich Young People's Theatre Centre (studio), schools, colleges, community venues. Advertise for actors in *The Stage*, the *Guardian* media page, *Asian Times* and *The Voice*. Do not welcome casting queries as all auditions are advertised as vacancies occur (on average, twice yearly). Do not require teaching qualifications, but 'a commitment to work with young people is essential and knowledge of education/teaching strategies an advantage. All actors are full company members with a role in developing the artistic and educational policy of the company. They are required to run workshops as well as perform. GYPT is a multi-racial company and equal opportunities employer. Policy development is towards diversity of cultural forms, and content that is educationally and socially relevant to inner-city young people.'

Half Moon Young People's Theatre

Dame Colet House, Ben Jonson Road, London E1 3NH
Tel (071) 265 8138
Artistic director Deborah Bestwick

Theatre-in-Education (TIE), young people's and touring community productions for an audience age range of 5 to 25. Perform in schools and community centres. Open-ended Equity contracts with an average company of four actors. Do not require teaching qualifications, but look for workshop and devising experience and a genuine interest in education. An ability to speak Bengali is very helpful. Advertise for actors in *The Stage*, *The Voice*, *Asian Herald* and *Surma*. As they have a small turnover of actors, do not welcome casting queries unless they have advertised; unable to maintain casting files. Hold auditions 'when necessary – about twice a year'.

Leicester Haymarket Youth Theatre

See **Repertory and regional theatres**.

M6 Theatre Company

See **Touring companies**.

Magic Carpet Theatre

18 Church Street, Sutton-on-Hull, N. Humberside HU7 4TS
Tel (0482) 709939
Artistic director Jon Marshall

Children's theatre productions and shows for family audiences performed in schools, theatres, arts centres, civic halls, village halls and out-of-doors. Company of four on one-year contracts; pay Equity rates. Occasionally advertise in *The Stage*, but welcome casting queries from actors. Approach in writing in the first instance. Do not require teaching qualifications – 'much of our work is based on circus and magical skills.'

Magic Roundabout Theatre Company

See **Touring companies**.

Merseyside Young People's Theatre Company

5 Hope Street, Liverpool L1 9BH
Tel (051) 708 0877
Artistic director Cathy Hawkes

Founded 1978. Tour schools and other venues in the Merseyside region, playing to audiences from 3 to 18 years old. In 1981, Willy Russell was commissioned to write *Blood Brothers* for the company. New plays, workshops and special emphasis on development of theatre for under-fives. Company of four or five actors on Equity contracts. Welcome casting queries from actors. The company operates on a local staffing policy. Letters and details are kept on file. Teaching qualifications not essential but require actors who have experience of working with children.

Molecule Theatre of Science for Children

Bloomsbury Theatre, 15 Gordon Street,
London WC1H 0AH
Tel (071) 388 5739 Fax (071) 388 5739
Producer Lally Carlton-Jones

Founded 1967. Tour scientific adventure plays for 7- to 11-year-olds to middle-scale theatres (one tour annually). Also a Theatre-in-Education company playing to 11- to 13-year olds in schools and museums. Company of ten actors for the middle-scale tour, and five actors for the TIE tours; all on Equity contracts. Advertise in *SBS*. Letters enclosing details should be sent only in May/June.

National Youth Theatre of Great Britain

443/445 Holloway Road, London N7 6LW
Tel (071) 281 3863
Artistic director Edward Wilson

Founded 1956 by Michael Croft who was the company's director until his death in 1986. Starting in the East End of London, the NYT proved so successful that soon young people from all over the country were applying to join. It reached the West End in 1959 and, in 1960, was given national status and financial support by the Department of Education and Science, which has grant-aided it ever since.

The NYT's record has been one of continual development and expansion, despite limited resources. It now presents an annual season of both contemporary and classical plays in London every summer, and has toured abroad many times with the British Council to such places as Moscow Art Theatre and Valencia's Principal Theatre. The NYT also mounts national and regional tours performing in such venues as the Tramway, Glasgow; Buxton Opera House and Cambridge Arts Theatre. From its earliest days, it has also played a key role in developing youth theatre in the provinces, and has helped to set up many of the over 800 regional youth theatres in Great Britain.

The NYT's aims are to give young people practical experience of the theatre, to set them high standards and, in doing so, offer them a valuable form of teamwork. Membership is open to young people aged between 14 and 21. Selection is by interview and audition, but the latter is often of secondary importance. Members are often selected because they have lively personalities or show qualities that seem to be suited to the teamwork essential in the NYT. It is hoped that technical members will show more evidence of ability, but this is not essential. Applications should be made in October of each year.

Comment
The 1988 NYT production of *The Caucasian Chalk Circle* attracted praise from reviewers, including John Coldstream of the *Daily Telegraph*: '. . . There is much to relish in the revitalization of this admirable troupe, now 32 years old and buffeted by the fates – above all, by the death in 1986 of its irrepressible founder, Michael Croft. A new permanent home has opened in the Holloway Road; there is miraculous talk of Arts Council support; Sainsbury's provide trolleyloads of fivers; and, to judge by the contingent at present mustered under Mr

Wilson's firm hand in WC1, morale is high.'

Oily Cart Company

209 Welsbach, Wandsworth Business
Village, Broomhill Road,
London SW18 4JQ
Tel (081) 877 0743

Comedy, puppet shows, participation plus day-long interactive drama projects at special schools. Shows for under 5s, 7- to 11-year-olds and mentally handicapped children aged 5–16. Perform in nursery schools, playgroups, one o'clock clubs, community centres, schools, arts centres, theatres, language units, libraries, festivals, etc. Company of three actors on contracts of varying lengths; pay Equity rates. Advertise in *The Stage*, and only audition in response to adverts.

Pandemonium Theatre

13 Royal Stuart Workshops, Adelaide
Street, Cardiff CF1 6BR
Tel (0222) 482821
Artistic director Paul Bassett

Perform to primary school children – infant and junior. 'We aim to produce entertaining pieces of live theatre to the primary age range (3–12). All of our plays have an educational content, but we are not TIE [Theatre-in-Education].' Recent productions: *The Forest of Fortune*; *In Lincoln Green*; *Alice in Wonderland*; *Through The Looking Glass*. Three companies of ten actors tour nationally during school terms; 12-week contracts, renewable if required (non-Equity). Advertise in *The Stage*, and welcome casting queries from actors. Approach in writing in the first instance.

Pilot Theatre

Old Woodhouse 1st School, Wakefield
Road, Normanton, Wakefield
WF6 1BB
Tel (0924) 220406

Annual performance project touring schools/colleges/youth clubs/small scale venues. Numerous community projects based in the Wakefield area with minority groups. The Company employs 1 full time administrator – 4 permanent company members on fixed contracts. Pilot Theatre is a company limited by guarantee with a board of directors who implement all major artistic policy and financial decisions. The Company is a member of ITC and all actors are members of Equity. Advertise for actors in *The Stage*, *Northern Star* and *The Voice*: do not welcome casting queries. Auditions held when Company members unavailable. Teaching qualifications not required but a genuine commitment to the Company's work is essential.

Pit Prop Theatre

See **Touring companies**.

Polka Children's Theatre

240 The Broadway, Wimbledon,
London SW19 1SB
Tel (081) 542 4258
Artistic director Vicky Ireland

Full stage productions for children and young people, including musicals and straight drama. Audience age range of 3 years to early teens, performing in main theatres. Company of six, contracted per production (approximately two months); pay Equity rates. Advertise in *SBS*, and do not welcome casting queries from actors. General auditions are held once a year, with restricted auditions per production. Teaching qualifications are not required; they look for skills in mime and movement, mask work, puppetry, singing and musical skills.

Quicksilver Theatre for Children

4 Enfield Road, London N1 5AZ
Tel (01) 241 2932
Artistic director Guy Holland

Founded 1978. Tour 2–3 productions per year for the 3–5, 5–9 and 7–11 age ranges. Tours of 8–12 weeks, one or two shows daily; perform in schools, community and arts centres, small- and middle-scale theatres in London and the regions. Company of 3–6 actors on contracts of 12–16 weeks' duration; pay ITC/Equity small-scale touring rates. Advertise in *The Stage* and *SBS* – send letter and CV. 'As a member of ITC, Quicksilver Theatre is committed to a policy of integrated casting, and actively seeks applicants from ethnic minorities.'

Rainbow Theatre Company

See **Touring companies**.

Red Ladder Theatre Company

Cobden Avenue, Lower Wortley,
Leeds LS12 5PB
Tel (0532) 792228

Socialist, feminist company performing to young people in youth clubs and similar venues. Tours nationally and in West Yorkshire. Productions include: *One of Us*; *The Best*; *Bhangra*

Girls; *Who's Breaking*; *Breaking the Silence*; *The Scrappie*. Advertise in *The Stage*. Welcome queries from individual actors, for specific productions. Particularly anxious to hear from disabled actors. Write with CV, photograph and SAE. Details kept on file.

Royal Court Young People's Theatre

309 Portobello Road, London
W10 5TD
Tel (081) 960 4641
Artistic director Elyse Dodgson

Youth theatre productions. Perform in community venues. *The Royal Court Young People's Theatre never requires actors*: 'Actors – especially drama school leavers – think it appropriate to write to the company [but it] is a non-professional organization for young people.'

Salamander Theatre

Hogarth School, Duke Road,
London W4 2JR
Tel (081) 994 4969

Run co-operatively by the actor-/teachers and the administrator, Salamander provides TIE plays and workshops, with a particular interest in those for whom English is a second language. Perform in schools, colleges, special schools, community centres, libraries, parks, small theatres and arts centres. Equity rates. Advertise in *The Stage*, and welcome casting queries from actors – 'all applications are given equal consideration.' Approach in writing in the first instance. Require actors to have teaching qualifications – 'but not every company member has to be a teacher. Languages are a help, also musical skills. We like actors with all-round skills: acting/musical and physical.'

Scottish Youth Theatre

The Old Atheneum Theatre,
179 Buchanan Street, Glasgow
G1 2JZ
Tel (041) 332 5127
Artistic director Robin Peoples

Offers young people, 12–21, the chance to take part in most aspects of performance, working with theatre professionals, as a means of encouraging self, social, and artistic development. Extensive Summer Festival, workshops, classes and projects available throughout Scotland.

Professional company Skint Knees produces educational theatre for primary and pre-school kids. (See separate entry).

Skint Knees

The Old Atheneum Theatre,
179 Buchanan Street, Glasgow
G1 2JZ
Tel (041) 332 5127
Artistic director Robin Peoples

The professional company of the Scottish Youth Theatre, providing educational and entertaining theatre for primary and pre-school children. Launched in June 1990, the company immediately won critical acclaim. It provides projects and workshops for special-needs children, tours, and performs at the Atheneum Theatre. Queries should be in writing, with photograph, CV and SAE.

Snap Theatre Company

Millars One House, Southmill Road,
Bishop's Stortford, Herts. CM23 3DH
Tel (0279) 504095/503066
Artistic director A.M. Graham

Schools-based project residencies, youth club workshops, infant, primary and junior school programmes, small-scale tours and national children's, adults and family theatre tours. Perform in schools, arts centres, village halls, youth clubs, small- and middle-scale theatres. New adaptations of novels/stories and new plays. Starting to work with European Children's Theatre Companies. Company of 3–25 on contracts which range in length from 6 to 20 weeks; pay Equity rates. Advertise for actors in *The Stage*, *SBS* and *Rep Report*. Welcome casting queries from actors; approach in writing in the first instance. Hold auditions four times a year. Teaching qualifications 'useful but not essential'. 'Prepare audition pieces most suited to you. Gain as much experience as you can in working with young people – i.e. youth clubs, schools, etc. Skills: mime (drama school alone won't do), musical instruments an advantage, ability to sing, devising and improvisation skills essential, drivers preferred. State on application why the interest apart from the job prospects. Send SAE and *up-to-date* photo. Arrive on time; phone if any problems. Files on actors are only kept if actors up-date Snap's administration – i.e. a postcard on what they've been doing.'

Soapbox Theatre Company

Durning Hall, Earlham Grove, Forest Gate, London E7 9AB
Tel (081) 519 4394
Artistic director Russell Allen

Educational theatre for young people aged 3 to 17 years old. Perform in schools and community venues. Company of four actors on 12-week contracts; pay Equity rates. Advertise in *The Stage*, and welcome ('within reason') casting queries from actors; approach in writing in the first instance. Auditions held twice a year. Teaching qualifications not required but 'an advantage'. 'We have a policy of mixed race and gender casting.'

TAG (Theatre About Glasgow)

Citizens Theatre, Gorbals, Glasgow G5 9DS
Tel (041) 429 2877
Artistic director Alan Lydiard

Founded 1967. Perform new plays, small-scale adaptations of Shakespeare, plays for primary and secondary schools as well as plays for adults. 'The plays must have a strong storyline and reflect aspects of modern life, and are produced in a strong visual way.' Venues range from school halls to 2000-seat theatres. School tours are usually in the Strathclyde region, and adult tours all over Scotland, Northern Ireland and the north of England. Recent productions: *Dancer* by John Harvey; *Sailmaker* by Alan Spence; *Twelfth Night*; *From Glasgow to Saturn* based on the poetry of Edwin Morgan. Average company of eight actors on 12-week Equity contracts. Do not advertise for actors, and do not particularly welcome casting queries, as 'we usually cast inside Scotland.' Will consider letter with CV, photo and SAE.

Taking Steps Community Theatre Co. Ltd

c/o 24 Turves Green, Northfield, Birmingham, B31 4AA
Tel (021) 475 1921
Artistic director Karen Benjamin

Perform Theatre-in-Education (TIE), street theatre and circus in schools, youth clubs, community centres and out-of-doors. Audience age range of 5–90, with school ages of 6–11 and 12–16 years. Company of two or three on 10/12-week contracts; pay Equity rates 'when on contract'. Sometimes advertise in *The Stage*, and welcome casting queries from actors; send letter giving full details. Auditions held annually. Do not require actors to have teaching qualifications, but sometimes need teaching experience or circus skills – depending on tour.

Theatre Centre

Hanover School, Noel Road, London N1 8BD
Tel (071) 354 0110 Fax (071) 359 7562
Artistic director Libby Mason

Theatre Centre is Britain's longest established young people's theatre company, touring schools and small scale venues nationally and internationally. The performing companies are supported by an education unit, which develop written educational resource material and workshops. The company commissions up to five new plays a year for young people. Audience age range: 4–8, 9–14, 15–18. Presently, actors are engaged on short term contracts. Auditions are held annually, with periodic special auditions for specific projects, advertised in *The Stage*, *Asian Times* and *The Voice*. Theatre Centre positively welcomes applications from Asian/African and Afro-Caribbean people. The company does not discriminate on the grounds of gender, sexual orientation or physical disability.

Theatre West Glamorgan/Gorllewin Morgannwg

Unit 3, Millands Road Industrial Estate, Neath, SA11 1NJ
Tel (0639) 641771
Artistic director Tim Baker

Theatre-in-Education (TIE) for junior schools and secondary schools in English and Welsh language; community theatre productions in English and Welsh languages touring throughout Wales. Company of 7 on one-year or single-tour contracts; Equity rates. Advertise for actors in *The Stage*, the *Guardian*, *Western Mail* and *Y Cymro*. Welcome casting queries – send letter explaining interest in this field of work. Auditions held annually, although the present company has been maintained for six years. Teaching qualifications not required, but look for 'talent and musical ability'. The company's policy is very locally based – 'members need an interest and commitment to Wales and the Welsh language. The company writes its own material, therefore writing/devising skills are necessary. Singing skills (not necessarily trained) are almost essential, musical skills an advantage. Operate an equal-wage policy for all members. Any interested actors welcome to write for "package"

including details of nature of work and company policy.'

Theatr Powys

See **Touring companies**.

Theatre Workshop Edinburgh

See **Touring companies**.

Unicorn Theatre

6/7 Great Newport Street, London WC2H 7JB
Tel (071) 379 3280
Artistic director Richard Williams

Leading London young people's theatre company which produces plays 'that help children understand their world and gain power within it'. Audience age ranges from 4 to 12 years old. Perform in their own theatre in Great Newport Street. Average number of actors in the company is six. Try to cross cast as much as possible. Equity contracts. Do not usually advertise for actors, but welcome letters enclosing CV and photograph, which are kept on file. Sometimes hold general auditions. Teaching qualifications not required.

Upstream Children's Theatre

Ilderton Primary School, Ilderton Road, London SE16 3LA
Tel (071) 232 2869
Artistic director Rosemary Poole

Founded 1978 as part-time project; became full-time company in 1980. Performances and drama workshops, usually devised by the company, with emphasis on themes of anti-racism, anti-sexism and non-violence for children aged 4 to 11 years old. Perform in infant and junior schools, youth clubs, community play schemes plus the Upstream Theatre. Summer tour to community venues and a Christmas tour to schools plus a week in the Upstream Theatre. Permanent company of three actors – the company is extended according to production requirements. Equity/ITC contracts of varying lengths. Advertise in *The Stage*, *The Voice* and through other companies. Prefer responses to advertisements rather than general enquiries, although the director will meet actors who have a genuine interest in the work of the Upstream Children's Theatre. The company is committed to working as a mixed sex/racial company.

Whirligig Theatre

14 Belvedere Drive, Wimbledon, London SW19 7BY
Tel (081) 947 1732 Fax (081) 879 7648
Artistic directors David Wood & John Gould

Full-length musical plays for children of primary school age. Perform in middle-scale and large theatres at low seat prices. Company of 8 to 12 actors on 12-week contracts; pay Equity rates. Advertise for actors in *SBS* and *PCR*, and welcome casting queries – by letter only. Hold auditions for every production, usually once a year. Do not necessarily require actors with teaching qualifications, but look for

'good acting, singing and moving plus a genuine interest in the work. Please do not approach us if you see children's theatre work as simply a rung on the ladder, a stepping stone to "greater things". The work demands great commitment as well as skills and the ability to be on top form for morning and afternoon performances, working in front of audiences of up to 1500 children. When coming to an audition, it is essential that you have a couple of songs under your belt and do not arrive with no music, or ask to look over the pianist's shoulder. Although we sometimes like people to play musical instruments, an audition is best sung with piano accompaniment provided.'

Zuriya Theatre Company

38 Brixton Road, London SW9 6BT
Tel (071) 582 9479
Artistic director John Adewole

Perform traditional African storytelling, musical and full dramatic productions plus workshops for schools, for audiences from primary school age to further education. Venues include schools, community centres and fringe theatres. Company of six actors on contracts of 3–6 months; Equity/ITC. Advertise for actors in educational and local publications, and also at venues; welcome written casting queries. Teaching qualifications not essential but favour experience of working with children. Musical and dance skills required. Auditions held according to demand.

15 Theatre-in-Education (TIE) Companies

Action Transport Theatre Company

West Cheshire College, Regent Street, Ellesmere Port, South Wirral, L65 8EJ
Tel (051) 357 2120
Administrator Margaret Housley

Action Transport Theatre is a professional Theatre in Education company working in schools, colleges, youth clubs and community venues throughout the county of Cheshire. Recent productions include: *Wounded, Operation Starwatch, Bag Dancing, Billy The Kid*. Write in the first instance with CV, photograph and SAE.

Big Brum Theatre-in-Education Company Ltd

Midlands Arts Centre, Cannon Hill Park, Birmingham B12 9QH
Tel (021) 440 2087
Artistic director Peter Wynne-Willson
Administrator Lynne Carney

TIE programmes for secondary school children (11–18 years), mostly devised but a few commissioned; always aimed specifically at Birmingham schools and colleges. Occasionally perform in studio and community venues. Company of (on average) 3–4 actors on contracts of one term to one year in length; pay above Equity rates. Advertise for actors – usually in the *Birmingham Post & Mail*, local radio and careers services, and sometimes nationally in *The Stage* and *TES*; also in Afro-Caribbean and Asian papers. Particularly welcome casting queries from local Birmingham actors. Approach in writing or by telephone. Only hold workshops and interviews (no auditions) for specific vacancies – on average, twice yearly. Do not specifically require actors with teaching qualifications, but look for teaching *ability*. 'We tend to look much more closely at abilities and instincts than at qualifications. We have always taken on a number of untrained local people alongside more experienced actor/teachers. Acting ability and experience probably come lower down in our priorities than many applicants realize – instinctive grasp of the point of our work, commitment, ability to communicate with young people, suitability for the balance of the company at the time, all these can turn out to be more important. The best actors in the world might be disastrous company members. Genuine feeling for young people in Birmingham is the most sought-after attribute for Big Brum.'

Big Wheel Theatre Company

P.O. Box 461, Oxford OX1 4NL
Tel (0865) 241527
Directors Roland Allen and Jeni Williams

Theatre workshops for schools in Europe. Language and literature workshops in English. Company members employed on short term contracts. Advertise for members in *The Guardian* and *The Stage*. Welcome enquiries – approach in writing in the first instance. Do not require teaching qualifications. 'Performers must be genuinely interested in working with young people. This kind of work is extremely demanding and exhausting, you need an iron constitution and . . . yes . . . a Gorilla sized . . . wait for it . . . sense of humour.'

Cambridge Syllabus Players Ltd

12 Guilford Street, London WC1N 1DT
Tel (071) 242 8672
Artistic director Timothy Seward

Perform plays, adaptations of novels, poetry in connection with GCSE and 'A' Level examination texts for audiences of 12–18-year-olds in school halls and occasionally in theatres or arts centres. Company of seven on contracts for one term, although the actors 'often stay for two or even three terms'; non-Equity. Advertise in *The Stage*, and welcome letters from actors: 'We do not have time to reply to them

as they come in, but examine them all at our next casting session and reply to them all then.' Hold auditions on average once or twice a year, with major auditions usually in August or September. Do not require teaching qualifications. 'We tend to take people who have previous TIE experience and usually some form of drama training, but this is not a hard and fast rule. As members of ITC, we abide by all their rulings with regard to equal opportunities, etc., though we are not as yet an Equity company. We look not only for acting talent but also for a personality that we feel will work well under the exacting conditions of eight- or nine-week tours and will respond in a friendly way to secondary school children. Our workshops always involve close work with students as well as performance.' 1991 will see the start of a sister company working alongside C.S.P., called *The Light Blue Summer Syndicate*. This will also perform work in schools but the emphasis will be upon new work which is less academic, and which will also find audiences in small- to middle-scale venues, drawn from the general public.

Channel Theatre TIE Company

Granville Theatre, Victoria Parade, Ramsgate, Kent CT11 8DG
Tel (0843) 588280
Artistic director Philip Dart

Productions and occasional workshops for infant-to-secondary pupils in Kent schools. No teaching qualifications required. Advertise once a year in *The Stage*, and hold general auditions following that.

Cwmni'r Frân Wen

Coleg Harlech, Harlech, Gwynedd
LL46 2PU
Tel (0766) 780179
Artistic director Carys Huw

TIE company that works through the medium of Welsh in schools and colleges in Gwynedd for 5–18 year olds. Recent projects for the secondary sector have dealt with HIV and AIDS and the ethic of work; and in the primary schools projects dealing with gypsies, language and culture and a scientific project dealing with the environment. Company of three/four actors on three-month contracts; pay Equity rates (MRSL 1). Advertise for actors in *Y Cymro*, *Liverpool Daily Post*, *Western Mail* and *The Stage*. Welcome casting queries from actors; approach in writing in the first instance. Hold auditions once a year.

Cwmni Theatr Outreach Theatre Company

Outreach Theatre Centre, Glanrafon Road, Mold, Clwyd CH7 1PA
Tel (0352) 56331 ext 298
Company manager Stuart Seller

Perform to a wide range in schools, colleges and community venues in Clwyd. 1989/90 Productions included: *Storytelling Stone* (7–9 yrs.), *Carreg Hanesion* (Welsh junior), tour of Wisconsin, U.S.A., *Kachiri* (top infants), *Leonardo* (1st & 2nd year secondary Welsh learners), *The Tempest*

(8–13 yrs.), *The Withered Arm* (community). Usual company of four actor-/teachers; Length of contract varies. Pay Equity rates. Teaching qualifications are useful but not essential. Advertise in *The Stage*, and welcome written casting queries from actors. Auditions held when a vacancy occurs. 'The Company devises a lot of its work, so experience of devising, research and improvisation is important. The Company performs work in English and Welsh, and is interested in hearing from Welsh-speaking performers as well as English-speaking ones. Commitment to T.I.E. and community theatre is essential.'

Electric Theatre Company

21 Slagrove Place, London SE13 7HT
Tel (081) 690 6164 and 314 5676
Artistic directors (partnership) David Zoob, David Annen

TIE for fourth-year GCSE students and above. Programmes mix performance with active participatory drama work. Programmes complement aims and content of exam syllabi. Perform in secondary schools throughout ILEA and surrounding boroughs; occasional performances in youth centres, clubs, etc. Do not advertise, but use actors on other TIE companies' recommendation, via word of mouth and those who contact the company – 'these channels have satisfied requirements in the past.' Approach in writing or by telephone call. Auditions are held 'as required'. Ideally prefer actors with teaching qualifications, devising and administrative ability and a genuine concern and interest in education.

Gazebo Theatre-in-Education Company Ltd

Darlaston Multi-Purpose Centre,
Victoria Road, Darlaston,
W. Midlands WS10 8AP
Tel (021) 526 6877
Artistic director Annie Lambert

TIE programmes for all ages and abilities, serving schools and Youth Clubs within the Wolverhampton & Walsall LEA. Company of seven permanent members, others taken on as required; pay Equity rates. Advertise for actors in *The Stage*. Hold auditions only when, on the rare occasion, a vacancy arises; do not therefore welcome casting queries. Teaching qualifications not a necessity.

Gwent Theatre in Education Company

The Drama Centre, Pen-y-Pound,
Abergavenny, Gwent
Tel (0873) 3167
Artistic director Gary Meredith

Theatre-in-Education projects and Welsh-language productions for infant, junior and secondary schools (6–7; 10–12; 16–18 years); community touring. Perform in schools, village halls, leisure centres, theatres ('we occasionally present "on site" productions – venues to date have included a large country house, a castle and a colliery'). Company of nine. Contracts renewable every six months, but 'we prefer people to stay with us for at least a year – most stay for two or more years.' Pay Equity rates (MRSL 1). Advertise in *The Stage*, Equity *Jobgrapevine* and a circular to all theatre companies in Wales; welcome

casting queries from actors. 'It is important that the letter is detailed and demonstrates clearly the reasons why the writer wants to work in TIE and the qualities they feel they have that make them suitable for this kind of work. Casual enquiries and duplicated letters receive a polite acknowledgement only. As the average length of stay for team members is a couple of years, auditions are infrequent – perhaps once a year or every 18 months. Teaching qualifications are desirable but not essential – a genuine interest in education and working with young people is far more important. We prefer actors to have had some formal professional training. Most of the company's work is devised and written by the team under the direction of the artistic director. Strong performing skills are essential, as well as devising skills or the desire to develop them. Music plays an important part in our work, and although it is not a requirement for anyone seeking work with the company to be able to play a musical instrument, it is important that they are able to sing reasonably well. We welcome visitors; anyone wishing to see our work should contact our administrator, Julia Davies, to arrange a visit.'

Humberside Theatre in Education

Hessle High School, Lower School,
Boothferry Road, Hessle, nr Hull
HU13 9AR
Tel (0482) 640876
Director Amanda J. Smith

Perform existing work, new work and company-devised shows for 5–18-

year-olds in schools. Company of four actor/teachers on contracts that vary from short to long term; pay Equity/ITC rates. Advertise for actors in *The Stage, Minority Arts Advisory Service Job Bulletin* and ITC *Job Bulletin*. Do not necessarily require actors with teaching qualifications, although 'educational background/experience may be useful.' Welcome casting queries and will keep CVs on file; hold auditions when necessary. 'The company works as a cooperative. Members have to: take responsibility; be honest and open; work under pressure and as a team; be fair; challenge in a creative way.'

Learning Through Action

Learning Through Action Centre, Cumberland Road, Reading, Berks. RG1 3JY
Tel (0734) 665556
Director Annette Cotterill

Team of seconded teachers studying for the Learning Through Action Diploma (awarded by University of Reading) introducing active learning/cross-curricular projects into schools throughout Berkshire and the U.K. Separate programmes devised for infant, junior and secondary schools. At least three programmes are presented each year and the scope of subject matter is very wide – emphasis is always placed on multi-cultural and conservation related issues. Teaching qualifications required. Do not advertise and do not welcome casting queries from actors. Teachers use role play and artefacts to create simulated environments that facilitate learning.

Skin and Bones Theatre Company

Skin and Bones Theatre Collective, Ouseburn Warehouse Workshops, Lime Street, Newcastle upon Tyne NE1 2PN
Tel (091) 232 3276
Contact George Smyth

Productions for young people including TIE, participatory work and pantomime in schools, colleges and community centres. Audience age range of 3–18 years. Company of six on an initial contract of 3–6 months, often extended, with the possibility of a permanent contract; pay Equity rates. Do not usually advertise for actors. Do not object to receiving casting queries from actors, but 'cannot often respond'. Approach in writing in the first instance. Usually hold auditions once a year. Teaching qualifications would be an advantage. 'Find out something about us before applying. CVs which just list the parts you have played are of no use to us. We value other experience – other jobs, voluntary work, etc. – as well as acting experience. Tell us about it.'

The Theatre Company Blah Blah Blah

48 Harold Mount, Leeds LS6 1PW
Tel (0532) 754091
Artistic director None – 'artistic decisions are taken by the company'

Junior and senior programmes for schools and youth clubs (ages: 5–7, 7–11, 14 upwards). 'We devise our own shows, and would expect any person joining the company to enter into the devising process. The content of the show reflects questions that company members confront in their work and which are then tested against the age range for which we devise the show.' Average company of four actors on three-month contracts; non-Equity. Advertise in *The Stage*, and do not welcome general casting queries from actors. Hold auditions annually. Teaching qualifications required or 'at least a good knowledge of theories of learning'.

Theatre of Fact

Stantonbury Campus, Stantonbury, Milton Keynes, Bucks. MK14 6BN
Tel (0908) 322568
Artistic director Roy Nevitt

Issue-based TIE plays and participatory programmes for 9–16-year-olds. Perform in schools, small-scale theatres and community centres. Company of four actors on 14-week contracts; Equity rates. Advertise for actors in *The Stage*. Welcome casting queries from actors; approach by telephone call in the first instance. Auditions held as necessary – once or twice a year. Teaching qualifications not required.

TIE Break Theatre in Education

St William's Primary School, St William's Way, Norwich NR7 0AJ
Tel (0603) 39965
Artistic director David Farmer

Production themes include disability, conservation, racism, prejudice, sexism and local history for an audience age range of 5 to 25 years. Perform in schools, youth clubs and arts centres. Company of 3–6 on contracts that vary from two months to a year; pay Equity rates. Advertise in *The Stage*, and prefer to hear from actors only in response to these adverts. Auditions held, on average, twice a year. Teaching qualifications not always required, but welcome drama or teacher training and preferably some experience in TIE/YPT. 'We look for company members who have good experience in TIE/YPT or who wish to make this their chosen area of work.'

16 TIE Companies attached to Rep/Regional Theatres

Belgrade Theatre in Education Company

Belgrade Theatre, Belgrade Square,
Coventry CV1 1GS
Tel (0203) 56431

Half-day, whole-day and multi-visit TIE programmes: 'A combination of performance pieces, workshops and participation in role work.' Audience age ranges from 4 to 18. Perform in school halls and classrooms, with occasional performances in the Belgrade Studio Theatre. Average size of the company is 13, pay above MRSL 2. Advertise in *The Stage*; hold auditions when a company member leaves. 'Applications are helped if they are accompanied by a letter clearly stating the applicant's ideas on and commitment to TIE and education, and why they have applied to this company in particular.' Do not require teaching qualifications – however, 'such applicants might be viewed with more interest.'

Duke's Theatre in Education Company

Duke's Playhouse, Moor Lane,
Lancaster LA1 1QE
Tel (0524) 67461
Artistic director Warwick Dobson

A range of productions for primary and secondary school children (7–18 years), including *The Big Lie*; *Voices In The Crowd*; *In Good Faith*; and *Killing Time*. Perform in schools. Company of five actor/teachers on open-ended permanent contracts; pay Equity rates. Advertise in *The Stage*; do not generally welcome casting queries from actors as they only hold auditions as and when a vacancy occurs, which is not often. Teaching qualifications are a 'decided advantage' as is a degree. 'If young actors are *genuinely* interested in TIE, they should take every opportunity to see companies at work. (From our point of view this is the best kind of preliminary approach.)'

Harrogate Theatre-in-Education

Harrogate Theatre, Oxford Street,
Harrogate, N. Yorks. HG1 1QF
Tel (0423) 502710
Artistic director Nobby Dimon

Biased towards role-play and inter-active drama, but do occasionally mount 'plays' for young people. Audience age ranges from 5 to 18. Perform in schools in North Yorkshire; and to adult audiences in village halls. Average size of company is three, with an average contract length of eight weeks; pay Equity rates. Welcome casting queries from actors; approach in writing in the first instance. 'Pro-forma letters such as the drama schools seem to encourage, with a string of productions listed and parts played, are, as far as we are con-cerned, useless without a letter which gives us some idea about the person behind the boring statistics, his or her attitudes to TIE, children, hopes, fears, etc.' Do not exclusively require actors with teaching qualifications but do prefer them: 'Improvisational skills essential.'

Leeds Theatre-in-Education

The New West Yorkshire Playhouse,
Quarry Hill Mount, Leeds, LS9 8AW
Tel (0532) 442145

Present company-devised pro-grammes plus some scripted work. Advertise in *The Stage* and *Leeds Other Paper*; do not welcome casting queries from actors – 'we only advertise when we need to replace a company member.'

Palace-go-Round Outreach

Palace Theatre, 430 London Road,
Westcliff-on-Sea, Essex SS0 9LA
Tel (0702) 347816
Artistic director Christopher Dunham

Tours of Infant, Junior, Senior Schools and Old People's Homes.

Roundabout Theatre Company

Nottingham Playhouse, Wellington
Circus, Nottingham NG1 5AF
Tel (0602) 474361
Artistic co-ordinator Fraser Dunworth

Founded in 1973, this is the TIE and community touring company of Nottingham Playhouse whose aim is 'to use theatre as a medium for learn-ing'. Play to schoolchildren from 5 to 18 years, including those with special needs; there is also a community tour through Nottinghamshire and the East Midlands to non-theatre-going aud-iences. Six TIE programmes per year plus one tour. Productions include: *Fen* and *Do As You're Told*. Company of up to eight actors; core company on open-ended contracts (having com-pleted probationary period) and free-lance on fixed-term contracts; 56 days' notice, TMA/Equity Esher TIE contract – MRSL II. Advertise in *The Stage*, actors' centres, the black press and through other TIE companies. Prefer letters from actors only in response to advertisements. Do not require teach-ing qualifications.

Royal Theatre-in-Education Company

Royal Theatre, Guildhall Road,
Northampton NN1 1EA
Tel (0604) 27566
Artistic director Gavin Stride

Tour schools in the county, and studio work at the Royal, playing to four age ranges between years 4 to 18. Also community shows each year, touring village halls. Average company of two to five actors on Equity contracts, usually of twelve weeks. Advertise for actors in *The Stage*, and welcome casting queries, 'although we do not keep extensive files'. The company operates a 'rolling rep' system. Do not require teaching qualifications.

Salisbury Playhouse Theatre-in-Education Company

Malthouse Lane, Salisbury, Wilts.
SP2 7RA
Tel (0722) 320117
Associate director/YPT Lynn Wyfe

Tour schools in Wiltshire, Dorset and part of Hampshire, playing to children from 5 to 18 years old. Company of four actors on Equity contracts of 6–9 months. Sometimes advertise in *The Stage*. Hold auditions once a year. Welcome casting queries from actors; approach in writing in the first instance, enclosing CV, photograph and SAE. Teaching qualifications not 'entirely' essential.

Sheffield Crucible Education Department

Crucible Theatre, 55 Norfolk Street,
Sheffield S1 1DA
Tel (0742) 760621
Artistic director Lawrence Till

Education support to main house productions. All casting is through central casting at the Crucible. Welcome letters enclosing CV and photograph, expressing interest in the Education Department.

Thorndike Young People's Theatre Company

Thorndike Theatre, Church Street,
Leatherhead, Surrey KT22 8DF
Tel (0372) 363729
Artistic director Beth Wood

Tour primary and secondary schools twice a year (autumn and spring terms) – workshops as well as performances. Average company of 4/5 actors on Equity contracts of 8–10 weeks. Hold general auditions once a year – usually in September. Welcome casting queries from actors; approach in writing, enclosing CV and photograph. Do not require teaching qualifications.

Tynewear Theatre in Education

67a Westgate Road, Newcastle upon
Tyne, NE1 1SG
Tel (091) 232 3366
Fax (091) 261 9699
Artistic director Christopher Bostock

Infant, junior and secondary projects plus pre-school shows and projects for young people with severe learning difficulties. Audience age ranges from 3 to 18+. Perform in school and community venues plus small studio theatres. Average company of 4–8 performers; Equity contract of three months' to one year's duration. Advertise in *The Stage*, and hold auditions once or twice a year. Welcome casting queries from actors either by telephone or letter. Do not necessarily require actors with teaching qualifications, but musical skills are 'useful'.

Watford Palace Theatre in Education

Theatreyard, Grosvenor Road,
Watford WD1 2QT
Tel (0923) 33439/35455 ext 48

Plays, participatory drama and teachers' workshops. Perform mainly in schools, community venues and youth clubs (community show planned). Audience age ranges from 5 upwards. Company of four actors with contracts of 9–46 weeks; pay Equity rates. Advertise in *The Stage* and various ethnic-minority papers; do not particularly welcome casting queries from actors. Hold auditions 'once a year whenever possible; try to do all casting in July.' Teaching qualifications not essential. 'When applying to the company, a full letter of application is preferred, detailing why the actor wishes to work in TIE.'

Wolsey Theatre-in-Education

Wolsey Theatre, Civic Drive, Ipswich,
Suffolk IP1 2AS
Tel (0473) 226092
Director Andrew Breakwell

Policy and programmes: actors employed on termly contracts; salary above Equity. Programmes usually have some element of participation either in the form of workshops or simulations; experience of children, young people and schools therefore desirable. Particularly interested in enquiries from older actors interested in TIE, and have strong commitment to multi-racial casting. Recent work includes: *Wild Child* (4–6 yr. olds), *Journey to Jo'burg* (8–12), *Message In A Bottle* (Health Ed. for 14+).

17 *Film, Video and Independent Production Companies*

This is the area in which the humblest and least well-known actor has the ability to make large sums of money (sometimes for very little apparent effort) and to become a nationally-recognised face, by apparently random casting in a successful television commercial. The unpredictable success of some beer and coffee advertising has led to tiny but perfectly-formed television soap-operas, continuing the adventures of the same product-related actors, sometimes over several years.

Success of this kind truly is random. Access to casting-sessions is normally only at the invitation of independent casting directors, frequently at very short notice. If you are not represented by an agent, there is little chance of such an invitation. It is vital for the actor to glean as much information as possible about the character, and the story-line and style of the commercial. Try your best to dress the part, and take some thought as to how to present yourself. You will then find yourself in a room full of identical actors, identically dressed, behaving identically: this can be unnerving. There is likely to follow the briefest encounter with a number of strangers, while you sit under a spotlight being video-taped and photographed. If you are lucky enough to be chosen, you will be told very quickly, usually within a day. The criteria for selection are beyond the ken of almost everybody; the only sensible advice is try to look right for the part, maintain your humour, and keep your fingers crossed.

The film industry can also lead to substantial rewards and very great fame, but rarely for no apparent effort. Again, access is though the casting director. Quite some time will be devoted to casting for any major film, and competition will be fierce for even the smallest role. There is however always a demand for the young and beautiful, and in this category experience is not so important. Established British actors

244

are much sought-after for supporting roles in large-budget motion pictures. There are examples aplenty of British star actors who are not dependent on stereotyped looks and performances, and these provide example and encouragement for all. Casting – especially in the initial stages – may involve nothing more than an informal chat. It is only sensible to do what homework you can, and to dress appropriately.

Lower-budget films and corporate training-material provide a less pressurized (and less highly-paid) opportunity. Again, these are mostly available through casting directors and agents, but many independent film and audio-visual production companies keep files on actors and are happy to be contacted. Working for such companies can provide a very decent income. For quite a lot of these productions, actors should expect to provide their own costume, usually smart business-wear.

Many actors accustomed to the theatre find the practices of film-making disorientating and discouraging. The understandable tendency to cast to type for film sometimes seems to be carried to an excess where the acting ability of actors is simply ignored. Actors can also feel completely without guidance as to what is wanted from them, frustrated by lack of rehearsal, and frustrated by lack of contact with the director.

Because film and video is a technology-dominated medium, a vast percentage of available energy and imagination has to be expended on the machinery. Directors tend to have more experience and understanding of picture composition, than of working with actors. In any case they will not have the time available to deal with actors, in the way that a theatre director would. Actors must accept that they must be very self-reliant. Camera operators can frequently give very sound advice about the technical requirements of a particular shot, and a chance to study play-back monitors can prove invaluable.

Student films can be a useful way to learn about acting to a camera, but you are unlikely to be paid for appearing in them.

Voice-overs

Voice-over work for commercials, dubbing for film, and the like, is a highly lucrative area. Consequently it is fiercely competitive and very difficult to break into. A demo-tape is crucial, and to be effective this must be professionally produced. This will not be cheap. If the demo tape is successful, and work comes your way (normally through the efforts of a specialist agent) you will need to be a brilliant sight-reader capable of instant performance without direction or rehearsal. Great powers of concentration, stamina, inventiveness and unflappability are required.

ANV Productions

47a Kendal Street, London W2 2BV
Tel (071) 262 3074
Contact Antony Norris

Film and video business TV; corporate and training programmes. Always use casting directors. Do not welcome casting queries from actors, but will consider demo tapes for voice-overs.

AVC Group

Walters Farm Road, Tonbridge, Kent
TN9 1QT
Tel (0732) 365107 Fax (0732) 362600
Telex 95586 PROBES G
Contact Brian Darnley

Video – corporate and training. Always use casting directors, and do not welcome queries from individual actors.

AVP

School Hill Centre, Chepstow, Gwent
NP6 5PH
Tel (0291) 625439 Fax (0291) 279671
Contact Laurence Nauen

Film and video – documentary, training, educational. Always use casting directors. Do not welcome casting queries from actors. Occasional voice-over opportunities, but do not welcome unsolicited demo tapes.

Abacus Film Productions Ltd

31 Shelton Street, London WC2H 9HT
Tel (071) 240 1277 Fax (071) 836 7014
Contact Ron Trainer

TV commercials, documentaries, corporate videos. Usually use casting directors. Do not welcome casting queries from actors, but will consider demo tapes or video show reels. Advice to newcomers: 'Keep in touch with casting directors; get a good agent. Demo tapes are important.'

Acme Arts Ltd

12 Vauxhall Grove, London SW8 1SY
Tel (071) 735 9099
Contact Jim Field

Horticultural and educational films for TV and video. Do not welcome enquiries from individual actors.

Aisling Films

Lyndon House, 112–4 Lisburn Road,
Belfast BT 6AH
Tel (0232) 661638 Fax (0232) 661614
Contact Bill Miskelly

Documentary and drama film. *Output*: *End of the World Man* (BBC children's drama serial); *In the Name of God* (Channel 4 documentary); *Hidden Ground-Maurice Leitch*. Use casting directors, but also welcome casting queries from actors. Will consider demo tapes and video show reels.

Allied Stars

17 Waterloo Place, London SW1 4SR
Tel (071) 839 5285
Contact E.M. Fayed

Feature films. *Output*: *Chariots of Fire*; *Breaking Glass*; *F/X Murder by Illusion*; *Government Issue*; *Rocket*; *F/X 2*.

Amber Films

5 Side (rear), Newcastle upon Tyne
NE1 3JE
Tel (091) 232 2000
Contact Peter Roberts, Murray Martin, Ellin Hare

Broadcast and non-broadcast video; broadcast film drama and documentary. *Output*: *Byker* (Channel 4 documentary); *Seacoal* and *T. Dan Smith* (Channel 4 docu-drama features); a ten-part series *Shields Stories*, and a full-length feature *In Fading Light*. Welcome casting queries from actors. Approach by letter in the first instance. Occasional voice-over opportunities; will consider demo tapes. 'Our work is almost exclusively based in the north-east of England, concentrating on subjects rooted in contemporary working-class life. Actors with this kind of background are therefore obviously of main interest to us.'

The Animation Partnership Ltd and Carl Gover Associates

8 Percy Street, London W1P 9FB
Tel (071) 636 3300 Fax (071) 580 9153 Telex 297002
Contact Carl Gover

Film, video and TV – documentary and commercials, with a possibility of forthcoming drama production. Use casting directors, but also welcome casting queries from actors. Prefer to be approached in writing, 'because the information contained in a letter can be filed for future use'. Welcome demo tapes and video show reels. 'Many voice-over opportunities on the animation side of our business because every character needs a voice. Demo tapes are always useful for reference, but video show reels demonstrate the use of the right voice for the appropriate occasion.'

Antelope Films Ltd

3 Fitzroy Square, London W1P 5AH
Tel (071) 387 4454
Fax (071) 388 9935
Telex 266205 AFL G

Makers of TV documentaries. *Output*: *The Triple Crown: The Paradox of the Papacy*; *The Spirit of the Alcazar: 50 Years in a Spanish City*; *Vidal in Venice*; *Heart of the Dragon*, 12-part series on China for Channel 4; *Portrait of Russia*, 7-part series for Turner Broadcasting; *Testament*, 7-part series for Channel 4. Do not normally use actors.

Antonine Productions/ Black Cat Studios

830 Springfield Road, Glasgow G31
Tel (041) 554 4667
Contact Paddy Higson, Mr Smith

Films for TV, feature films, commercials. *Output*: *The Girl in the Picture*, 1985; *Brond*, Channel 4, 1987; *Silent Scream*, 1990. Always use casting directors.

Apple Television

A2 Connaught Business Centre,
Hendon, London NW9 6JL
Tel (081) 205 6687/7514
Contact Ronnie Cairnduff

Videos – corporate, business, commercials, documentary, training films. Use casting directors, but also welcome casting queries from actors. Contact by telephone in the first instance. Welcome demo tapes and video show reels. 'A straight-to-camera photo – updated each year. If an accent is asked for, say no if you can't do it rather than bodge it.'

Aspect Film & Television Production Ltd

36 Percy Street, London W1P 9FG
Tel (071) 636 5303
Fax (071) 436 0666
Contact Catey Sexton

Corporate films and videos. Do not mind receiving casting queries from actors, but do not have many opportunities for them. Send a letter in the first instance. 'Prefer to contact agents.'

Aspen Spafax Television

1 Gayford Road, London W12 9BY
Tel (081) 743 8618
Fax (081) 740 9333 Telex 25221
Contact Mike Raggett, Amanda Thompson

Corporate film and video for promotion, training and communications using presenters, actors and voice-overs. *Output*: promotional dramas for Leeds Building Society; training programmes for British Gas, British Telecom, Marks & Spencer, Woolworth; communications for *Financial Times*, Pearson, TieRack, RHM, Glaxo and Wellcome; commercials for Post Office's QTV. Occasionally use casting directors, but welcome casting queries from actors. Approach by letter in the first instance. Frequent voice-over opportunities; welcome demo tapes and video show reels.

Aurora Sound & Vision

5 Hellesdon Park Road, Norwich
NR6 5DR
Tel (0603) 789509
Contact Steve Bloomfield, Christina Costelloe

Video sales and training films; radio commercials; conference presentations. Welcome casting queries from actors. Approach by letter in the first instance. Will consider demo tapes for voice-overs.

Barclays Bank PLC Video Department

Park House, Station Road,
Teddington, Middx TW11 9AD
Tel (081) 977 8800
Contact Mrs C M Abbassy

Corporate training films. Do not welcome telephone enquiries from individual actors, but will consider voice-over demo tapes or video show-reels if they come with SAE.

BBC Enterprises Ltd

Woodlands, 80 Wood Lane, London
W12 0TT
Tel (081) 576 0216 Fax (081) 743
0393 Telex 934678
Contact Denise Evans (business
affairs director, consumer products)

Responsible for the release of BBC
Video, BBC Record and BBC Radio
Collection titles, usually reflecting
BBC-TV and BBC Radio output. No
outlet for actors apart from occasional
voice-overs. Do not welcome unsolicited demo tapes.

Behr Cinematography

22 Redington Road, London
NW3 7RG
Tel (071) 794 2535
Contact Arnold Behr, Betty Burghes

Documentary, educational and corporate film and video, on subjects
ranging from care of the terminally ill
through sport for the handicapped to
custom building of motor cars. Do not
normally use actors, and find them
through casting directors. Limited use
of voice-overs, and demo-tapes are
welcomed.

Bentorm Ltd

26b Thorney Crescent, London
SW11 3TR
Tel (071) 585 1592
Contact David Deutsch

Films and TV drama. *Output*:
Shakespeare Lives and *Reflections* (Channel 4); *Tales of the Unexpected* (Anglia
TV); *The Chain* (Rank). Always use
casting directors. Do not welcome
casting queries from actors. Welcome
demo tapes and video show reels.

Paul Berriff Productions Ltd

The Chesnuts, Woodfield Lane,
Hessle, N. Humberside HU13 0EW
Tel (0482) 641158
Contact Paul Berriff

TV documentary features. *Output*:
Lakeland Rock for Channel 4; *Lifeboat*
series and *Animal Squad* for BBC1; *Fire*
for BBC *40 Minutes*; *Dianne's Children*
for BBC2; *Rescue* for ITV. Uses casting
directors, and does not welcome
enquiries from individual actors.

Blackrod Ltd

The Chrysalis Building, Bramley Road,
London W10 6SP
Tel (071) 221 2213
Fax (071) 221 6337
Contacts Michael Rodd, Tracey
Garrett

Corporate TV – drama and documentary. Always use casting directors. Do
not welcome casting queries from
actors, but will consider demo tapes
and video show reels.

Matt Boney Associates

'Woodside', Holdfast Lane,
Grayswood, Haslemere, Surrey
GU27 2EU
Tel (0428) 56178
Contact Matt Boney

Video, TV – documentary, commercials, travel and sport. Do not use
actors.

British Film Institute

29 Rathbone Street, London
W1P 1AG
Tel (071) 636 5587
Fax (071) 580 9456
Telex 27624 BFILDNG
Contact Davina Nicholson, Eliza
Mellor

Film, video, drama. *Output: Friendship's Death; On the Black Hill; Distant
Voices/Still Lives; La Deuda Interna.* Use
casting directors. Do not welcome
casting queries from actors. Do not
consider unsolicited demo tapes or
video show reels.

British Lion

Pinewood Studios, Iver, Bucks.
SL0 0NH
Tel (0753) 651700 Telex 847505
Contact Peter Snell (chief executive),
Lesley Keane

Film and TV. *Output: Turtle Diary, Lady
Jane, Prayer for the Dying* (all feature
films); *Tears in the Rain* (Yorkshire TV);
A Man for All Seasons (Turner Network
TV, USA); *Treasure Island;* and *The
Crucifer of Blood.* Use casting directors,
but will respond to casting queries
from actors 'only when in production'.

CHG Communications

108 Clarendon Road, London
W11 2HR
Tel (071) 727 4388
Fax (071) 727 3918
Contact Charlotte Cain, Anthony
Smith

Film, video, TV – drama/documen-
tary, corporate. Occasionally use casting directors, but welcome casting
queries from actors. Approach by letter and follow up with a telephone
call. A lot of opportunities for experienced voice-over actors. Welcome
demo tapes. 'Provide realistic photographs, accurate, well-presented CVs
and a demo tape of your work (if available). We avoid rude agents who have
chips on their shoulders about non-
broadcast programmes.'

CTR Productions

31 Lismore Crescent, Broadfield,
Crawley, W. Sussex RH11 9DA
Tel (0293) 548475
Contact Ian Cunningham, Roseanne
Coils

Video, TV and Radio – documentary,
music, children's, religious. Welcome
casting queries from actors. Approach
in writing in the first instance. Very
occasionally have voice-over opportunities. Will consider demo tapes and
video show reels.

The Callender Company

4th floor, 82 Wardour Street, London
W1V 3LF
Tel (071) 240 8644
Fax (071) 240 8647
Contact Andi Wright

Major drama series and feature films.
Output: The Belly of an Architect (Peter
Greenaway); *The Bretts* (co-produced
with Central TV for Mobil Masterpiece
Theatre).

Carnival (Films and Theatre) Ltd

12 Raddington Road, London
W10 5TG
Tel (081) 968 1818
Contact Brian Eastman

Feature films, drama serials and theatre. *Output: Father's Day* (Channel 4); *Blott on the Landscape* (BBC); *Whoops Apocalypse*; *Porterhouse Blue*; *Traffic*; *Wilt* (film); *Forever Green*; *Poirot*; *Jeeves and Wooster*. Use casting directors, and do not welcome queries from individual actors.

Carpenter Audio Visual

10 Skyport Drive, Harmondsworth,
Middx UB7 0LB
Tel (081) 897 2736
Fax (081) 759 3565
Contact John S. Carpenter

Video – documentaries, drama, training, commercials. Use casting directors, and do not welcome casting queries from actors, but will consider demo tapes and video show reels. 'An appropriate SAE for return of show reels or demo tapes always earns a plus point – but if possible, we like to retain material for future casting.'

Pearl Catlin Associates

16a Carlisle Mansions, Carlisle Place,
London SW1P 1HX
Tel (071) 834 1660
Contact Pearl Catlin, Philip Bond

Film and video – corporate and educational; TV commercials, some programme material. Do not welcome queries from individual actors.

Celador Productions Ltd

39 Long Acre, London WC2E 9JT
Tel (071) 240 8101 Fax (071) 836 1117 Telex 264593 COMCEL G
Contact Paul Smith (managing director)

Primarily specialize in development and production of entertainment programmes for British and international television markets. *Output: Canned Carrot* (BBC); *Everybody's Equal* and *Classic Country* (BSB); *British Oscars* (Sky TV).

Always use casting directors. Do not welcome casting queries from actors.

Centre Films Ltd

118 Cleveland Street, London
W1P 5DN
Tel (071) 387 4045 Fax (071) 388 0408 Telex 23733 CENTRE G
Contact Kent Walwin, Jeffrey Taylor, Derek Granger

Film and TV drama. *Output: Happy Valley* (BBC co-production); *The Four-Minute Mile* (co-production BBC/ABC Australia/CB Films); *Death of a Son* (BBC co-production). Use casting directors, and do not welcome casting queries from actors. 'If actors will insist on writing to us, we would ask that they make their letters clear, short and an enjoyable read, which give some insight into their personality and not just a dry, monotonous list of what they have done (or worse, what they would like to do).' Very limited opportunities for voice-over work. Will consider demo tapes and video show reels.

Charisma Films

Russell Chambers, Covent Garden,
London WC2E 8AA
Tel (071) 379 4267
Contact James Apherton

Contrary to popular belief, do not
make music promos (the company
grew out of Charisma Records).
Theatrical and drama TV producers.
Welcome enquiries from individual
actors.

Cinexsa Film Productions Ltd

209 Manygate Lane, Shepperton,
Middx TW17 9ER
Tel (0932) 225950
Telex 266389 KINLON G
Contact Mr J.E.F. Wright (director)

Film, video, documentary, shorts.
Clients include: British Telecom, Shell
UK Ltd, Manpower Services Commission, St Dunstan's, British Red
Cross Society and RYA Seamanship
Foundation. Use casting directors, but
also welcome casting queries from
actors. Contact by telephone in the
first instance.

Cleveland Productions

5 Rainbow Court, Oxhey, Herts.
WD1 4RP
Tel (0923) 54000
Contact Michael Gosling

Film and video – commercials, corporate, sales, promo programmes. Use
casting directors, but welcome casting
queries from actors. Approach by letter or telephone. Welcome demo tapes
for voice-overs.

Colstar Communications and Entertainment Ltd

11 Wythburn Place, London W1H 5WL
Tel (071) 437 5725
Fax (071) 706 1704
Contact Claire Peterken

Colstar is a producer and international
distributor of broadcast programming
for all media: documentaries, short
films, drama, programme specials and
series. Normally uses casting directors.

Compass Film Productions Ltd

Third floor, 18–19 Warwick Street,
London W1R 5RB
Tel (071) 439 6456
Contact Simon Heaven

Specialists since 1974 in documentary,
educational and promotional programmes for TV and corporate clients.
Output: *Another Way of Life*, on mental
handicap, for Channel 4; *Music of the
Outsiders* for Channel 4. Usually employ casting directors. Do not welcome enquiries from individual actors.

The Crew Multi-Media

186 Monkmoor Road, Shrewsbury,
Salop SY2 5BH
Tel (0743) 233684
Contact Simon Rea

Film, video, TV – documentary, commercials, sales, training, corporate and
feature. Use casting directors, but also
welcome casting queries from actors.
Approach by letter in the first instance. Will consider demo tapes and
video show reels.

Cromdale Films Ltd

12 St Paul's Road, London N1 2QN
Tel (071) 226 0178
Contact Ian Lloyd

Film, video, TV, drama and documentary. *Output*: *The Face of Darkness* (feature film); *Drift to Dawn* (rock music drama); *The Overdue Treatment* (documentary). Usually use casting directors. Do not welcome enquiries from individual actors.

Crystalvision Productions Ltd

Communications House, Blue Riband Estate, Roman Way, Croydon,
Surrey CR9 3RA
Tel (081) 681 7171
Fax (081) 681 2340
Telex 8814079
Contact Julia Bartle (corporate),
Frazer Ashford (broadcast television)

Corporate and industrial film and video; TV documentaries, commercials, sport and children's programmes. Do not welcome casting queries from actors, but will consider demo tapes for voice-overs.

Cygnet Ltd

CBC, 14 Blenheim Road, Cressex,
High Wycombe, Bucks. HP12 3RS
Tel (0494) 450541
Fax (0494) 462403
Telex 83659 BIGGS
Contact Philip Lee

Film and video: corporate, educational (medical) and TV commercials. Sometimes use casting directors, but welcome casting queries from actors. Send letter in the first instance. Will consider demo tapes and video show reels.

DBI Communication

21 Congreve Close, Warwick,
Warwicks. CV34 5RQ
Tel (0926) 497695
Contact David Impey

Video – corporate, training, safety, promotional. Clients have included: Massey Ferguson, Courtaulds, ICI, Peugeot Talbot, Forte International. Welcome casting queries from actors. Send letter in the first instance. Welcome demo tapes and video show reels.

Dareks Production House

58 Wickham Road, Beckenham, Kent BR3 2RQ
Tel (081) 658 2012 Telex 265871
MONREF G (Quote ref: MAG10088)
Contact David Crossman, Barry Wale

Broadcast and sponsored film and video drama. *Output*: *Horace's Day Out*; *The Pocket Money Programme* (Channel 4). Use casting directors, but also welcome casting queries from actors. Send letter with CV and photograph – no phone calls. Will consider video show reels if on VHS format (SAE essential). 'Please provide details of where we can see your work – including theatre.'

Dateline Productions Ltd

79 Dean Street, London W1V 5HA
Tel (071) 437 4510/1834
Contact Miranda Watts

Film and video – broadcast documentary, corporate, drama, commercials. Occasionally use casting directors, but also welcome casting queries from actors. Approach by letter in the first instance. Will consider demo tapes and video show reels.

Dibgate Productions Ltd

Studio 4, Parkstead Lodge, 31 Upper Park Road, London NW3 2UL
Tel (071) 722 5634
Contact Nicholas Parsons

Make documentary and travel films for TV, cinema and industrial films. *Output*: *A Fair Way to Play*, *Mad Dogs and Cricketers*, *Relatively Greek*, *Viva Menorca* and *Terribly British*.

The Directors Video Company Ltd

89a Victoria Road, Aldershot, Hants GU11 1JE
Tel (0252) 316429 Fax (0252) 344362
Contact A.J. Barton

Video: documentary, corporate, training, promotional. Welcome casting queries from actors. Approach by letter in the first instance.

Diverse Productions Ltd

6 Gorleston Street, London W14 8XS
Tel (071) 603 4567
Contact Frank Dynes

Corporate video; TV (current affairs, satellite business news, educational programmes). *Output*: *Checkout*, *Europe Express*, *The New Age* (all for Channel 4); *In Search of the Perfect Garden*, *The Rough Guide To Careers* (for BBC 2). No outlets for actors.

Drake A–V Video Ltd

89 St Fagans Road, Fairwater, Cardiff CF5 3AE
Tel (0222) 560333 Fax (0222) 554909
Contact Ian Lewis

Corporate A–V film and video – mostly documentary and promotional. Voice-over demo-tapes welcomed.

Duncan of Jordanstone College of Art

(Postgraduate diploma in electronic imaging)
Perth Road, Dundee DD1 4HT
Tel (0382) 23261
Contact Stephen Partridge (production) Colin Macleod (course leader)

Corporate video and TV drama. Welcome casting queries from actors. Send letter in the first instance. Will consider demo tapes and video show reels. 'We train young, aspiring writers, directors and producers who often need actors, and welcome the opportunity of testing themselves against fellow aspiring professionals. Budgets are extremely limited but enthusiasm is high!'

EPM Production

The Production Office, 8b St Vincent Street, Edinburgh EH3 6SH
Tel (031) 557 4609
Fax (031) 557 4365
Contact Kenneth Andrew, Avis Moore

Corporate video – promotion, training, company information, documentary. Do not welcome casting queries from actors, but will consider demo tapes for voice-overs.

Ecce Productions

3/73 Station Road, Sidcup, Kent
DA15 7DR
Tel (081) 302 1667
Contact Stuart McKears

Film and video – documentary and
drama. Do not use casting directors.
Will consider demo tapes and video
show reels. No telephone calls.

Enigma Productions Limited

The Old Stable Block, Pinewood
Studios, Iver Heath, Bucks, SL0 0NH
Tel (0753) 630555

Enigma films include: *Chariots of Fire,
The Killing Fields, Cal, The Frog Prince,
The Mission, Defence of the Realm, The
Memphis Belle.* Always use casting dir-
ectors and do not welcome queries
from actors.

Enlightenment AV & Video Productions

The Studio, Warrens Lane, Botesdale,
Diss, Norfolk IP22 1BW
Tel (0379) 898434 Fax (0379) 898987
Contact Adrian Taylor, Phil Whetter

Video – training, industrial sales, conferences. Welcome casting queries
from actors with demo tapes and
video show reels – 'more useful than
picture and CV'.

The Epic Interactive Media Company Ltd

VPS House, 22 Brighton Square,
Brighton, E. Sussex BN1 1HD
Tel (0273) 728686/821567
Contact Alan Holden (production
director), Cathy White (production
manager)

Film and video – corporate training
medical, interactive video production,
computer-based video training. Welcome queries from individual actors.

Eurofilm Productions Ltd

47 Ossington Street, London W2 4LV
Tel (071) 243 1613
Contact Andrzej Swoboda

Output: *Modern Polish Composers* for
Channel 4 and *King Size*, a short
science-fiction comedy feature.

Euston Films Ltd

365 Euston Road, London NW1 3AR
Tel (071) 387 0911
Fax (071) 388 2122
Contact Andrew Brown, Bill Launder

Feature films; TV series and serials.
Output: *The Fear; Consuming Passions;
Bellman & True, Capital City, Minder.*
Always use casting directors. Do not
welcome casting queries from actors.

Farnham Film Company Ltd

34 Burnt Hill Road, Lower Bourne,
Farnham, Surrey GU10 3LZ
Tel (0252) 710313 Fax (0252) 725855
Telex 265871 ref: MMU279
Contact Ian Lewis, Melloney Roffe

Film and TV drama, documentary,
corporate. Use casting directors, but

welcome casting queries from actors. Send letter in the first instance. No unsolicited demo tapes or show reels.

Filmworks

65 Brackenbury Road, Hammersmith, London W6
Tel (081) 741 5631 Fax (081) 748 3198 Telex 8954111 REPLAY
Contact Geraldine Easter

Film, video, TV (drama and documentary); corporate programmes for business TV. Use casting directors. No unsolicited demo tapes or video show reels. Do not welcome enquiries from individual actors.

Fitting Images Ltd

Alfred House, 127a Oatlands Drive, Weybridge, Surrey
Tel (0932) 840056 Fax (0932) 858075
Contact Sue Fleetwood, Venetia Rickerby

Video – corporate, promotion and training films. Use casting directors, but welcome casting queries from actors. Contact by writing in the first instance. Will consider demo tapes and video show reels, but 'we can't guarantee a speedy return. We expect a sympathy with the demands and expectations of our clients – mainly blue chip, Conservative organizations – i.e. attitude to content of scripts should be serious; clients' dress code and behaviour rules on smoking, drinking and swearing should be observed.'

Five Lamps Television Ltd

West Avenue, Derby DE1 3HR
Tel (0332) 383322
Contact Mollie Kirkland, David Regan

Usually employ casting directors. Do not welcome queries from individual actors but will consider voice-over demo tapes.

Forever Films

82d Warwick Avenue, London W9 2PU
Tel (071) 286 1948
Contact Clare Downs

Feature films. *Output*: *The Dress* and *High Season*. Always use casting directors. Do not welcome casting queries from actors.

Formula Enterprises Ltd

19a Marlowes, Hemel Hempstead, Herts. HP1 1LA
Tel (0442) 250427
Contact Colleen Bending, Steve Arnold

Video – commercial, corporate, training; AV multi-image production, conferences, presentations. Do not welcome casting queries from actors, but will consider demo tapes and video show reels.

Mark Forstater Productions Ltd

8A Trebeck Street, London W1Y 7RL
Tel (071) 724 0287
Contact Nicola Lund

Active in the selection, development and production of material for film, TV. *Output*: *Monty Python and the Holy Grail*; *The Grass Is Singing*; *Forbidden*; *The Fantasist*; *Separation*; *The Wolves of Willoughby Chase*. Always use casting directors. Do not welcome enquiries from individual actors.

Freeway Films

67 George Street, Edinburgh EH2 2JG
Tel (031) 225 3200
Contact John McGrath, Susie Brown

Film outlet for John McGrath's work. *Output*: *Blood Red Roses* and *There Is a Happy Land* (Channel 4); *The Dressmaker*, from the novel by Beryl Bainbridge, scripted by John McGrath (Film on 4 International/British Screen). *Border Warfare*, a three-part series on Anglo-Scots relations; *John Brown's Body* (Channel 4). Projects in development include *Sunday Best*, *My Old Flame* (feature-length film). Normally use casting directors but don't mind enquiries from individuals.

Frontroom Films Ltd

79 Wardour Street, London W1
Tel (071) 734 4603
Contact Robert Smith

TV and cinema, both short and full-length features. *Output*: *Acceptable Levels*, *Ursula Glenys*, *Intimate Strangers*, *The Love Child* and *Wild Flowers*. Do not mind enquiries from individual actors.

Futuremedia Ltd

Media House, Arundel Road,
Walburton, Arundel, W. Sussex
BN18 0QP
Tel (0243) 555000 Fax (0243) 555020
Telex 86402
Contact Dr Peter Copeland

Video – training programmes and company promotional films. Always use casting directors. Do not welcome casting queries from actors, but will consider demo tapes for voice-overs.

GPA Films

14 Pembroke Road, Dublin 4, Eire
Tel (Dublin) 600122
Contact Celine Cawley (producer)

TV commercials for UK, Ireland, Italy, Africa and the Far East. Some voice-over opportunities for actors. Always use casting directors. Do not welcome casting queries from actors.

Gateway Audio Visual & Video

472 Green Lanes, London N13 5XF
Tel (081) 882 0177 Telex 896462
Contact Graham L. Smart

Corporate and training video and film. Always use casting directors. Do not welcome casting queries from actors, but will consider demo tapes for voice-overs.

Gibb Rose Organization Ltd

Pinewood Studios, Iver, Bucks.
SL0 0NH
Tel (0753) 651700 Fax (0753) 656935
Telex 847505 PINEW G
Contact Sydney Rose (managing director), Keith Belcher (creative director)

Film, video, TV. Corporate and sales videos through to independent productions for ITV (music, film, documentary) and full-length feature films. Normally use casting directors, but welcome enquiries from individual actors.

Goldcrest Films and Television

36–44 Brewer Street, London
W1R 3HP
Tel (071) 437 8696
Fax (071) 437 4448

Feature films. Do not consider telephone queries from individual actors, but CVs and stills are accepted and kept on file.

Grandplay Ltd

Orchard House, Adam & Eve Mews,
169 Kensington High Street,
London W8 6SH
Tel (071) 938 4766
Fax (071) 938 4992
Telex 917293
Contact Yves Pasquier, Katri Skala

TV and feature film drama. *Output*: *Hemingway*, Channel 4 series starring Stacey Keach.

Grasshopper Productions Ltd

50 Peel Street, London W8 7PD
Tel (071) 229 1181
Contact Joy Whitby

Children's programmes and adult drama. Do not welcome enquiries from individual actors.

Greenpark Productions Ltd

'St Wilfrids', 101 Honor Oak Park,
London SE23 3LD
Tel (081) 699 7234
Fax (081) 291 6319
Telex 25247 GPK
Contact David Morphet

Short film and video production. Always use casting directors. Do not welcome casting queries from actors, but will consider demo tapes for voiceovers.

Greenpoint Films

5a Noel Street, London W1V 3RB
Tel (071) 437 6492
Contact Ann Scott, Patrick Cassavetti

A small company whose members act as individual producers and directors. Always use casting directors and do not welcome enquiries from individual actors.

Colin Gregg Films Ltd

Floor 2, 1/6 Falconberg Court, London
W1V 5FG
Tel (071) 439 0257
Contact Colin Gregg

Feature films for Channel 4 and BBC2. *Output*: *Remembrance; To the Lighthouse; Lamb; Hard Travelling.*

Griffin Productions Ltd

3 Fitzroy Square, London W1P 5AH
Tel (071) 636 5066
Fax (071) 388 9830
Telex 8813271 GECOMS G
Contact Adam Clapham

Drama, documentary, arts and current-affairs TV. *Output: Painting with Light*, with Tom Keating (Channel 4); *The Bombay Hotel*, for *Forty Minutes* (BBC2); *Odyssey*, monthly magazine (Channel 4); *Maharajas* (BBC2).

Guild Sound & Vision Ltd

6 Royce Road, Peterborough, Cambs.
PE1 5YB
Tel (0733) 315315
Fax (0733) 315395
Telex 32683 GSV G
Contact John Dent

Film and video (training and educational); sponsored corporate videos (usually drama with 3–5 actors). Always use casting directors. Do not welcome casting queries from actors. 'Get a good agent or get yourself known to casting directors.'

David Hall Productions

30–38 Dock Street, Leeds LS10 1JF
Tel (0532) 422586
Contact David Hall

Makers of TV drama and documentaries, film, corporate video. *Output: Maggie's Children* and *All of You Out There* (both documentaries for Channel 4); *To Everything a Season* (feature film

in development). Do not welcome enquiries from individual actors.

Hamilton Film & Television Ltd

Lee International Studios, Shepperton, Middx TW17 0QD
Tel (0932) 562611 Fax (0932) 68989
Telex 929416 MOVIES G
Contact Christopher Hamilton

International co-productions, film, TV, drama, commercials.

Handmade Films

26 Cadogan Square, London
SW1X 0JP
Tel (071) 581 1265
Fax (071) 584 7338
Telex 8951338 EURODO

Output: Mona Lisa; Shanghai Surprise; A Private Function; Privates on Parade; The Missionary; Time Bandits; Withnail and I; Five Corners; Bellman & True; Track 29; The Lonely Passion of Judith Hearne; Nuns On The Run. Use casting directors. Do not welcome queries from actors.

Charles Harris

17 Langland Gardens, London
NW3 6QE
Tel (071) 435 1330
Contact Charles Harris, Elaine Harris

Feature films, TV drama, drama documentary. Always use casting directors. Do not welcome casting queries from actors.

John Hemson Associates

The Bakehouse Media Resource
Centre, Bedford Road, Aspley Guise,
Milton Keynes MK17 8DH
Tel (0908) 583062
Contact John Hemson

Film and video – corporate, documentary and drama. Welcome casting queries from actors. Approach by letter in the first instance. Will consider demo tapes and video show reels. 'Our output is mainly corporate video, using actors where possible plus voice-overs.'

Holmes Associates Ltd/
Holmes Productions plc

10–16 Rathbone Street, London
W1P 1AH
Tel (071) 637 8251
Fax (071) 637 9024
Contact Stephen Taylor, Andrew
Holmes

Film and video for both broadcast and non-broadcast TV. *Output*: *Piece of Cake* (LWT drama); *Arts Weekly* and *Well Being* (Channel 4 documentaries); *Chish 'n' Fips* (Central TV); *Video & Chips* (HTV); *Four Up Two Down* (Channel 4 music programme). Always use casting directors; do not welcome casting queries from actors. 'Our needs, when they occur, are very specific, and it just isn't worth your while sending us material "on spec" – we won't have time to look at it.'

HP: ICM

53 Frith Street, London W1V 5TE
Tel (071) 434 3041 Fax (071) 437
1586 Telex 894039

Video production. Corporate videos and face-to-face communications for a wide range of clients in the UK and Europe. Welcome enquiries from individual actors.

HTV Corporate
Communications

2 Nimrod Way, Elgar Road South,
Reading, Berks. RG2 0NH
Tel (0734) 751400 Fax (0734) 861482
Contact Sue Smith (producer)

Corporate television. Rarely use casting directors; welcome casting queries from actors. Approach by letter in the first instance. Will consider demo tapes and video show reels.

ICM International

ICM House, 20 Queen Street,
London W1
Tel (071) 629 8089/0
Contact Linda Lewis

Prominent makers of corporate videos for major commercial and industrial clients.

Ice International Video
Films Ltd

31–33 King Street West, Manchester
M3 2PN
Tel (061) 834 3992
Contact David Kent-Watson
(executive director)

TV commercials and films; video presentations. Welcome casting queries from actors. Send CV with photograph. Also welcome demo tapes and video show reels. 'Films are budget – outside UK, usually exotic. Opportunities for actors and actresses to gain experience and suntan!'

Illuminations

19/20 Rheidol Mews, Rheidol Terrace,
London N1 8N
Tel (071) 226 0266
Telex 23152 MONRET G
Contact Linda Zuck

Primarily a documentary production
company, making cultural programmes for a Channel 4 and BBC
audience. *Output*: *State of the Art*, six-
part documentary series; *Ghosts in the
Machine*, six-part video series; *A-Z of
TV*; *White Noise*; and *Shooting Star*; plus
other documentaries about art and TV.

Imagicians

34 Fouberts Place, London W1V 2BH
Tel (071) 439 2244
Fax (071) 734 6813
Telex 299200 MOLI G
Contact Alan Scales

Diverse productions, from TV documentary features to in-flight videos,
broadcast, corporate and home
videos. *Output*: *The Great Palace: The
Story of Parliament*. Do not welcome
enquiries from individual actors.

Independent Business Television Ltd

22–25 Portman Close, London
W1A 4BE
Tel (071) 487 4474
Fax (071) 997 8738
Telex 24672 CFSLAB
Contact Sue Tramontini, Patrick Veale

Corporate film and video. Always use
casting directors. Do not welcome
casting queries from actors, but will
consider demo tapes for voice-overs.

Independent Film Production Associates

87 Dean Street, London W1V 5AA
Tel (071) 734 3847
Fax (071) 734 0776
Telex 265871 Ref: MMU 441
Contact Aileen McCracken

Makers of documentary and entertainment TV, plus corporate video.
Always use casting directors, and do
not welcome enquiries from individual
actors.

Infovision Ltd

63 White Lion Street, London N1 9PP
Tel (071) 837 0012
Contact John Mayhew (managing
director)

Corporate video makers in the area
of training, marketing and internal
communications. Household-name
clients. Always use casting directors,
and do not welcome enquiries from
individual actors.

Insight Productions Ltd

Gidleigh Studio, Gidleigh, Chagford,
Newton Abbot, Devon TQ13 8HP
Tel (0647) 432686
Contact Brian Skilton

Feature film, arts, documentary,
entertainment, drama (TV). *Output*:
Playing Away (Film 4 International);
Dartmoor, the Threatened Wilderness
(4 one-hour environmental documentaries); *Streets Ahead* (contemporary dance & music). Use casting
directors, but welcome written casting
queries from actors. Do not telephone.

Do not welcome unsolicited demo tapes or video show reels.

and do not welcome enquiries from individual actors.

Integrated Video

5 Burton Close, Harpenden, Herts.
AL5 4QT
Tel (05827) 64302/460921
Contact Dave Howell

Video – promotional, pop and corporate. Use casting directors, but also welcome casting queries from actors. Will consider demo tapes and video show reels.

Peter Isaac Ltd

94 High Street, Bildeston, Suffolk
IP7 7EB
Tel (0449 741) 248
Contact Peter Isaac

Film, video, TV, documentary, commercials. Special interest in medical subjects and animal husbandry. Very few opportunities for actors, but welcome enquiries from individual actors.

Interesting Television Ltd

Boundary House, Old Warwick Road,
Lapworth, Warwicks. B94 6LU
Tel (0564) 783958
Contact John Pluck

Independent broadcast TV productions – documentaries, corporate film and video programming, and popular factual programmes. Do not welcome casting queries from actors.

International Broadcasting Trust

2 Ferdinand Place, London NW1 8EE
Tel (071) 482 2847
Telex 946240 Attn 19020600
Contact Paddy Coulter

Documentary company specializing in Third World and environmental issues and drama. No opportunities for actors. Always use casting directors,

Paul Joyce Productions

5 Townley Road, Dulwich, London
SE22
Tel (081) 693 6006
Contact Paul Joyce

Development and production of drama, documentary, music, arts, adventure and current affairs TV and cinema. *Output*: *Nothing as It Seems*; *Summer Lightening* (Film on 4); *Tickets for the Titanic: Everyone a Winner* with Jonathan Pryce and Anna Carteret.

Kay Communications Ltd

Gauntley Court Studios, Gauntly
Court, Nottingham NG7 5HD
Tel (0602) 781333 Fax (0602) 783734
Contacts John Alexander

Makers of industrial video programmes and training programmes.

King Rollo Films Ltd

Dolphin Court, High Street, Honiton,
Devon EX14 8LS
Tel (0404) 45218/9 Fax (0404) 45328
Telex 24637 WIGMOR
Contact Clive Juster

Animated films for TV – mostly for
children but some for adults. *Output*:
Mr Benn; *King Rollo*; *The Adventures of
Spot*; *Ric*. Do not welcome casting
queries from actors as this is inappro-
priate to their work, but will consider
demo tapes for voice-overs if relevant
to their specialist output. 'For our type
of work, it is useful to know if actors
can also sing!'

Knaves Acre Productions

The Crest, Hoe Lane, Abinger
Hammer, Dorking, Surrey RH5 6RL
Tel (0306) 731007 (071) 379 4441
Fax (071) 240 3982
Contact Brian Izzard

Makers of broadcast television, principally for Channel 4 and ITV. Unusual
biographies of unusual composers,
comedy (particularly sit-com), popular
drama (live soaps). *Output*: *The Middle
of the Road* (HTV); *The Garden of Evelyn*
(Channel 4); *Video Alice*, 90-minute
special (Channel 4).

LTV Productions

53 Kirkgate, Shipley BD18 3LU
Tel (0274) 585289
Contact Simon Allison

Video drama, documentary, commercials. Always use casting directors,
and do not welcome queries from individual actors.

Landseer Film & Television Productions

140 Royal College Street, London
NW1 0TA
Tel (071) 485 7333

Drama, documentary, music, arts,
children's, adventure and current
affairs TV. *Output*: *Mr Pye* with Derek
Jacobi; *A Penny for Your Dreams*, co-
production with BBC Wales and S4C;
Sinfonietta (Channel 4) and *Valentine
Falls*. Always use casting directors,
and do not welcome queries from individual actors.

Lawson Productions Ltd

2 Clarendon Close, London W2 2NS
Tel (071) 706 3111
Contact Sarah Lawson

Film and TV – drama and comedy.
Output: *You Again?* (NBC comedy
series for USA); *The Dawning* (feature
film); *That's Love* (TVS comedy series);
Life After Life. Always use casting directors; do not welcome casting queries
from actors.

Lewis Productions

Unit 3, River Gardens Business
Centre, Spur Road, Feltham, Middx
TW14 0SN
Tel (081) 890 1111
Fax (081) 751 5797
Contact Jonathan Lewis (managing
director), Caroline Hardy (project
manager)

Film and video – in-house promotional. Do not use casting directors.
Welcome casting queries from actors.
Send letter in the first instance. Will
consider demo tapes and video show
reels.

Limehouse Productions

Limehouse Studios, Canary Wharf,
West India Docks, London E14 9SJ
Tel (071) 987 2090
Telex 296149 LIMHSE D
Contact Janet Walker, Terence
Pritchard

Dramatic adaptations made for TV and
video. *Output*: *But What if It's Raining?*;
Rocket to the Moon; *To Have and to Hold*.

Linkward Productions Ltd

Shepperton Studios, Shepperton,
Middx TW17 0QD
Tel (0932) 562611 Fax (0932) 568020
Contact Phil Bowden

Video – medical and educational (children's); TV programmes. *Output*:
Bodytalk (Channel 4). Occasionally use
casting directors, but also welcome
casting queries from actors. Write with
photograph in the first instance. Will
consider demo tapes and video show
reels.

Little King Productions

13–14 Bateman Street, London
W1V 6EB
Tel (071) 437 9611
Fax (071) 734 7143
Contact Dr Simon Nicholas, Simon
Manley Cooper

Film and video documentary (mainly
medical). Do not generally welcome
casting queries from actors, but will
consider demo tapes and video show
reels.

London Film Productions Ltd

44a Floral Street, London WC2E 9DA
Tel (071) 222 8151
Contact Susan Chapman

Makers of a wide range of inter-
national TV and film. *Output*: *The
Scarlet Pimpernel*; *Kim*; *Country Girls*;
Poldark; *I Claudius*.

M2 Video

The Forum, 74–80 Camden Street,
London NW1 0EG
Tel (071) 387 5001
Contact Peter Muir

Video, documentary, corporate, commercials. Do not welcome casting
queries from actors, but will consider
demo tapes for voice-overs.

Magic Hour Productions Ltd

143 Chatsworth Road, Willesden
Green, London NW2 5QT
Tel (081) 459 8987/8
Contact Ms Bianka Ford

Makers of TV and films for a serious
adult audience. TV and feature films,
drama series, serials, documentaries,
shorts. Always use casting directors,
and do not welcome queries from individual actors.

Magic Lantern Ltd

Metropolitan Wharf-BGL, Wapping
Wall, London E1 9SS
Tel (071) 480 6811
Fax (071) 702 3509
Contact Bill Johnson, Sylvia Johnson

Mainly corporate video, training and
promotional programmes on both

film and video. Clients include: British Airways, RCA Records, Coates Viyella. Hardly ever use actors, and do not welcome individual enquiries.

Malone Gill Productions Ltd

Canaletto House, 39 Beale Street, London W1R 3LD
Tel (071) 287 3970
Fax (071) 287 8146

Principally documentary series on film for TV, but some drama and drama documentary. *Output*: *Vintage: The Story of Wine*; *Paul Gauguin*; *The Savage Dream*; *No Man Hath Seen God*; *Matisse in Nice*; *How to Handle a Wine* (all documentaries); *The Ghost Writer* (drama). Do not welcome casting queries from actors, but will consider demo tapes for voice-overs, giving range of accents and dialects. 'Our drama output is so limited that it is simply not worth applying to us speculatively.'

Mar-Com Presentations

6 Heathlands, Heath Gardens, Twickenham, Middx TW1 4BP
Tel (081) 744 1818
Contact Peter Kay, Robin Evans

Film and video – corporate drama/ documentary. Welcome casting queries from actors. Approach by letter in the first instance, and follow up with a telephone call. Voice-over opportunities: welcome demo tapes and video show reels.

Marking Inc Productions

18 Sandringham Court, Dufours Place, London W1V 1FB
Tel (071) 494 1555
Contact Stacy Marking

TV drama and drama documentary. *Output*: *Channel 4 Guide to Genius: 'Freud'* and *'Einstein'*. Always use casting directors. Do not particularly welcome casting queries from actors, but 'the one useful piece of information is notification of an upcoming TV performance. But it must be *enough* of a part to be worth catching.'

Medical & Scientific Productions

PO Box 493, Cookham, Maidenhead, Berks. SL6 9TD
Tel (06285) 31148 Fax (0628) 810029
Telex 849462
Contact Peter Fogarty

Corporate – medical programmes for health-care professionals.

Meditel Productions Ltd

Bedford Chambers, The Piazza, Covent Garden, London WC2 8HA
Tel (071) 836 9216/9364
Fax (071) 831 9498 & (071) 405 1656
Telex 262284 Ref: 3348
Contact Joan Shenton

Intelligent documentaries; afternoon programmes, factually based but with an element of fun; evening programmes with hard story lines. *Output*: *Who Cares?*, series of four health-care documentaries; *Kill or Cure?*, two series on the international drugs industry; *10 Million*, two consumer series for the over-60s; *Despatches – The Unheard Voices* and *The Aids Catch*; and *Health Circuit* (26-part series). Do not welcome queries from individual actors.

Merchant Ivory Productions

46 Lexington Street, London W1P 3LH
Tel (071) 437 1200
Fax (071) 734 1570
Telex 94013757 MIPLG
Contact Paul Bradley

Output: *The Europeans; Heat and Dust; The Bostonians; Maurice; The Deceivers; Room with a View; Slaves of New York; Mr and Mrs Bridge; The Ballad of the Sad Café*. Use casting directors, but also welcome casting queries from actors. Approach by letter in the first instance. Will consider demo tapes and video show reels.

Mersey Casting

Campus Manor, Childwall Abbey Road, L16 0JP
Tel (051) 722 9122
Contact Dorothy Andrew

Film, TV, video – pop videos and commercials. *Output*: *Brookside* and all Mersey TV programmes; *First of the Summer Wine* and *Truckers* (BBC); *Business as Usual* (feature film); *Waterfront Beat* and *Final Frame*.

Metropolis Pictures Ltd

147 Crouch Hill, London N8 9QH
Tel (081) 340 4649
Contact Nick Dubrule, Elizabeth Taylor-Mead

Film for TV: documentary and drama documentary. Feature films in development. *Output*: *Of Muppets and Men; John Cooper-Clarke – Ten Years in an Open-necked Shirt; Pottery Ladies; My Mama Done Told Me*. Always use casting directors. Do not welcome casting queries from actors.

John Mills Video Productions

11 Hope Street, Liverpool L1 9BJ
Tel (051) 709 9822
Contact Andrew Mills

Video documentary, sales and training films. Clients include: Nabisco, AC Delco, Alfred McAlpine. Welcome casting queries from actors. Approach by letter in the first instance. Will consider demo tapes and video show reels.

Mosaic Film & Video Productions

68 Clarence Road, Teddington, Middx TW11 0BW
Tel (081) 977 5554
Contact Adrian Antrum

Film, video and TV documentaries; training and public service films. Always use casting directors; do not welcome casting queries from actors.

Moving Direction

Ground floor, 97 Strawberry Vale, Twickenham, Middx TW1 4SJ
Tel (081) 891 2604
Contact Shaun Gale (director/producer)

Makers of documentary, corporate and fictional productions on video and film. *Output*: *Truckers Delight; Dick Head* (gangster spoof for children's TV); *Thriving on Steam; Introduction to Desk-Top Publishing*. Welcomes queries, particularly when accompanied by video show-reels.

Moving Picture Company

25 Noel Street, London W1V 3RD
Tel (071) 434 3100
Fax (071) 437 3951
Contact David Jeffers

Drama and documentary for TV, corporate video, interactive videos and commercials. *Output: In the Shadow of Fujisan* (BBC); *Heinz Superchamps* (children's programme for Channel 4); *The Assam Garden* and *Stormy Monday* (features). Normally use casting directors, and do not welcome queries from individual actors.

Multiple Image Productions

Milton Road Baths, Milton Road,
Swindon SN1 5JA
Tel (0793) 611741
Contact John Hay, Tim Langford

Non-broadcast drama and documentary. *Output: We're Not Mad . . . We're Angry!* (drama/documentary); *Looking Back* (drama). Do not use casting directors; welcome casting queries from actors. Approach either by letter or telephone in the first instance. Will consider demo tapes and video show reels.

Network 5

11 Ospringe Road, London NW5 2JA
Tel (071) 267 9492
Contact Kathy O'Neil

TV current affairs, documentary and drama. Welcome casting queries from actors. Approach by letter in the first instance. Will consider demo tapes and video show reels.

Normandy Film Productions

49 Observatory Road, East Sheen,
London SW14 7QB
Tel (081) 568 6025
Contact David Turnbull

Broadcast TV: documentary and drama. *Output: The Song and the Story*, Prix Jeunesse winner (Munich 1982), BAFTA nominated.

North West Video Productions

9a New Street, Carnforth, Lancs.
LA5 9BX
Tel (0524) 735774
Contact Steve Le Cheminant (managing director)

Corporate and training videos. Clients include: K Shoes, British Steel, Rexel. Welcomes individual queries, demotapes and videos, particularly from Northern-based actors and presenters.

Original Film & Video Productions Ltd

13 Bateman Street, London W1V 6EB
Tel (071) 734 9721
Fax (071) 734 7143
Contact Boyd Catling

Corporate video, sponsored film documentaries, commercials, video publishing, broadcast. Always use casting directors. Do not welcome casting queries from actors, but will consider demo tapes and video show reels.

Pace Productions Ltd

12 The Green, Newport Pagnell,
Bucks. MK16 0JW
Tel (0908) 618767 Fax (0908) 617641
Contact Chris Pettit, Aileen Spankie

Film and video – drama, commercials, documentaries, broadcast series, corporate. Clients include: TSB, Kodak, The Post Office and Mars. Rarely use casting directors, preferring to deal with agents, but will consider letters and keep them on file. Welcome demo tapes for voice-overs. 'Prefer actors with some camera experience, but not averse to giving some their first break. At casting sessions, listen to the way the director wants the character played. Do not lose native accents.'

Pacesetter Productions Ltd

New Barn House, Leith Hill Lane,
Ockley, Surrey RH5 5PH
Tel (0306) 70433 Fax (0306) 881021
Contact Adele Spencer

Feature and documentary films, TV, corporate and educational material. Usually use casting directors, and do not welcome queries from individual actors.

Palace Productions

16–17 Wardour Mews, London
W1V 3FF
Tel (071) 734 7060
Contact Stephen Wooley, Nik Powell

Output: *Company of Wolves*; *Letter to Brezhnev*; *High Spirits*; *Scandal*; *Mona Lisa*; *The Big Man*; co-produced *Absolute Beginners*. Use casting directors, but also welcome casting queries from actors. Write in the first instance.

Peak Viewing Film & Video Productions Ltd

130 Canalot Production Studios,
222 Kensal Road, London W10 5BN
Tel (081) 969 7139
Contact Wendy Smith, Carl St. Hill

Film, video – documentary and drama/documentary. Welcome letter with photograph and CV. Greater opportunities in voice-overs; will consider demo tapes.

Picture Palace Productions Ltd

65–69 Beak Street, London W1R 3LF
Tel (071) 439 9882
Fax (071) 734 8574
Contact Malcolm Craddock, Camilla Holloway

Film/video: commercials, drama, documentary TV programmes, corporate. *Output*: *Ping Pong* (feature film); *Tandoori Nights* (Channel 4 comedy drama series); *Eurocops – Hunting the Squirrel* (Channel 4 drama); *The Orchid House* (Channel 4). Always use casting directors; do not welcome casting queries from actors.

Poseidon Film Productions Ltd

113–117 Wardour Street, London
W1V 3TD
Tel (071) 734 4441/5140
Contact Frixos Constantine

TV and film makers/distributors, for an adult, educated art-loving audience. *Output*: *Pavlova* (drama); series for Channel 4 on the Greek philosophers. Welcome queries from individual actors.

Pretty Clever Pictures Ltd

Rushes, 66 Old Compton Street,
London W1V 5PA
Tel (071) 437 8676/(0483) 222890
Contact Geraldine Morgan

Film and video, broadcast television – commercials, promos, corporate. Clients include: Philips, Barclays Bank. Rarely use casting directors. Welcome casting query letters from actors. Will consider demo tapes and video show reels.

Primetime Television Ltd

Seymour Mews House, Seymour Mews, Wigmore Street, London W1H 9PE
Tel (071) 935 9000
Fax (071) 487 3975
Telex 22872 TV FILM G
Contact Helen Stroud (assistant to directors)

Specialize in international co-productions: adult and family drama series/serials and TV films. *Output*: *Nicholas Nickleby* and *Deliberate Death of a Polish Priest* (filmed theatre productions); *John Silver's Return to Treasure Island, Seal Morning, Lost Belongings* and *Fortunes of War* (drama series); *Durrell in Russia, Ourselves and Other Animals* and *Amateur Naturalist* (natural history documentaries); *Great Expectations; Jupiter Moon; Tales of Helpman; Othello; First Circle*. Always use casting directors. Do not welcome casting queries from actors.

Priory Production Ltd

40 Priory Road, Kew, Richmond,
Surrey TW9 3DH
Tel (081) 940 9062
Contact Alexandra Collison

Film, video and TV documentaries. Do not welcome casting queries from actors. No unsolicited demo tapes or video show reels.

The Production Pool Ltd

52 Tottenham Street, London
W1P 9PG
Tel (071) 323 0691
Contact Ann Wingate

Film and TV drama. *Output*: *Making Waves*, short film for screen and Channel 4. Usually use casting directors, and do not welcome queries from individual actors.

Professional Magnetics Ltd

Cassette House, 329 Hunslet Road,
Leeds LS10 1NJ
Tel (0532) 706066 Fax (0532) 718106
Telex 55293 CHACOM G PROTAPE
Contact Hilary Rhodes, Barrie Rhodes

Video and audio duplication and standards conversion. Video – corporate, sales and training. Do not use casting directors; welcome casting queries from actors. 'We frequently use voice-overs on our technical videos, and welcome demo tapes or show reels for casting purposes.'

Public Image Productions Ltd

22–25 Portman Close, London
W1A 4BE
Tel (071) 487 4474
Fax (071) 997 8738
Telex 24672 CFSLAB
Contact Sue Tramontini, Patrick Veale

Drama and documentary. Always use casting directors. Do not welcome casting queries from actors, but will consider demo tapes for voice-overs.

Quad Production Company

Studio One, 2 Downshire Hill, London
NW3 1NR
Tel (071) 435 6953
Contact Andy Dean, Sue Osborne

Promotional and training programmes for commerce and industry. Welcome queries from individual actors, and will consider demo-tapes and video show reels.

Quanta Ltd

Old Forge House, Rodbourne Road,
Corston, Malmesbury SN16 0HA
Tel (0666) 825626
Contact Nicholas Jones

Documentary makers, specializing in science. Also produce interactive corporate material. Opportunities for voice-overs, and welcome demo-tapes.

Ragdoll Productions

49 High Street, Henley-in-Arden,
W. Midlands B95 5AA
Tel (0564) 794076
Contact Anne Wood

Makers of children's TV programmes. *Output*: *Pob's Programme* and *Pob's Playtime* (Channel 4); *Playbox* (Central TV); *Rosie and Jim*; *BOOM*.

Cyril Randell Pictures Ltd

47 Brewer Street, London W1R 3FD
Tel (071) 437 3331
Fax (071) 734 4166
Telex 261426 ADFONE G
Contact Jeremy Phipps

Film, video and TV – documentary. Always use casting directors; do not welcome casting queries from actors. Do not welcome unsolicited demo tapes.

Recorded Picture Company

8–12 Broadwick Street, London
W1V 1FH
Tel (071) 439 0607
Fax (071) 434 1192
Telex 9419035

Feature films. Always use casting directors. Willing to give telephone information on current casting information – i.e. name of casting director involved. Credits include: *The Last Emperor* and *Merry Christmas Mr Lawrence*; *The Sheltering Sky*.

Rediffusion Films Ltd

Buchanan House, 3 St James's
Square, London SW1Y 4LS
Tel (0298) 77623
Contact Jette Bonnevie

Video (training and educational); film
and TV drama. *Output: The Irish RM*
(Channel 4); *The Bostonians* (feature
film). Use casting directors, but will
consider demo tapes and video show
reels.

Red Rooster Films

11–13 Macklin Street, London
WC2B 5NH
Tel (071) 405 8147
Contact Linda James, Christian Routh

Independent film and TV production
company, with productions ranging
from drama series and feature films to
light entertainment, all destined for
international distribution. A speciality
in the past has been quality drama for
children. *Output: Joni Jones* (five-part
drama series about 1940s Welsh childhood); *Coming Up Roses* (feature film
for SC4); *The Falcon's Malteser* (comedy
feature film); *Just Ask for Diamond; The
Gift; South by South-East; Kersplat.*
Always use casting directors, and do
not welcome queries from individual
actors.

Regent Productions

The Mews, 6 Putney Common,
London SW15 1HL
Tel (081) 789 5350
Contact William G. Stewart, Christine
Rye

Drama, situation comedy, current
affairs, quiz shows. *Output: The Lady Is
a Tramp; Tickets for the Titanic* (Channel
4 series); *Fifteen-to-One; The Nineteenth
Hole.* Use casting directors; do not welcome casting queries from actors, but
will consider demo tapes for voice-
overs.

Renaissance Vision

Unit 16, Drayton Industrial Estate,
Taverham Road, Drayton, Norwich
NR8 6RL
Tel (0603) 260280
Contact Brian Gardner

Corporate video, 16mm films, documentaries and commercials. Welcome
casting queries from actors: approach
by letter in the first instance. Will consider demo tapes and video show
reels. 'We already have several contacts, but we are always interested to
hear from different people.'

Right Angle Productions Ltd

31 Ransomes Dock, 35 Parkgate
Road, London SW11 4NP
Tel (071) 228 9968
Fax (071) 223 8116
Contact Anise Driessen, Mike
Goodman

Corporate video. Occasionally use
casting directors. Will consider demo
tapes and video show reels.

Riverfront Pictures Ltd

Dock Cottages, Peartree Lane, Glamis
Road, London E1 9SR
Tel (071) 481 2939
Contact Jeff Perks

Arts, comedy, documentary, drama,
music and young people's pro-
grammes. *Output: Our Lives, A Wee Bit
Cheeky, Everyone a Special Kind of Artist,
Breaking Through, The New Eastenders,
Cola Cowboys, Raag Rung* and *Chorus
Theatre of Manipur* (all for Channel 4);
Night Moves (for BBC); *Present
Imperfect; The Sentence.* Always use
casting directors, and do not welcome
queries from individual actors.

SBM Vision Ltd

18 Whitfield Place, London W1P 5SF
Tel (071) 387 9808
Fax (071) 387 9106
Contact Mike Brown

Corporate video programmes for
training, information and marketing.
Do not welcome casting queries from
actors. 'We use actors occasionally in
recreating business situations. We also
use professional presenters on camera
and as voice-overs. However, the person appointed to direct a drama is
responsible for suggesting the cast
who will then be auditioned.'

Sands Films Ltd

Grice's Wharf, 119 Rotherhithe Street,
London SE16 4NF
Tel (071) 231 2209
Telex 886040 SANDS G
Fax (071) 231 2119

Feature films. *Output: Little Dorrit.*
Welcome casting queries from actors.
Send letter with CV and photograph.

Sankofa Film and Video

Unit K, 32–34 Gordon House Road,
London NW5 1LP
Tel (071) 485 0848
Contact Robert Crusz

Films, TV, commercials and training
course acting work. Do not welcome
telephone queries from individual
actors, but photographs and CVs welcome for files. These are consulted before a production.

SAV Communications PLC

70–72 Tanners Drive, Blakelands,
Milton Keynes, MK14 5BP
Tel (0908) 612586
Contact Tess Harris

Specialize in corporate communications, especially training and marketing videos, using actors and
presenters for drama and voice-overs.
Do not welcome telephone queries
from individual actors but will consider demo tapes and video show-
reels if they come with SAE.

The Saville Group

Millfield Lane, Nether Poppleton,
York YO2 6PQ/
17 The Crescent, Salford, Manchester
M5 4PF
Tel (0904) 782782/(061) 736 6221
Fax (0904) 782700
Contact Sue Atkinson, Richard Hagan

Video – training, promotional, corporate. Sometimes use casting directors,
but welcome 'intelligent' casting queries from actors. Approach in writing in
the first instance. Welcome demo
tapes and video show reels: 'We often
require actors for voice-overs.'

Scan Film Productions

30 Heol Aradur, Danes Court,
Llandaff, Cardiff CF5 2RE
Tel (0222) 552469
Telex 497492 CHACOM G ATT SCAFIL
Contact Frances Gallaher, Geoffrey
Thomas, Robert Thomas

Film, TV, video – drama documentary
and commercials. *Output: The Welsh
Connection* (drama/documentary series);
George Borrow (drama series); *Pastor
Dan* (drama); *Through the Eye of the
Needle* (drama). Do not welcome cast-
ing queries from actors.

Scimitar Films Ltd

6–8 Sackville Street, London
W1X 1DD
Tel (071) 734 8385
Fax (071) 602 9217
Contact Michael Winner (chairman)

Feature films for the international mar-
ket. *Output: The Sentinel; The Big Sleep;
Death Wish I, II* and *III; The Wicked
Lady; Appointment with Death; Chorus of
Disapproval; Bullseye.* Accepts queries
from individual actors.

Screen First

Studio 1, 40 New Oxford Street,
London WC1A 1EP
Tel (071) 436 3863
Contact Mairede Thomas

Film and TV. Do not welcome telephone queries from individual actors,
or materials sent through the post.

Shand Pictures Ltd

Rosehill House, Rose Hill, Burnham,
Bucks. SL1 8NN
Tel (0628) 605129
Contact Ian Shand

Documentaries, commercials, TV, feature films. *Output: Wombling Free*
(feature film); *Homes of History* (TV
series); training and corporate videos.
Use casting directors, but welcome
casting queries from actors. Write in
the first instance. Voice-over opportunities. Will consider demo tapes and
video show reels.

Skyline Productions Ltd

1st floor, 24 Scala Street, London
W1P 1LU and
4 Picardy Place,
Edinburgh EH1 3JT
Tel (071) 631 4649
Fax (071) 436 6209 and
Tel (031) 557 4580
Fax (031) 558 1555
Contact Steve Clark-Hall (London),
Trevor Davis (Edinburgh)

Major supplier of programmes to
Channel 4, Skyline also make health,
educational and corporate films.
*Output: Years Ahead, Radicals, 98 Not
Out, Roy and Bob* (all for Channel 4).
Always use casting directors, and do
not welcome queries from individual
actors.

Smith Bundy Video & Film

10a The Pavement, Clapham
Common, London SW4 0HY
Tel (071) 582 4700
Contact Beryl Richards, Gill Brown

Video (training, commercials); documentaries for broadcast TV. *Output:*

Dispatches (Channel 4); *Moving Away from Home* (drama for Shelter). Use casting directors, but also welcome casting queries from actors. Write in the first instance with 'short' CV.

Spectacle Films Ltd

16 Chelmsford Road, London
E11 1BS
Tel (081) 539 2306
Contact Roger Ashton-Griffiths

Film and video drama; business TV. Always use casting directors, and therefore do not welcome casting queries from actors. 'In common with most people, we look for what we want *when* we want it and not otherwise. This company is run by people with an acting background, so we are quite well placed to emphasize that the only route to the studio floor for an actor is through a casting director via an agent. The first qualification an actor needs is sufficient tenacity to get an agent – without this, therefore, there is no hope.'

Strictly The Business Ltd

31 The Grove, W. Denton, Newcastle upon Tyne NE5 5AX
Tel (091) 264 2887
Contact Geoff Wonfor

Pop videos, training films, drama and documentary. Use a local casting director when necessary. Do not welcome casting queries from actors.

Supervision Ltd

St Andrews House, 17 St Andrews Road, Croydon, Surrey CR0 1AB
Tel (081) 680 4612
Fax (081) 680 3127
Contact Charles Marriott (director/producer)

Film and video – documentary, industrial and corporate.

Swanlind Ltd

The Production Centre, Stafford Road, Fordhouses, Wolverhampton
WV10 7EL
Tel (0902) 784848/789212 Fax (0902) 788840 Telex 338490
Contact Mike Davies, Tom Coyne

Video and TV – drama, documentary, commercials, corporate. *Output: Great Western Railway* (Channel 4); *Ar-y-Frordd* (S4C Welsh motoring series); *Hidden Attractions* and *It's No Big Deal* (award-winning dramas). Use casting directors, but welcome casting queries from actors. Approach by letter in the first instance. No unsolicited demo tapes or video show reels.

Teliesyn

3 Mount Stuart Square, The Docks, Cardiff CF1 6EE
Tel (0222) 480911 Fax (0222) 481552
Contact Mary Simmonds, Richard Staniforth

Film and video – broadcast TV drama, documentary music and sport. Involved in the Celtic Film Festival and Cyfle (Welsh language film training course). *Output: Will Six* (1920s period drama); *Paris–Dakar Motor Rally; Dihirod Dyfed* (West Wales murder series); *In Two Minds* (feature film); *Cracking Up* (documentary series for Channel 4). Normally use casting directors, and do not welcome queries from individual actors.

Topaz Productions Ltd

Manchester House, 46 Wormholt
Road, London W12 0LS
Tel (081) 749 2619
Contact Anne Taylor

Corporate and broadcast TV. Clients include: Lloyds Bank, GKN, Alliance & Leicester Building Society. Usually use a casting director, but also welcome casting queries from actors. Send a letter with SAE in the first instance. 'We constantly use *Spotlight*, and suggest it is almost a prerequisite for actors to take space in this publication. It rarely happens that an actor writing in is suitable for imminent casting; they are better off concentrating mail shots to individual casting directors rather than small, independent companies.'

Torbay Video

58 Dolphin Crescent, Paignton, Devon
TQ3 1JZ
Tel (0803) 558138
Contact David C. Jackson

Industrial videos. Do not welcome casting queries from actors, but will consider demo tapes for voice-overs.

Transport in Vision

20 Chancellors Street, London
W6 9RL
Tel (081) 741 8691
Contact Barry Coward

Film and video documentary. Do not welcome casting queries from actors, but will consider demo tapes for voice-overs.

Transworld TV Productions Ltd

Whitecrook Centre, Whitecrook Street,
Clydebank, Glasgow G81 1QS
Tel (041) 952 4816
Contact Peter McNeill

Video, non-broadcast TV (documentary). Clients include: Glasgow Airport, John Brown Engineering, Clydesdale Bank, Silverstream Films, Rolls Royce Hillington, Strathclyde Regional Council. Welcome casting queries from actors. Approach in writing in the first instance. Will consider demo tapes and video show reels.

Tridec Television Ltd

2 Dinsdale Road, Croft Industrial
Estate, Bromborough, Wirral,
Cheshire L62 3PY
Tel (051) 647 4673
Contact Belinda Talbot Smith

Industrial and commercial video covering corporate, training, promotion, sales and public information. Use casting directors, but also welcome casting queries from actors. Approach by letter in the first instance. Will consider demo tapes and video show reels. 'A great proportion of our requirement is for new and interesting voice-overs. Please be quite clear what rate is going to be charged, and do not think that you can record a voice-over without some experience and practice.'

Tripod Productions Ltd

111a Wardour Street, London
W1V 3TD
Tel (071) 439 0729
Fax (071) 437 0304
Contact Evan Morgans

Film and video – TV documentary, corporate, commercials. Always use casting directors, and do not welcome queries from individual actors.

Triskel Communications Ltd

Horizon House, 28 Upper High Street, Epsom, Surrey KT17 4RS
Tel (03727) 42468
Contact W. A. Eakins, J. Hutchens

Video – training and education programmes in the field of finance; company promotional videos. Do not welcome casting queries from actors, but will consider demo tapes and video show reels.

Turners Film & Video Productions/Television Media Associates

Pink Lane House, 7–15 Pink Lane, Newcastle upon Tyne NE1 5HT
Tel (091) 232 1809
Fax (091) 232 9823
Contact John Grant, Hilton Davis

Film and video: TV documentary, commercials and dramatized documentary. Always use casting directors, but welcome demo tapes for voice-overs.

TV Choice Productions

80–81 St. Martin's Lane, London
WC2N 4AA
Tel (071) 379 0263

Drama-based videos, training films, television and film. Welcome queries from individual actors. Write with CV and photograph. Video show-reels welcomed.

Ty Gwyn Films Ltd

Y Ty Gwyn, Llanllyfni, Caernarfon, Gwynedd LL54 6DG
Tel (0286) 881235
Contact Gareth Wynn Jones

Situation comedy, contemporary gritty Welsh subjects, spy thrillers. Bilingual productions. Their primary role is to provide output for the Welsh channel, S4C. Welcome queries from individuals.

UBA Ltd

Pinewood Studios, Pinewood Road, Iver Heath, Bucks SL0 0NH
Tel (0753) 651700
Contact Peter Shaw, Richard Gregson

Feature films and TV drama. Use casting directors, and only welcome casting queries if the actor is known to them. Send letter with 'extensive CV' and photograph; these will then be put on their casting file.

Upstream

Ridings House, 66 Alma Road, Windsor, Berks. SL4 3EZ
Tel (0753) 858895 Fax (0753) 864123
Contact David Ingham

Corporate film, video and multi-image production. Use casting directors, but welcome casting queries from actors. Send letter in the first instance. Will consider demo tapes and video show reels.

Video Arts Ltd

Dumbarton House, 68 Oxford Street, London W1N 9LA
Tel (071) 637 7288
Production executive Margaret Tree

Training videos. Creative team includes John Cleese. Occasionally use casting directors but mainly cast from a core of actors known to the company.

Video at Work

10 King Street Lane, Winnersh, Berks. RG11 5AS
Tel (0734) 790500
Telex 847423 COCRG
Contact Mr G.A. Clarke

Video, corporate. Use casting directors; do not welcome casting queries from actors. Voice-over opportunities for actors, but will not consider unsolicited demo tapes or video show reels.

Video Express

Canalot Studios, 222 Kensal Road, London W10 5BN
Tel (081) 969 4502
Fax (081) 969 5337
Contact Beata Romanowski, David Lindsay

Video – corporate, drama, documentary. Welcome casting queries from actors. Send letter in the first instance. Will consider demo tapes and video show reels.

Video One Professional

155 Baird Street, Glasgow G4 0PT
Tel (041) 552 7865
Fax (041) 553 1794
Contact Harry Woolfries

Video: documentary, commercials, training. Clients include: British Rail, Strathclyde Regional Council, Sony Centre. Welcome casting queries from actors. Approach by letter in the first instance. Will consider demo tapes and video show reels.

Videotel Productions/ Living Tape Productions

Ramillies House, 1–2 Ramillies Street, London W1V 1DF
Tel (071) 439 6301
Contact Nick Freethy

Film, video, TV, mainly but not exclusively of a broadly educational nature. *Output*: *Catering with Care* (Open College/Channel 4); *Tourism: The Welcome Business* (Open College/ Channel 4); *Dead Ahead – AIDS Advice for Seafarers* (Royal Navy).

Vidox Video Productions Ltd

Milton House, Roper Close, Canterbury, Kent CT2 7EP
Tel (0227) 763888 Fax (0227) 450744
Contact Robin Ochs, Chantal Cleven

Video – corporate, training, promotional, TV commercials. Use casting directors and do not welcome casting queries from actors.

Virgin Films & Video

MEG Virgin Vision Ltd, Atlantic House, Rocksley Road, London W14 0DL
Tel (081) 740 5500

Cinema, educational and animated films. *Output*: *Gothic* (directed by Ken Russell, 1987); *Absolute Beginners*; *Captive*. No TV at present. Likely to bid for one of Britain's new national commercial radio stations. Not producing at this time.

The Visual Connection (TVC) Ltd

1 Rostrevor Mews, London SW6 5AZ
Tel (071) 731 6300
Fax (071) 736 9462
Telex 995801 Ref V1
Contact Ann Dieckmann

Conference, corporate film and video. Clients include: Glaxo, BT, English Heritage. Use casting directors, but also welcome casting queries from actors. Send letter in the first instance. Will consider demo tapes for voiceovers.

Vulgar Productions

1 Cowcross Street, London
EC1M 6DR
Tel (071) 608 2131
Fax (071) 490 1864
Contact Sue Hayes

Makers of TV documentary programmes. *Output*: *Arthur & Phil* (Channel 4). Welcome queries from individual actors.

The Walnut Production Partnership

Crown House, Armley Road, Leeds LS12 2EJ
Tel (0532) 456913 Fax (0532) 439614
Contact Alison Hughes (production assistant)

Corporate video. Sometimes use casting directors, but welcome casting queries from actors. Approach by letter in the first instance. 'Telephone queries are of little use because of the small amount of drama work we do. However, information received through the post is retained in our files for reference.' Will consider demo tapes and video show reels.

Warner Sisters

21 Russell Street, London WC2B 5HP
Tel (071) 836 0134
Fax (071) 836 6559
Contact Lavinia Warner, Jane Wellesley

One of the leading UK independent production companies specialising in drama and documentary. It has worked with all the British Broadcasters and a number of international co-producers. *Output includes*: *Tenko*; *Wish Me Luck*; *GI Brides*; *That's Entertainment*; *No Place Like Home*; *Riddle of Midnight*. *Current productions include*: *She-play*; *Selling Hitler*; *In Search of the White Rajahs*.

Watershed Television Ltd

53 Queen Square, Bristol BS1 4LH
Tel (0272) 276864
Contact Chris James

Corporate film and video; commercials; broadcast drama and documentary. Use casting directors, but also welcome casting queries from actors. Send a letter with photograph. Will consider demo tapes and video show reels, but 'always write first'.

Michael White Productions Ltd

13 Duke Street, St James's, London SW1Y 6DB
Tel (071) 839 3971
Fax (071) 839 3836
Telex 923753
Contact Michael White

Feature films and theatre. *Output*: *White Mischief*; *Rocky Horror Picture Show*; *Monty Python and the Holy Grail*; *Ploughman's Lunch*; *My Dinner with André* and the *Comic Strip* series, including *The Strike*; *Nuns On The Run*; *The Pope Must Die*. 'Casting is not done through our office – always through a casting director.'

Wood Visual Communications

500 Leeds Road, Bradford, W. Yorks. BD3 9RU
Tel (0274) 732362 Fax (0274) 736164
Contact David Wood

Film, video and TV – documentaries and commercials. Do not welcome casting queries from actors, but will consider demo tapes for voice-overs.

Working Title Ltd

1 Water Lane, London NW1 8NZ
Tel (071) 911 6100
Contact Tim Bevan, Sarah Radclyffe

Feature films. Its subsidiary 'WTTV Ltd' handles television. *Output*: *My Beautiful Launderette*; *Wish You Were Here*; *Sammy and Rosie Get Laid*; *A World Apart*; *For Queen and Country*; *The Tall Guy*; *Diamond Skulls*; *Chicago Joe and The*

Showgirl; *Fools of Fortune*. Use casting directors; do not welcome queries from actors.

Wyvern Corporate Communications Ltd

18 Lansdown Road, Swindon, Wilts. SN1 3NE
Tel (0793) 615615
Contact Leslie Jenkinson

Film, video, TV – drama, commercials, documentary, corporate training, communications training and development. Sometimes use casting directors, but welcome casting queries from actors. Send letter with CV and photograph. Will consider demo tapes and video show reels.

Yorkshire Film Company Ltd

Tong Hall, Tong, Bradford, W. Yorks. BD4 0RR
Tel (0532) 441224 Fax (0532) 441220
Contact Keith Hardy

Film and video – corporate, training, information, TV commercials. 'Actors are quite frequently used – video compilations of any actor's range of work might be useful.'

Greg Younger Associates

Barons Croft, Hare Lane, Blindley Heath, Surrey RH7 6JA
Tel (0342) 832515 Fax (0342) 833768
Contact Greg Younger, Christine Younger

Film, video, TV, documentaries, commercials, corporate, training. *Output*: corporate, training and product video for Ford; corporate and sales video for Canary Wharf.

Yo-Yo Films

108 Grove Park, London SE5 8LE
Tel (071) 733 1806
Contact Philip Bartlett, Laurens
Postma

Film, video, TV – drama, documentary
and commercials. Always use casting
directors. Do not welcome casting
queries from actors, but will consider
demo tapes for voice-overs.

ZED Ltd

KJP House, 11 Great Marlborough
Street, London W1V 1BE
Tel (071) 494 3181
Contact Ruth Walsh

Film and TV drama. Do not welcome
telephone queries from individual
actors, but welcome client updates
from agents.

Zenith Productions Ltd

43–45 Dorset Street, London
W1H 4AB
Tel (071) 224 2440
Fax (071) 224 3194
Contact Scott Meek (head of
production)

Feature films and TV. Formerly the
feature arm of Central TV. *Output: The
Hit; The Dead; Insignificance; Wetherby;
Personal Services; Prick Up Your Ears;
Slam Dance; Wish You Were Here.*
Television: *Heart of the Country;
Finnegan Begin Again; Fields of Fire;
Escape from Sobibor; Inspector Morse; The
Paradise Club.* Always use casting dir-
ectors – 'not always the same ones'.
Do not welcome casting queries from
actors. 'Make yourself known to all the
main casting directors.'

18 *National TV and Radio*

Television is without question the principal medium of modern entertainment. Television drama, in one form or another, provides a staple source of employment for many actors, and can readily lead to success. There is a constant demand for new products and new faces of all types. Although deregulation and uncertainty over the renewal of TV franchises may have produced a hiccup in new production, it must be assumed that this will not last very long.

Television drama permits many more one- or two-line characters (and generally features much larger casts) than the modern stage can afford. This is particularly true of the long-running naturalistic serial, which also features a relatively large number of substantial characters who appear in virtually every episode. Even the most humble role gives an actor an opportunity to be seen by millions, including future employers. Almost any appearance on a networked series seems to exercise a fascination over the public, and as a result may make an actor more attractive (at least from the publicity angle) for casting in stage productions.

Casting for television is normally arranged through agents, although there are companies whose casting departments keep files on individual actors. Decisions are frequently the result of an informal interview, perhaps with a couple of pages of script more-or-less sight-read, and often a five-minute chat. First impressions can be crucial. Dress appropriately, if possible.

Many one-off television dramas are as carefully constructed as feature-films and offer very satisfying roles. They also give a chance for the relatively inexperienced to learn the skills required for the camera. In the longer-running serials the atmosphere can be much more that of a treadmill, with everyone required to work very fast. Involvement for any length of time in a serial provides an excellent chance to learn and develop skills, although in the rush to beat the clock the actors' performance will be the first casualty of compromise. The episodic nature of television production can mean isolation from other actors, and an actor may find the situation fiercely competitive.

Radio offers many opportunities, but it should be thought of as a specialist area. Acting for a microphone is as different from stage or filmwork as can be imagined. The BBC Radio Drama Auditions are open to those with at least one year's professional experience, but there can be very long waiting-lists. The audition requirement is three or four pieces of about one minute each, and it is advisable to keep to your native accent unless you have absolute confidence of the accuracy of an adopted one. After the audition your details are filed and are available to all radio drama producers. The BBC Radio Drama Company recruits new members by invitation only.

There is a reasonable output of drama on the radio, and wonderful variety, from major classics to popular entertainment. Educational and children's radio also require actors regularly. Acting which depends on the voice alone is peculiarly revealing and requires a high degree of concentration, together with some understanding of microphone technique and the rather surreal world of the radio studio. The pay is not high, and only presenters and DJs are likely to become famous, with the honourable exception of some soap operas, in particular the BBC's beloved *Archers*.

BBC Radio & Television

BBC Radio Drama

Room 6070, BBC Broadcasting House, London W1A 1AA
Tel (071) 927 4251
Contact Karen Rose (auditions and publicity assistant)

Radios 3 and 4 transmit some 500 new plays every year – 50 times more than the National Theatre and the Royal Shakespeare Company put together. This output amounts to an annual 96 hours on Radio 3 (1.5 per cent of the total) and 852 hours on Radio 4 (11 per cent). No other country does so many radio plays.

The main slots are on Radio 4:
The Monday Play (repeated on Saturday afternoons – 75 or 90 minutes, sometimes longer). Original plays often on complex themes, but also a showcase for classical stage plays and the occasional dramatization of novels.

Saturday Night Theatre (repeated Monday afternoons – 75 or 90 minutes). Family entertainment with a strong narrative line.

The Afternoon Play (Wednesday & Thursday – 45–55 minutes). A balanced diet of original, entertaining and demanding plays.

Thirty-minute Theatre (Tuesday afternoons). Drama equivalent of the short story.

'To qualify for a radio drama audition, an actor must have had at least a year's professional acting experience with an emphasis on playing as many varied roles as possible, and be resident in the south-east region. Radio experience is not essential but an awareness is. Listen to as much radio drama as possible in order to recognize the range of work the department produces. Unfortunately, it is not enough to merely demonstrate a "pleasant" voice. Once you have done a radio drama audition, it is not possible to re-audition for another eight years. Auditions are not held specifically for the Radio Drama Company. Vacancies are discussed as they occur – some artists may be asked to attend a workshop at a later date; however, these cannot be applied for, although a general drama audition is the first step to this end.' Write to Karen Rose for further information.

BBC Natural History Unit

Broadcasting House, Whiteladies Road, Bristol BS8 2LR
Tel (0272) 73221
Senior producer Michael Bright

'Actors for Natural History Unit TV programmes are usually obtained via agents, publicity material and *Spotlight*. Actors for Natural History Unit radio programmes (usually narrators for radio features) are obtained via personal contacts. It is useful for actors to send audition tapes (cassette is best), to include straight narrative readings.'

BBC Northern Ireland

Broadcasting House, 25–27 Ormeau Avenue, Belfast BT2 8HQ

Radio Drama
Tel (0232) 244400 ext 516
Senior radio producer Jeremy Howe

Usually cast from a pool of actors based in Northern Ireland, with additions from the Radio Drama Company, but are interested to hear from actors either living in Northern Ireland or from actors who are going to be working there in the future (give at least two months' notice).

TV drama
Tel (0232) 244400 ext 240
Head of TV drama Robert Cooper

Welcome casting queries from actors: 'Write, if enquiring about a specific production; telephone, if a general enquiry.' Do not hold general interviews.

BBC Radio Scotland (Drama Department)

5 Queen Street, Edinburgh EH2 1JF
Tel (031) 225 3131
Contact Stewart Conn (senior producer), Patrick Rayner, Hamish Wilson

'We don't cast exclusively either Scottish actors or for Scottish parts. At the same time, we have an obvious obligation to our catchment area and to artists resident in Scotland. A worthwhile reminder to young actors and those newly out of college is that radio is not the easy option some seem to think, but a specialized field of acting, requiring timing, sensitivity and awareness of expression and considerable technique. For audition purposes, we prefer an indication of someone's emotional and vocal range and an understanding of the text – rather than an ability to double or play what in the theatre would be thought of as character roles.' Welcome letters giving advance notice if actors from the south are coming to work in Scotland. General auditions are held periodically.

BBC Scotland (Television Drama)

Queen Margaret Drive, Glasgow
G12 8DG
Tel (041) 330 2345
Head of drama Bill Bryden
Producers Norman McCandlish,
David Blair, Aileen Forsyth, Paddy
Higson

Output has included: *Tutti Frutti; The Dunroamin' Rising; Down Where the Buffalo Go; The Dark Room*. Welcome casting queries from actors, either by telephone or letter. Do not hold general auditions.

BBC Television

Television Centre, Wood Lane,
London W12 7RJ
Tel (081) 743 8000

Casting of actors in BBC TV programmes is the responsibility of individual producers, directors and their production staff. There is no point of contact for general auditions. Producers or directors occasionally engage freelance Casting Advisers for special projects but they do not negotiate fees or contracts. That is the responsibility of the BBC's Artists Contracts department, and members of this department will give general casting advice.

BBC Wales (TV & Radio)

Broadcasting House, Llantrisant Road,
Llandaff, Cardiff CF5 2YQ
Tel (0222) 564888
Head of drama John Hefin
Contact Dawn Walters (drama manager)

Welcome casting queries from actors, either by telephone or letter. Will consider demo tapes. Occasionally hold general auditions – usually when planning a major series.

Commercial Television

Anglia Films

48 Leicester Square, London
WC2H 7FB and Anglia House,
Norwich, Norfolk NR1 3JG
Tel (071) 321 0101
Fax (071) 930 8499
Tel (0603) 615151
Fax (0603) 631032
Managing director Graeme
McDonald
Head of drama John Rosenberg

Output includes: *Tales of the Unexpected* series; P.D. James murder mysteries such as *Devices and Desires*; police drama *The Chief*.

Border Television

The Television Centre, Carlisle
CA1 3NT
Tel (0228) 25101

Very little drama output, apart from two productions in the children's drama series, *Dramarama*. No in-house casting directors.

Central Independent Television

35/38 Portman Square, London W1H 9AH and Central House, Broad Street, Birmingham B1 2JP and East Midland TV Centre, Nottingham NG7 2NA
Tel (071) 486 6688
Tel (021) 643 9898 Tel (0602) 863322
Controller of drama Ted Childs
Head of casting Barry Ford
Casting directors Jane Arnell, Derek Barnes, Pam O'Connor, Sally Fincher (light entertainment) – all at 8 Great Titchfield Street, London W1

Large drama output, including: the Birmingham-based series, *Boon*; *Inspector Morse*; *Hard Cases*; *Les Girls* and *The Bretts*.

In 1988, Central Television set up a new film arm, Central Films, to replace Zenith. Managing director: Ted Childs. Recent output has included two mini-series, both filmed in Australia: *Tananmera* and *Edens Lost*; and a TV film, *The Grass Cutter* starring Frances Barber and Ian McElhinney. Central Films use freelance casting directors for each project.

Grampian Television

Queen's Cross, Aberdeen AB9 2XJ
Tel (0224) 646464

No drama output, apart from very occasional independent commissions.

Granada Television

Granada TV Centre, Manchester M60 9EA and 36 Golden Square, London W1R 4AH
Tel (061) 832 7211 Tel (071) 734 8080
Casting directors Carolyn Bartlett (head of casting) (London office), James Bain and Judi Hayfield (Manchester office)

Britain's longest-established independent television company has a very large drama output including series, films and plays. Past successes include: *Brideshead Revisited*, *The Jewel in the Crown* and *The Adventures of Sherlock Holmes*, and *Coronation Street* continues to be as popular as ever. Recent productions include: *Game, Set and Match*; *The Return of Sherlock Holmes*; *The Hound of the Baskervilles*; *A Tale of Two Cities*; *After the War*; *El Cid*; *The Casebook of Sherlock Holmes*; *Pied Piper*; *Prime Suspect*; and *Families*.

HTV (Wales)

The Television Centre, Culverhouse Cross, Cardiff CF5 6XJ
Tel (0222) 590590

HTV (West)

The Television Centre, Bath Road, Bristol BS4 3HG
Tel (0272) 778366

London Weekend Television

South Bank Television Centre, London SE1 9LT
Tel (071) 620 1620

LWT provides a significant proportion of the network's drama. Output includes: *London's Burning*; Agatha

Christie's *Poirot*; *A Perfect Hero*; *Come Home Charlie and Face Them*; *Forever Green*; *Trouble In Mind*; *Second Thoughts*; *The Piglet Files*; *Palmer*.

Scottish Television

Cowcaddens, Glasgow G2 3PR
Tel (041) 332 9999
Controller of drama Robert Love

Scottish Television's networked drama continues to draw increased viewing figures, particularly the Glasgow detective series, *Taggart* starring Mark McManus (two or three 3-part series are screened annually). The networked soap, *Take the High Road*, which is mainly filmed on location at Loch Lomond, consists of 104 twice-weekly episodes each year. Apart from this regular output, they also produce occasional one-off dramas and series such as *Bookie* and *Winners and Losers* (starring Leslie Grantham).

No in-house casting directors. Freelance casting directors have been increasingly employed.

Thames Television

Thames Television House, 306 Euston Road, London NW1 3BB
Tel (071) 387 9494
Controller of drama Lloyd Shirley
Casting directors Linda Butcher (The Bill), Pat Hayley (light entertainment), Pat O'Connell (The Bill), Julian Oldfield, Shirley Teece (light entertainment)

Large drama output, including: *The Bill* (twice weekly). Thames also has a subsidiary company – Euston Films – which produces filmed drama such as *Minder*, *The Fear*, *Jack the Ripper*, *Van der Valk*, *Capital City*, *Shrinks*, and *Selling Hitler*.

TSW (Television South West)

Derry's Cross, Plymouth, Devon
PL1 2SP
Tel (0752) 663322

Very limited drama output, including some drama documentaries. Freelance casting directors used.

TVS (Television South)

Television Centre, Northam, Southampton SO9 5HZ
Tel (0703) 634211
Controller of drama Graham Benson

Output includes: *Gentlemen and Players*; *Act of Betrayal*; *Murder Is Among Us – Simon Wiesenthal*; *Heroes*; Ruth Rendell mysteries such as *A Guilty Thing Surprised* and *Shake Hands Forever*.

Use freelance casting directors.

Tyne Tees Television

The Television Centre, City Road, Newcastle upon Tyne NE1 2AL
Tel (091) 261 0181
Controller of Drama, Arts and Entertainment Michael Chaplin

Recent successes with drama for ITV Network. Currently producing a series of Catherine Cookson adaptations with World Wide International. *Black Velvet Gown*; *The Black Candle*. Also producing regional drama and children's series.

Ulster Television

Havelock House, Ormeau Road,
Belfast BT7 1EB
Tel (0232) 328122

Not one of the major drama-producing companies, but output includes: *The Hidden Curriculum*; *The Last of a Dyin' Race* by Christina Reid; *Undertow of the Armada* (for *Dramarama*); *God's Frontiersmen* (a four-part drama documentary on the Scots-Irish emigration to America); *William's War* (drama-documentary celebrating Tercentenary of the Battle of the Boyne); *December Bride* (feature film produced in association with Little Bird Films, RTE, Film Four International, CTE and British Screen).

Use freelance casting directors.

Yorkshire Television

Television House, 32 Bedford Row,
London WC1R 4HE and
The Television Centre, Leeds LS3 1JS
Tel (071) 242 1666 Tel (0532) 438283
Head of casting Malcolm Drury
(London office)
Casting directors Ruth Boyle and
Paddy Stern (London), Linda Kremer
(Leeds)

Output includes: *The Beiderbecke Tapes*; *Emmerdale Farm*; *Cloud Waltzer*; *Dreams Lost, Dreams Found*; *The Refuge*.

Welcome casting queries – in writing only.

Part 3 *Directors*

19 *Directors*

Directors exercise great power over actors. Their casting decisions dictate who will work and who won't. Their responses to scripts, and guidance of actors in rehearsal (or lack of it) have a crucial effect on individual performances. It's only sensible to understand some of the concerns which preoccupy directors – it may help you to find work, and may help to make that work more productive.

Even when specific production plans are not on the horizon, directors receive a lot of letters from actors seeking employment. When a production is planned, they can be buried under a flood of correspondence. Those with the financial resources may well retreat behind a casting director in these circumstances. Some heroes try to consider every application, *and* to reply in person – at least to those who have thought to enclose a stamped addressed envelope. In general however, actors can expect no more than impersonal standard acknowledgement to their applications.

It's very much to your advantage to write with a specific part in mind. Theatre directors find personally-written applications preferable to rather impersonal notifications from agents: take note of the advice offered in the Basics section (p 000). If you are invited to an audition, prepare yourself to the best of your ability. Read the script thoroughly if it is available to you. Try to ensure that all your time with the director is helpful: your professionalism here can stand you in good stead, even if a particular job does not come your way. Do not waste anybody's time: you will not be forgiven by directors, who are always short of time.

Outside the rehearsal room, directors find themselves dealing with administrative details, planning ahead and trying to raise funding. Finance has become a major headache, severely restricting the scope and scale of production plans. Directors find that they cannot commission new work, and that cast-sizes are so limited that vast numbers of established classic plays cannot be attempted. Adequate rehearsal time is all too often a remote dream.

Should you wish to become a director, there is no established pattern of training or career structure. Some drama schools and other educational establishments offer directors' training courses. Many people derive their experience from involvement in fringe theatre. The Battersea Arts Centre Young Director's Award give a professional production at Battersea Arts Centre in London, with a bursary from the Arts Council of Great Britain, and further training at a regional theatre. Temporary attachment to established theatres may be possible under bursary schemes from various charities, the Scottish Arts Council and the Thames Television Regional Young Theatre Directors' Scheme. Staff directors are employed by the RSC and the National, and many other theatres employ assistant directors to assist with rehearsal, research and shows in production. The quality of experience as an assistant varies considerably and may depend very much on a personal relationship.

In the search for experience in different types of play, directors may work in youth theatres (which may give a rare opportunity for large-scale productions); at drama schools (if you have a particular skill or method); and in opera. There is very little cross-over between theatre and film/television, although a BBC scheme exists for experienced theatre directors to gain television experience.

Maria Aitken

Theatre director and actress. Credits include: *Happy Families* and *Private Lives* for the theatre. Devised and presented a chat show on television (*Private Lives*) and also devised a television drama series: *Poor Little Rich Girls*.

Bill Alexander

Theatre director. One of the six associate directors of the Royal Shakespeare Company, the others being John Barton, John Caird, Ron Daniels, Barry Kyle and Adrian Noble. His first production for the RSC was *Richard III* with Antony Sher in 1984. This subsequently transferred to the Barbican and then toured Australia. In 1985, he opened the Stratford season with *The Merry Wives of Windsor* and directed three new productions for the Pit at the Barbican: *Today* by Robert Holman, and *Downchild* and *Crimes in Hot Countries* by Howard Barker. In 1986, *The Merry Wives of Windsor* opened in London and won the Laurence Olivier Award for Best Production. At Stratford in 1986, Bill Alexander directed *A Midsummer Night's Dream* and *Country*

Dancing by Nigel Williams, both of which transferred to the Barbican the next year. In 1987, he was artistic director of The Other Place in Stratford and directed *The Merchant of Venice*, *Twelfth Night* and *Cymbeline* there, all of which transferred to London in 1988.

Mike Alfreds

Theatre director and writer. Founded Shared Experience Theatre Company in 1975 (where his credits included *Too True to Be Good* and *The Three Sisters*), and though he has now left and is freelancing, he still works largely with classic texts. Has been voted 'Best Director' by the London critics for the production of *The Cherry Orchard* that he directed for Ian McKellen at the Cottesloe, and has directed and co-written (with Michelene Wandor) a five-hour production of *The Wandering Jew* at the Lyttelton.

In *Plays and Players* (August 1987), he said that he likes to adapt novels for the stage because: '19th-century novelists were frustrated playwrights, perhaps unable to work on the frivolous, artless, stage of that day . . . There's a sense of purpose; of meeting; of struggling; something that's lacking in contemporary writing where you get a lot of wit and comment, but rarely any real, rich theatrical blood. There seems to be an inability to mesh together characters and concepts . . . technology is crushing the actor. It is the suggestiveness of theatre that is so wonderful, but we're losing it. There's nothing except competence around. We are dull – no one's breaking new ground.' Recent direction include *Ghosts*, *The Miser*, *Cosi Fan Tutte*.

Jonathan Alwyn

TV producer and director. Credits (all BBC-TV) include: *The Trial of Lady Chatterley*; episodes of *Juliet Bravo*; *By the Sword Divided*; episodes of *Bergerac*; *Chelworth* and *Campion*.

Sarah Pia Anderson

Theatre and TV director. Theatre credits: *The Caucasian Chalk Circle* (Crucible Theatre, Sheffield); *The Nest* by Frank Xavier Kroetz; *Rosmersholm* (National Theatre, 1987) *Mary Stuart* (Washington DC Theatre, 1989). TV credits: *A Woman Calling* by Ann Devlin (BBC N. Ireland); *This Is History*, *Gran* by Robert Holman and *Pity in History* by Howard Barker (both BBC-TV); *The Bill* (1990, Thames).

Michael Apted

TV and film director. Credits include: *Coal Miner's Daughter* (1980); *Continental Divide* (1981); *Gorky Park* (1982); *P'tang Yang Kipperbang* (Channel 4, 1982); *First Born* (1984); *28-Up* (Granada TV, 1984); *Bring on the Night* (1985); *Critical Condition* (1986); *Gorillas In The Mist* (1987).

Moira Armstrong

TV and video director. Credits include: *Testament of Youth* (1979), *Minor Complications*, *How Many Miles to Babylon?* (1982), *Freud* (1984) and

Bluebell (all BBC-TV); *Inside Story* (location video for Anglia); *Dun Roaming Rising*.

Michael Attenborough

Theatre director. Son of Sir Richard Attenborough. Was artistic director at Hampstead Theatre for over four years and is now setting up a new production company, Turnstyle. Previous posts include: associate director of the Mercury Theatre, Colchester, Leeds Playhouse and Young Vic; artistic director of Watford Palace Theatre. Recent productions include *The Summer* by David Edgar.

While at Hampstead, he persuaded the Board of the need for a literary manager to cope with the volume of new scripts being sent in – around 600 per year. In an interview with Robert Gore-Langton in *Plays & Players* (May 1988), he said: 'If there's a good play out there, it will get done. Talent will out . . . Not enough new work is being re-done. Plays are coming and going far too fast. Very few new plays get an after-life, so the writer's income suddenly stops and they are immediately forced to accept another commission before they are ready.' He was sorry to leave Hampstead, but 'the sheer facts of subsidized theatre are stark at the moment.'

Sir Richard Attenborough, CBE

Film director. Began his career as an actor, undertaking an ambitious range of characterizations including Pinky in *Brighton Rock* (1947). Went on to produce and direct. Among his credits as a director are: *Oh! What a Lovely War* (1969); *Young Winston* (1972); *A Bridge Too Far* (1977), *Magic* (1978) and, most recently, *A Chorus Line, Gandhi* starring Ben Kingsley (for which director, actor and film all received Academy Awards), and *Cry Freedom* about the life and death of Steve Biko.

David Attwood

TV, video and pop promo director. Credits include: *Flowers in the Rain, All Together Now, Airbase, Killing Time* and *Rockliffe's Babies* (all for BBC-TV); *Crossroads* (Central TV).

Alan Ayckbourn

Theatre director and writer. Began directing at the age of 19 for Stephen Joseph's Studio Company in Scarborough, and has directed approximately 150 plays to date. As a BBC radio drama producer in Leeds, he directed an average of two plays a month for six years, working mostly with new writers. He left the BBC in 1970 to become artistic director of Scarborough's Library Theatre, responsible for a summer repertoire of four or five plays, one of which traditionally was his own annual offering. He managed to establish the company on a permanent basis and, in 1976, masterminded the transfer of the company from the Library Theatre into a converted Victorian high school, where it became the Stephen Joseph Theatre-in-the-Round (*see* Rep/Regional Theatres).

Ayckbourn usually re-directs the London productions of his own plays when they transfer from Scarborough. These have included: *Ten Times Table*; *Joking Apart*; *Season's Greetings*; *Way Upstream*; *Intimate Exchanges*; *A Chorus of Disapproval* and *Woman in Mind*. In 1977, he was nominated for a Broadway Tony award for his co-direction, with Peter Hall, of the National Theatre production of *Bedroom Farce*.

In 1986, Ayckbourn took a two-year sabbatical from Scarborough to work with his own group of actors at the National Theatre. He has directed the 1920s farce *Tons of Money*; his own play, *A Small Family Business*; Arthur Miller's *A View from the Bridge* (for which he was nominated for 'Director of the Year' in the Olivier Awards, and won the *Plays & Players* Award); and *'Tis Pity She's a Whore*. In 1988, he directed *Henceforward* in the West End; and *Man of The Moment*.

Roger Bamford

TV and video director. Credits include: *Auf Wiedersehen, Pet*; *Blott on the Landscape*; *Rumpole of the Bailey*; *Pulaski*; *Stolen*; *Come Home Charlie And Face Them* and various pop promos.

Frith Banbury

Theatre director and manager. As an actor in the 1930s, he appeared in many West End plays including John Geilgud's *Hamlet*. Turned to direction in 1947, and has since produced and/or directed over 50 plays in London, including the original productions in the West End of *The Deep Blue Sea*, *Flowering Cherry*, *Waters of the Moon*, *The Holly and the Ivy* and *The Wings of the Dove*. Vanessa Redgrave made her first London appearance under his direction in N. C. Hunter's *A Touch of the Sun* in 1958. Banbury has worked on and off Broadway, and in many other cities all over the world. Recent London credits include: *Dear Liar* (with Robert Hardy & Sian Phillips); *The Aspern Papers* (with Vanessa Redgrave, Christopher Reeves & Dame Wendy Hiller); and *The Corn Is Green* (with Deborah Kerr) at the Old Vic.

Humphrey Barclay

TV director (light entertainment and video drama). Credits include: *Relative Strangers*, *Hot Metal*, *Whoops Apocalypse*, *Me and My Girl*, *A Fine Romance*, *Two's Company*, *No Honestly* and *Doctor in the House*.

Lezli-An Barrett

Film director. Credits include: *An Epic Poem* (short film about suffragettes, screened by Channel 4 in 1982); *Business as Usual* (1987). Financed the latter film (her first) with £900 she saved from her job as a cinema usherette. It defeated work by more experienced women directors to win an award in Paris.

John Barton

Theatre and TV director. Associate director of the Royal Shakespeare Company. Joined the RSC in 1960 and devised two anthology programmes:

The Hollow Crown and *The Art of Seduction*. He co-directed the Stratford histories cycle with Peter Brook and edited *The Wars of the Roses*. Subsequent productions include: *Love's Labours Lost; Henry IV Parts I & II* and *Henry V* (co-direction); *All's Well that Ends Well; Julius Caesar; Troilus and Cressida; The Tempest; Othello; When Thou Art King; Richard II; King John; Cymbeline; Much Ado about Nothing; The Winter's Tale* (with Trevor Nunn); *King Lear* (with Trevor Nunn & Barry Kyle); *A Midsummer Night's Dream; The Merchant of Venice; Hamlet*. Non-Shakespearean work includes: *Dr Faustus; Perkin Warbeck; Pillars of the Community; The Way of the World*; and, recently, *The Three Sisters* at the Barbican. He has also directed *The School for Scandal* at the Haymarket Theatre, and *Waste* at the Lyric Theatre, Hammersmith. For TV, he has directed *Morte d'Arthur*, and has devised and presented the series *Playing Shakespeare*.

Roy Battersby

Film and TV director (documentaries and drama). Film credits include: *The Body* (1970); *Winter Flight* (1985); *Mr Love* (1986); *The Palestinian* (film documentary, 1978). TV credits: *No Excuses* (Central TV, 1983); *King of the Ghetto* (BBC-TV, 1986); *Yellowbacks* (1990; BBC); *Escape From Kampala* (1991; BBC).

Stephen Bayly

Film director. Credits include: *Coming Up Roses/Rhosyn A Rhith* for S4C – the first film to be both financed in Wales and made in the Welsh language, and

The Falcon's Malteser. Previously, he worked with Tony Scott and Ridley Scott before going to the National Film School.

Alan Bell

TV and video director: Credits include: *Chinese Puzzle, Gaskin* and *Death on the Mountain; King and Castle, Gems* and *Couples; Fallen Hero; Cats' Eyes; The Bill; The Beiderbecke Connection*.

Rodney Bennett

TV director. Credits include: *Dombey and Son* (BBC-TV); *Dearly Beloved* (Yorkshire TV); *Edwin* and *Love Song* (both for Anglia); *Monsignor Quixote* (Euston Films); *Rumpole of the Bailey* (Thames TV); *Darling Buds of May* (Yorkshire).

Bruce Beresford

Australian film, documentary and commercial director. Feature films include: *The Getting of Wisdom* (1977); *Breaker Morant* (1979); *The Club* (1980); *Puberty Blues* (1981); *Tender Mercies* (1982); *King David* (1984); *The Fringe Dwellers* (1985); *Crimes of the Heart* (1986); *Driving Miss Daisy* (1989).

Steven Berkoff

Theatre director, actor, writer and designer. Credits include: *Metamorphosis; The Trial; The House of Usher; East; Greek; West; Decadence; Salome.*

Most of these have been produced several times, on the fringe and in the West End – for example, *Greek* was recently seen at Wyndham's. He has also directed *Coriolanus* at Joseph Popp's Public Theatre in New York.

Kevin Billington

TV, theatre and film director. Theatre credits include: *The Deliberate Death of a Polish Priest* (Almeida, 1986); *Veterans Day* (Haymarket). Film credits include: *Interlude* (Columbia, 1968); *The Rise and Rise of Michael Rimmer* (Warner, 1969); *The Light at the Edge of the World* (1970). Television credits include: *Outside Edge* (LWT, 1982); *The Good Soldier* (Granada, 1981); *Henry VIII* (BBC-TV, 1979); *Reflections* (Court House Films/Channel 4, 1984); *Heartland* (BBC-TV).

Michael Blakemore

Theatre and film director, actor and writer. Born in Australia, and came to England in 1950. Studied at RADA and in 1966 joined the Glasgow Citizens Theatre as an actor and co-artistic director. Here he directed Peter Nichols' prize- winning play *A Day in the Death of Joe Egg*, which transferred to London and New York. Other prize winners he has directed include *Arturo Ui*; *Forget-Me-Not Lane*; and Michael Frayn's *Make and Break* and *Noises Off*. The latter two transferred from the Lyric, Hammersmith (where Blakemore was resident director) to the West End. The Broadway production of Frayn's *Benefactors* (also a prize winner) played on Broadway at the Brooks

Atkinson, as did *Noises Off*. His successes at the National Theatre included *The National Health*, *Plunder*, *Long Day's Journey into Night* and *The Front Page* (the latter two winning the *Plays & Players* 'Best Director' award); and *After The Fall*. Other West End credits include: *Design for Living*, *Knuckle*, *Candida*, *Separate Tables*, *Privates on Parade*, *Deathtrap* and *All My Sons*.

He directed the film version of *Privates on Parade*, and wrote, directed and acted in the film *A Personal History of the Australian Surf*, for which he received the Peter Sellers Award for comedy in the (London) *Evening Standard* Film Awards. He has also written a novel about the theatre called *Next Season*. Recent West End productions include: *Made in Bangkok* by Anthony Minghella at the Aldwych Theatre; *Lettice and Lovage* by Peter Shaffer at the Globe Theatre; and *Uncle Vanya* with Michael Gambon at the Vaudeville Theatre.

Les Blair

Television director. Productions include: *Blooming Youth*, *Law and Order*, *Beyond the Pale*, *Honest*, *Decent and True*, *London's Burning*, *The Accountant*, *News Hounds*.

Michael Bogdanov

Theatre, TV and opera director. Associate director, Tyneside Theatre Company (1971–3); director, Phoenix Theatre, Leicester (1974–7) and Young Vic (1978–80); associate director, National Theatre, since 1980; joint artistic director, English Shakespeare

Company. Work for the National Theatre includes: *Sir Gawain and the Green Knight*; *The Hunchback of Notre Dame*; *The Romans in Britain*; *Hiawatha*; *One Woman Play*; *The Mayor of Zalamea*; *The Hypochondriac*; *Uncle Vanya*; *The Caucasian Chalk Circle*; *The Spanish Tragedy*; *Macbeth*; *Lorenzaccio*; *You Can't Take It with You*; *Strider – The Story of a Horse*; *Orwell's England*; *The Ancient Mariner*. For the Royal Shakespeare Company productions include: *Shadow of a Gunman*; *The Knight of the Burning Pestle* (1981); *Romeo and Juliet* (1987). In the West End, he directed the musical *Mutiny*, and won the 'Director of the Year' SWET award for his production of *The Taming of the Shrew*. For TV, he directed his own series *Broad and Narrow* and *Shakespeare Lives*; and at the Royal Opera House, *Donnerstag aus Licht*. For the English Shakespeare Company in 1987, he directed *The Henrys*, which made a national tour and appeared at the Old Vic; and in 1990 *Coriolanus* and *The Winter's Tale*.

John Boorman

Film director. Began as a TV director, switching to films in the 1960s. Has since moved to the US and has spent much time recently trying to keep the Irish film industry afloat. Credits include: *Leo the Last* (1970); *Deliverance* (1972); *Zardoz* (1973); *Exorcist II – The Heretic* (1977); *Excalibur* (1981); *The Emerald Forest* (1984); *Hope and Glory* (1987). 'Hope and Glory confirms Boorman as a worthy inheritor of Powell's role as the great risk-taking romantic of British cinema' (Charles Barr, *Monthly Film Bulletin*).

Michael Boyd

Artistic director, Tron Theatre, Glasgow. Productions include: *A Midsummer Night's Dream*, *Commedia*, *A Passion In Six Days*, *Othello*, *Hedda Gabler*, *The Guid Sisters*, *Dr Faustus*, *Crow*.

Liz Brailsford

Theatre director. Has worked extensively in children's theatre. Credits include: *Now You See It* by Shirley Barrie (Tricycle Theatre); *The Iron Man* by Ted Hughes (Nottingham Playhouse); *Fantastic Mr Fox* by Roald Dahl (Theatre-in-Education direction for Nottingham Playhouse); *Something Wicked This Way Comes* by Ray Bradbury (Nottingham Playhouse; Crucible Theatre, Sheffield; Theatre Royal, York); *The Lion, the Witch and the Wardrobe* by C. S. Lewis (Westminster Theatre).

Kenneth Branagh

Theatre director, actor and writer. (*See* Young Actors section for biography and acting credits.)

Much of the profits from his leading role in BBC-TV's *Fortunes of War* went into the founding of Renaissance Theatre Company with fellow actor David Parfitt. As an independent operation aiming to create opportuni-

ties for people to stretch themselves
beyond their usual roles as actors, directors or writers, Renaissance has
proved highly successful. Branagh has
directed *Romeo and Juliet; Twelfth Night;
Look Back In Anger; A Midsummer
Night's Dream*. He has also directed
and starred in an acclaimed film of
Henry V. He has also written and
appeared in his own play *Public
Enemy*. To quote Kenneth Hurran in
Plays & Players (February 1988): 'What
a remarkable talent is amongst us in
young Branagh. I begin to think there
has not been such a boy wonder since
Orson Welles. Not only is he one of
the finest actors of his generation, he
also writes plays (not, so far, with
spectacular success, but that may well
come), has formed his own
Renaissance Theatre Company . . .
and he directs with, it may be said on
the evidence of his *Twelfth Night*, considerable distinction.'

Yvonne Brewster

Theatre director. Credits include: *The
New Hardware Store* (Arts Theatre);
Raisin in the Sun (Black Theatre
Cooperative); *Two Can Play* (Bristol
Old Vic); *The Good Doctor* (Arts
Theatre); *Black Jacobins* (Riverside
Theatre); *School's Out* (Theatre Royal,
Stratford East); *Flash Trash* (Half Moon
Theatre); *The Importance of Being
Earnest* (Talawa Theatre); *The Dragon
Can't Dance* (Stratford East); *Blood,
Sweat and Fears* (Riverside). Also
worked on the feature film *The Harder
They Come* in Jamaica.

Peter Brook, CBE

Theatre, film and opera director.
Educated at Oxford. Directed his first
theatre production, *Faustus*, at the
Torch Theatre in 1943. Other theatre
credits include: *Hamlet* (directed the
Stratford Shakespeare Memorial
Company at the Moscow Arts Theatre
in 1955 and in London in 1956); *The
Power and the Glory, A View from the
Bridge* and *La Chatte sur un toit brulant
(Cat on a Hot Tin Roof)* at the Theatre
Antoine, Paris (1956); *Titus Andronicus*
and *The Tempest* (1957; also composed
music and designed sets); *Irma la
Douce, The Visit* (opening play at the
Lunt–Fontaine Theatre) and *Eugene
Onegin* (Metropolitan Opera) (New
York, 1958); *The Fighting Cock* (New
York); *The Balcony* in Paris, *The Visit* in
London and *Irma la Douce* in New York
(1960); *King Lear* (1962; also designed);
The Physicists, The Perils of Scobie Prilt
and *Sergeant Musgrave's Dance* (1963);
Marat/Sade (1964 & 1965; New York
Drama Critics Award for Best
Director); *US* (London, 1966); Seneca's
Oedipus (London, 1968; also designed);
A Midsummer Night's Dream (New
York, London, Stratford, 1970–1).

In 1971, Brook founded the Centre
International de Créations Théâtrales
in Paris. Activities with the Centre
have included: *Orghast* for the Shiraz
Festival at Persepolis in Iran (1971); a
tour of central Africa in 1972, presenting mime plays; *Timon of Athens* (Paris,
1974); *The Ik*, tour 1975–6, including
the Round House, London; *Ubu*
(1977); *Antony and Cleopatra* (Royal
Shakespeare Company, 1978);
Conference of the Birds (1979); *The
Mahabharata ; Woza Albert; The Tempest*.
Film credits include: *The Beggar's Opera*
(1953); *Moderato Cantabile* (also co-
wrote; 1960); *Lord of the Flies* (also

screenplay; 1964); *Marat/Sade* (1967); *Tell Me Lies* (film version of *US*; 1967); *King Lear* (1969); *Meetings with Remarkable Men* (1979); *Carmen* (1983). Peter Brook also wrote two TV plays in the 1950s, and a book about directing: *The Empty Space*. His latest book, *The Shifting Point*, was published in 1988. He was made a Commander of the British Empire in 1965.

Pip Broughton

Artistic director, Nottingham Playhouse. Productions include: *She Stoops To Conquer* (Chester Gateway); *The Lady From The Sea* (Duke's Playhouse); *Joking Apart* (Coventry Belgrade); *War With The Newts* (Liverpool Everyman); *A Midsummer Night's Dream* (KNS Antwerp); *Paradise* (Nottingham playhouse); *Germinal* and *The Art Of Success* (Paines Plough); *Twelfth Night* (Birmingham Rep.); *Having A Ball* (The Comedy Theatre); *The Importance Of Being Earnest, Therese Raquin* and *Two-Way Mirror* (Nottingham Playhouse).

Michael Napier Brown

Artistic director, Royal Theatre, Northampton. Has been an actor and director for nearly thirty years. In the last ten years has been responsible for over sixty productions in London, Derby, Cheltenham, Canterbury and Northampton. Recent productions include: *Twelfth Night, Julius Caesar, The Merchant Of Venice, Noises Off, A Tale Of Two Cities, The Ragged Child, Jane Eyre, Intimate Exchanges, Is This the Day, How Green Was My Valley.*

Bill Bryden

Theatre, TV and film director and writer. Directed his first professional production, *Misalliance*, at the Belgrade Theatre, Coventry, in 1965, and then worked as assistant to William Gaskill at the Royal Court (1966–8). Productions for the Royal Court include: *Journey of the Fifth Horse, Backbone, Passion, Corunna* and *The Baby Elephant*. In 1971, Bryden was appointed associate director of the Royal Lyceum Theatre, Edinburgh, where his productions included: *Benny Lynch* and *Willie Rough* (both written by Bryden); *The Iceman Cometh; The Flouers of Edinburgh; How Mad Tullock Was Taken Away*. At this time he also wrote the libretto for the opera *Hermiston*. In 1975, he was appointed an associate director of the National Theatre, where he directed: *Spring Awakening; Romeo and Juliet; The Playboy of the Western World; Watch It Come Down; Il Campiello; Counting the Ways; The Passion* (co-director); *Old Movies* (also author); *The Plough and the Stars*. In 1978, he was appointed director of the Cottesloe Theatre, where he has directed: *Lark Rise* (co-director); *American Buffalo; The World Turned Upside Down; Dispatches* (co-adapted); *Candleford* (co-director); *The Long Voyage Home; Hughie; The Iceman Cometh*; the York mystery plays; *Glengarry, Glenross; A Midsummer Night's Dream; The Mysteries* (National Theatre/Lyceum Theatre). TV work has included: *Ill Fares the Land* (Channel 4, 1982); *The Holy City* (BBC-TV, 1986).

Stuart Burge, CBE

Theatre, TV and film director. Began his career as an actor and stage manager at the Old Vic and started directing in 1948 with a travelling repertory company. First London production: *Let's Make an Opera*, at the Lyric Theatre, Hammersmith, 1949. Since then he has run the Queen's Theatre, Hornchurch; Nottingham Playhouse; and, more recently, the Royal Court. Notable theatre productions have included: the first performance of *The Ruling Class* by Peter Barnes at Nottingham, and Wedekind's *Lulu*, which was seen at Nottingham and later at the Royal Court and the Apollo Theatre in London. Co-directed *The Devil Is an Ass* and *Measure for Measure* at the Edinburgh Festival with Birmingham Repertory Theatre, which transferred to the National Theatre in 1977. Other productions at the Royal Court have included: *Fair Slaughter*; *The Eclipse*; *The London Cuckolds* (also at the Lyric, Hammersmith, 1985). In 1982, he directed *Another Country* at the Queen's Theatre, *Curtains* by Stephen Bill at Hampstead Theatre Club, and *The Black Prince* at the Aldwych. Work for BBC-TV has included: *Sons and Lovers* (1981); *The Old Men at the Zoo* (1984); *Breaking Up* (1986); *Naming the Names* (1987). Films include: *There Was a Crooked Man* (1960); *Othello* (1966); *The Mikado* (1967); *Julius Caesar* (1970); *Circles Of Deceit* (1990). Made a Commander of the British Empire in 1974.

Cliff Burnett

Associate director, Dundee Repertory Theatre, with special responsibility for Youth and Community Drama. Productions include: *Private Lives*, *Death Of A Salesman*, *Macbeth*, *Funeral games*, *The Ruffian On The Stair*, *One For The Road*, *Metamorphosis*.

John Caird

Theatre director. Born in Canada, he worked there for a time in touring, fringe, community and university theatre before coming to England to train as an actor. He soon decided that he preferred directing to acting, and joined the Royal Shakespeare Company in 1977. He directed several successes at the Warehouse including: *Dance of Death*; *Savage Amusement* by Peter Flannery; *Look Out, Here Comes Trouble* by Mary O'Malley. In 1977, he began a series of productions co-directed with Trevor Nunn, starting with *The Merry Wives of Windsor* and *As You Like It*, continuing in 1979 with *Nicholas Nickleby*, which went on to achieve enormous success, with three seasons at the Aldwych, a transfer to Broadway and a TV film. This production won 16 awards in the UK and US, including four for 'Best Director'. Other collaborations with Nunn include *Les Miserables* and *Peter Pan*. Other work for the RSC (where he is now an associate director) includes the first production in The Pit – *Our Friends in the North* by Peter Flannery – as well as *Twelfth Night*, *Red Star*, *Philistines*, *The New Inn* by Ben Jonson and *A Midsummer Night's Dream*. Outside the RSC, he has directed *Song and Dance* (the Andrew Lloyd Webber musical); *As You Like It* in Stockholm, which was filmed for Swedish TV; and *Children Of Eden*.

Ken Campbell

Theatre director, actor and writer. Founded his own company, Ken Campbell's Roadshow, which toured from 1971 to 1974, visiting venues ranging from public bars to the Theatre Upstairs, in shows such as *Bar-room Tales*, *An Evening with Sylvester McCoy*, *The Human Bomb*, *Stonehenge Kit the Ancient Brit*, *The Furtive Nudist*, *Olympical Games*, and *Clowns On A School Outing*. His musical, *Bendigo* (co-written with Dave Hill & Andy Andrews) was performed at Nottingham Playhouse in 1974, and he played the part of Stu Lyons in his own play *The Great Caper* at the Royal Court in the same year. In 1976, he co-founded the Science Fiction Theatre of Liverpool and was artistic director until 1980. Their marathon *Illuminatus* (which he adapted) was the opening production at the National Theatre's Cottesloe. Other productions for this company include the ten-play cycle *The Warp* and *The Hitch-Hiker's Guide to the Galaxy* (Rainbow, London). Was director of the Everyman Theatre, Liverpool in 1980, where productions included *The Disco Queen* and *War with the Newts*. As an actor, he has recently been seen on TV in the Sherlock Holmes series with Jeremy Brett and Edward Hardwicke.

Martin Campbell

TV and film director. TV credits include: *Muck & Brass* (Central TV, 1979);
Reilly: Ace of Spies (Euston Films, 1981); *Charlie* (Central TV, 1983); *Edge of Darkness* (BBC-TV, 1985); *Frankie & Johnnie* (BBC-TV, 1985); also episodes of *Minder* and *The Professionals*. Films include *Criminal Law*; *Defenceless*.

Annie Castledine

Theatre director. Has worked as artistic director of the Northern Studio Theatre, and as associate director of Theatr Clwyd, Mold, where productions have included: *Hedda Gabler*, *Translations*, *The Three Sisters*, *Maria Marten*. Is currently artistic director of Derby Playhouse, where she is pursuing an adventurous policy with such productions as *The Children's Hour* and *Sunday's Children*.

Michael Caton-Jones

Film director. After appearing in films as 'hired brawn', went to night school and film school, and worked on his first feature, *Scandal*, with Bridget Fonda and Joanne Whalley. His TV film, *Lucky Sunil*, was seen on BBC-TV in 1988.

James Cellan Jones

TV and film director. Head of BBC plays in the 1970s. Film credits include: *Bequest to the Nation* (1971); two films for Video Arts (1982). TV credits include: *The Day Christ Died* (1980); *A Fine Romance* (from 1981); *Comedy of Errors* (1983); *Oxbridge Blues* (1984); *Slip Up* (1985); *Fortunes of War* (1988).

Robert Chetwyn

Theatre and TV director. Early experience in repertory, then became an associate director at the Mermaid Theatre, London. West End productions include: *There's a Girl in My Soup* (also Broadway and Australia); *The Flip Side*; *The Importance of Being Earnest*; *The Real Inspector Hound* (at one time had four simultaneous West End productions); *What the Butler Saw*; *The Bandwagon*; *When We Are Married*; *Hamlet* (with Ian McKellen). Other London productions include: *Arms and the Man* (with Felicity Kendall); *Brimstone and Treacle* by Dennis Potter; *Bent* (with Ian McKellen & Tom Bell); *Moving* (with Penelope Keith). In 1983, he directed a new play by Peter Ustinov at the Vaudeville Theatre: *Beethoven's Tenth*. TV work includes *The Irish RM* (Channel 4); *Making Faces* (six plays by Michael Frayn); *Private Schultz* (six-hour mini-series; BBC2); *Small World* (Granada).

Ted Childs

Film and TV director. Film credits include: *The Sweeney* and *Sweeney II* (EMI/Euston Films); *The Quatermass Conclusion* and *Charlie Muffin* (Euston Films); *Oliver Twist* (Claridge Films). TV credits include: *Special Branch*, *The Sweeney* and *Quatermass* (Euston Films).

Roger Christian

Film director. Worked as art director on *Star Wars* and *Alien*, and did second-unit work on *The Return of the Jedi*. Credits include: *Black Angel* (short film); *The Dollar Bottom* (Academy Award-winning short film); *The Sender*; *Lorca and the Outlaws* (1985, shot in Australia as *2084*).

Anthony Clark

Theatre director. Currently artistic director of Contact Theatre, Manchester. Previously ran the Orange Tree Theatre, Richmond and served as director to Tara Arts, as the only white member of the company. Now at Contact, he follows an integrated casting policy that is sometimes controversial: 'When you put black actors on stage, there is an assumption that it has to be about race. But it is about accessibility. Young audiences tend to be multiracial. An audience needs empathy with the characters on stage. They have to think, "I could be that character," and an all-white, middle-class cast adds extra barriers to a young black person's empathy' (*Plays & Players*, March 1988). Recent credits include: *The Snowman*, *Homeland*, *Mother Courage*, *To Kill a Mockingbird*, *Faustus*.

Alan Clarke

Film director. Credits include: *Road*; *Scum* (1979); *Rita, Sue and Bob Too* (Film Four International/Umbrella Entertainment). The latter has been compared to such 1960s slice-of-life films as *A Taste of Honey*.

Jack Clayton

Film director. Credits include: *The Bespoke Overcoat* (1956); *Room at the Top* (1958); *The Innocents* (1961); *The Pumpkin Eater* (1964); *Our Mother's House* (1968); *The Great Gatsby* (1974); *Something Wicked This Way Comes* (1983); *The Lonely Passion of Judith Hearne* (with Maggie Smith & Bob Hoskins, 1987).

Ray Cooney

Theatre and TV director, actor, writer and manager. Has worked extensively as a director of West End comedy and farce, founding the Theatre of Comedy Company in 1983. Credits as a director include: *Two into One*, *Pygmalion* and *See How They Run*; *Run for Your Wife*; *Wife Begins at Forty*; TV production of *See How They Run*.

Ted Craig

Artistic director, Croydon Warehouse. Has directed in Australia, America, The Middle East, and throughout Britain. Productions include: *Look Back In Anger* (with Malcolm McDowell); *The Elephant Man*; *The Frogs*; *The Astronomer's Garden*; *Sugar Hill Blues*; *Ripping Them Off!*

Kim Dambaek

Freelance director. Productions include: *Just Frank, Blending In, The Hour Of The Lynx* (Traverse Theatre); *Ghosts* (Lyric Belfast); *In The Solitude Of The Cottonfields* (Almeida).

Ron Daniels

Theatre director. Associate director of the Royal Shakespeare Company. Born in Brazil, where he was a founder member of the Workshop Theatre of São Paolo. Came to England and worked as an actor at St Andrews Repertory Theatre, and at the Victoria Theatre, Stoke-on-Trent, where he became assistant director in 1969 and directed: *Who's Afraid of Virginia Woolf?*, *Sweeny Todd*, *Major Barbara*, *Drums in the Night*, *Ghosts*. He also directed for the Shaw Theatre, Bristol Old Vic, Yale Repertory Theatre in Connecticut, RADA and the National Youth Theatre. On the London fringe, he directed *Female Transport* (Half Moon Theatre) and *By Natural Causes* (Cockpit Theatre). In 1974, he directed his first show at The Other Place – *Afore Night Come* by David Rudkin – and, in 1976, *Destiny* by David Edgar, which transferred to the Aldwych.

In 1977, he became director of The Other Place and directed: *'Tis Pity She's a Whore* by John Ford; *The Lorenzaccio Story* by Paul Thompson; *The Sons of Light* and *Hippolytus*, both by David Rudkin; *Women Pirates* by Steve Gooch (at the Aldwych); *Pericles*; *The Suicide* by Nikolai Erdman (transferred to The Other Place and the Aldwych). In 1980 at Stratford, he directed *Romeo and Juliet*, *Timon of Athens* and *Hansel and Gretel* by David Rudkin, all of which transferred to London; and in 1981, he directed *A Midsummer Night's Dream* in Stratford and *The Beastly Beatitudes of Balthazar B* with Simon Callow and Patrick Ryecart at the Duke of York's Theatre in London. Subsequent productions in Stratford, which have transferred to London, include: *The Tempest* and *Peer Gynt* (both starring Derek Jacobi); *Hamlet*; *Camille* by Pam Gems (transferred first to the Comedy Theatre and then to the Long Wharf Theatre in Connecticut). Other recent work includes: *Maydays* by David Edgar; *Breaking the Silence* by Stephen Poliakoff; *Real Dreams*; *The Danton Affair*; *Much Ado about Nothing*; *The Plain Dealer*; *Hamlet*; *A Clockwork Orange*; *Richard II*.

Howard Davies

Theatre director. Started work as associate director of Bristol Old Vic, where credits included: *Narrow Road to the Deep North*, *Candida*, *Long Day's Journey into Night*, *Early Morning*, *Fear and Miseries of the Third Reich*, *Woyzeck*, *Spring Awakening*. He then worked in fringe and repertory theatre for three years before joining the Royal Shakespeare Company to direct *Man Is Man*, *Schweyk in the Second World War* and *The Iceman Cometh*. A year later, he became an associate director of the RSC and established and ran the Warehouse Theatre in London for five years. Productions included: *Bandits*; *Bingo*; *The Fool*; *The Bundle*; *The Jail Diary of Albie Sachs*; *No Limits to Love*; *The Innocent*; *Outskirts*; *Good* and *Piaf* (which both transferred to the West End and Broadway). More recent RSC productions have been: *The Time of Your Life*; *Macbeth*; *Henry VIII*; *Softcops*; *The Party*; *Troilus and Cressida*; *Flight*; *Les Liaisons Dangereuses*, which is currently in the West End and was for a time on Broadway. He has also recently directed *Cat on a Hot Tin Roof* at the Lyttelton Theatre, with Ian

Charleson, Lindsay Duncan and Eric Porter, and the *Shaughraun* at the Olivier Theatre.

John Davies

TV and film director. Credits include: *Nana*; *Germinal*; *The Woodlanders*; *War and Peace*; *Clayhanger*; *Cover Her Face*; *Miss Marple*; *Kim* (three-hour film); *A Taste For Death*; *The Care Of Time*; *Devices And Desires*.

Tudor Davies

Theatre, dance, light entertainment and TV director. Theatre credits include: *Cowardy Custard*, *Call Me Madam*, *Dear Anyone*, *Aladdin*. TV credits include: *Pennies from Heaven* by Dennis Potter; *She Loves Me*; *Showstoppers*.

Barry Davis

Theatre, musicals, TV and radio director. Credits include: *Theatre*: *The Contractor* and *Romeo and Juliet* (both in New York); *Can You Hear Me at the Back?* (Piccadilly Theatre); *TV*: *Telford's Change*, *The Bell* (adaptation of Iris Murdoch novel), *Oppenheimer* and *Late Starter* (all for BBC-TV); *TV/Theatre*: *Wait until Dark* (US).

Ross Devenish

Film, TV and theatre director. Credits include: *Boesman and Lena* (Bluewater Films); *Marigolds in August* (Serpent

Films); *Bleak House* (BBC-TV); *Happy Valley* (BBC-TV); *Death Of A Son* (BBC-TV); *Madly In Love* (Channel Four).

Clive Donner

Film and TV director. Credits include: *Stealing Heaven; Dead Man's Folly; Babes in Toyland; A Christmas Carol; Nothing but the Best; The Caretaker; Some People; The Scarlet Pimpernel; Rogue Male; Not A Penny More, Not A Penny Less.*

Bill Douglas

Film director. Won a place at the London Film School with his drawings and went on to make an autobiographical trilogy of films: *My Childhood* (1971), *My Ain Folk* (1972) and *My Way Home* (1979). In 1986, made *Comrades*, about the Tolpuddle Martyrs.

Patrick Dromgoole

TV director and producer: Credits include: as producer: *Robin of Sherwood; Three Wishes for Jamie; The Canterville Ghost; Return to Treasure Island; King of the Wind; Eminent Domain;* as director: *Chateau Arsenic; Succubus; Meutres En Douce.*

Nancy Duguid

Theatre director. Born in Kentucky and came to England to study at the Central School of Speech and Drama. Has been associated with feminism and the gay movement (has directed

numerous productions for Gay Sweatshop) but believes that 'content and breadth are as important as the issue' (*Time Out*, September 1986). Credits include: *Angels Descend on Paris* by Noel Greig (Albany Theatre); *Passion Play* by Peter Nichols (National Theatre of Israel); *The Daughter-in-Law* (Duke's Playhouse, Lancaster); work with the Suzuki Company of Toga in Japan; *Request Programme* by Franz Xavier Kroetz (Donmar, Bush, Traverse, Edinburgh); and, recently, *Sore Throats* by Howard Brenton and *Roosters* by Milcha Sanchez Scott. She has also directed a Greek-language version of *A Street Car Named Desire* in Athens.

Peter Duguid

TV and theatre director. Theatre credits include: *Just Between Ourselves* and *Roll On Friday* (Palace Theatre, Watford). TV credits include: *Funny Man; King and Castle; Jury; Ladies in Charge.*

Han Duijvendack

Associate director, Liverpool Everyman 1983–87: *From A Jack To A King, Siamese Twins, Two Can Play, Something Wicked This Way Comes, The Resistable Rise of Arturo Ui.* With Glen Walford: *Threepenny Opera, Tosca, Return To The Forbidden Planet.* Freelance work with Leicester Haymarket, Chester Gateway, and Liverpool Philharmonic. Since becoming artistic director of Century Theatre in 1987, he has directed: *Hobson's Choice, I'll Be Back Before Midnight!, The Glass Menagerie,* and *City Sugar.*

Simon Dunmore

Freelance director. Productions include: *The Boys From Hibernia, The Prime Of Miss Jean Brodie, The Hole In The Top Of The World, The Crucible, The Unexpected Guest* (all for Belgrade Coventry), *The Weapons Of Happiness* (Mountview Theatre School), *When We Are Married* (Young Vic).

Christine Edzard

Film director. Credits include: *Stories from a Flying Trunk; The Nightingale; Biddy; Little Dorrit* (in two parts).

Ian Emes

Film director. Credits include: *Tent* (short); *Goodie Two Shoes* (short); *Knights and Emeralds* (feature); *The Yob* (for the Comic Strip in association with Channel 4).

Richard Eyre

Theatre, film and TV director. Succeeded Peter Hall as artistic director of the National Theatre on 1 September 1988. Started as an actor, but moved into directing after a depressing stint in the chorus of *The Boyfriend* at Leicester. Directed his first production – *The Knack* – at Leicester Phoenix Theatre in 1965. Became associate director of the Royal Lyceum Theatre in Edinburgh in 1967, and director of productions from 1970 to 1972. Productions there included: *The Three Sisters; Uncle Vanya; Trumpets and Drums; The White Devil; The Crucible; Juno and the Paycock; Othello; Macbeth; The Changeling; Random Happenings in the Hebrides; Confessions of a Justified Sinner.* He won STV awards for 'Best Production' in 1969, 1970 and 1971. As artistic director of Nottingham Playhouse, his productions included: *The Taming of the Shrew; The Plough and the Stars; The Government Inspector; The Churchill Play; Bendigo; The Comedians* (later also for the National Theatre and BBC-TV); *Bartholomew Fair; The Alchemist; Deeds; Touched; The Cherry Orchard.* Work in London has included his own adaptation of *The Ha-Ha* (Hampstead Theatre); *The Great Exhibition; Hamlet; Edmund; Kafka's Dick; The Shawl* and *High Society* (Leicester Haymarket and Victoria Palace, London). For the Royal Shakespeare Company, he has directed *Jingo*, and for the National Theatre (as associate director) *The Beggar's Opera; Schweyk in the Second World War; Guys and Dolls* (highly successful production that won the SWET and [London] *Evening Standard* Awards for 'Best Director'); *The Government Inspector; Futurists; The Changeling; Racing Demon;* and *Richard III.*

From 1978 to 1981, he was producer of the BBC *Play for Today* series, and also directed: *Waterloo Sunset; The Cherry Orchard; The Imitation Game; Pasmore* (his own adaptation); *Country; The Insurance Man* (Tokyo Prize winner); *'V'; Tumbledown.* Films include: *The Ploughman's Lunch* ([London] *Evening Standard* Award for 'Best Film'); *Loose Connections; Laughterhouse.*

In an interview with the *Sunday Times* on 26 June 1988, Eyre said, 'I have never created a public image, indeed I have been self-conscious about not doing so. Such publicity as I have attracted has come about through my work, and that's the way I like it. I have no desire to become a quasi-celebrity.' However, Trevor Griffiths warns: 'Just you watch, he will take hold of that place [the National Theatre] and start to make it what he thinks it should be. When people try to stop him, that's when things will happen.'

Ronald Eyre

Theatre, opera and TV director and writer. Theatre credits include: *London Assurance* (Royal Shakespeare Company, 1970); *Saint Joan*; *A Patriot for Me*; *When We Are Married*. TV credits include: *The Long Search* (BBC-TV, 1978); many plays, including some written by himself, such as *A Crack in the Ice* (BBC-TV, 1964), *Bruno* and *Are You There?*. Opera credits include: *Falstaff*; *Jason*; *Beatrice and Benedict*.

Christopher Fettes

Theatre and opera director. Productions include: *Dr Faustus* and *Faith Healer* (both starring the late Patrick Magee); Racine's *Britannicus* and *Berenice* (first professional London productions); *The Lonely Road* by Arthur Schnitzler (also co-author of English version with Ronald Adam); *Intermezzo* by Arthur Schnitzler; Handel's *Orlando* for Scottish Opera.

Bryan Forbes

Film, TV and theatre director, producer, screenwriter and actor. Started his career as an actor and appeared in many films, including *An Inspector Calls* (1954), *The League of Gentlemen* (also screenplay; 1960) and *The Guns of Navarone* (1961). Credits as a director (including many of his own screenplays) include: film: *Whistle Down the Wind* (1961); *The L-Shaped Room* (1962); *Seance on a Wet Afternoon* (1964); *King Rat* (1965); *The Raging Moon* (1971); *International Velvet* (1978); *The Naked Face* (1984); television: *Jessie* (BBC-TV); theatre: *Killing Jessica*.

Bill Forsyth

Film director and screenwriter. Formerly a maker of documentary films, whose first feature was made with boys from the Glasgow Youth Theatre. Credits include: *That Sinking Feeling* (1979); *Gregory's Girl* (1981); *Local Hero* (1983); *Comfort and Joy* (1984); *Housekeeping* (1987).

Giles Foster

Film and TV director. Credits include: *Northanger Abbey*, *Hotel Du Lac*, *Silas Marner*, *The Aerodrome*, *Last Summer's Child* and *The Obelisk* (all for BBC-TV); *Dutch Girls* (LWT). Feature film: *Consuming Passions* (1988). He has also directed three Alan Bennett films for LWT and the BBC.

Karl Francis

Film and TV director. A major Welsh talent, who has concentrated on the difficulties faced by the Welsh community. Credits include: *Above Us the Earth*; *Giro City*; *Ms Rhymney Valley*; *The Happy Alcoholic*; *Boy Soldier*.

Stephen Frears

Film and TV director. Worked as an assistant at the Royal Court Theatre on *Inadmissible Evidence* and *Waiting for Godot* in 1964, and then assisted Karel Reisz on *Morgan, a Suitable Case for Treatment*, Albert Finney on *Charlie Bubbles* and Lindsay Anderson on *If . . .* He has also worked on commercials. Credits include: film: *The Burning* (1967); *Gumshoe* (1971); *The Hit* (1984); *My Beautiful Launderette* (1987); *Prick Up Your Ears* (1987); *Mr Jolly Lives Next Door* (Comic Strip/Channel 4); *Sammy and Rosie Get Laid* (1987); television: *Walter* and *Walter and June* (1982; Channel 4); *Saigon – Year of the Cat* (1983; Thames); *Song of Experience* (BBC-TV). Directed Glenn Close and John Malkovich in *Les Liaisons Dangereuses* in Hollywood.

Martyn Friend

TV director. Credits include: *Survival of the Fittest* (1990), *Summer's Lease* (1989), episodes of *Rumpole of the Bailey, All Passion Spent, The Daily Woman, The Daughter-in-Law, Anna of the Five Towns, Shackleton* (1983), *Fair Stood the Wind for France* (1981) and *The Voyage of Charles Darwin* (1978).

Patrick Garland

Theatre, opera and film director. Began career as actor with Bristol Old Vic. First directing credits include *Brief Lives* (which he also wrote, and which was produced in London, on Broadway, and for TV) and Alan Bennett's *Forty Years On* (1970). After directing *An Enemy of the People, The Apple Cart* and *Look after Lulu* at Chichester, he was made artistic director there in 1980. During his four-year stint, eight productions transferred to London, including *Kipling*, a one-man show starring Alec McCowen. Opera credits include *Don Giovanni* for Pavilion Opera, and two Royal Gala Performances: *Fanfare for Europe* (1976) and *Fanfare for Elizabeth* (1971). He has also directed the musicals *Billy* (with Michael Crawford), *Hair* (in Israel) and *My Fair Lady* (in the US). Film credits include *The Doll's House*, nominated at the Cannes Film Festival in 1974. Most recently, he directed *The Secret of Sherlock Holmes*, with Jeremy Brett and Edward Hardwicke, at Wyndham's Theatre.

William Gaskill

Theatre director. One of the young directors brought on by George Devine in the early years of the English Stage Company at the Royal Court, where he directed plays by Osborne, Wesker, Arden and N. F. Simpson. Directed for the Royal Shakespeare Company for a short period – *Cymbeline, Richard III, The Caucasian Chalk Circle* – and then became one of Laurence Olivier's associates at the National Theatre (*The Recruiting Officer, Mother Courage, The Beaux Stratagem*). From 1965 to 1972, he was artistic director at the Royal Court, where he directed the first productions of Edward Bond's *Saved, Early Morning, Lear* and *The Sea*, and a controversial version of *Macbeth* with Alec Guinness and Simone Signoret. Since 1972, he has been a freelance. He was a founder–director of the Joint Stock Theatre Group, for whom he directed or co-directed *The Speakers*, *Fanshen*, *A Mad World My Masters*, *Yesterday's News*, *The Ragged Trousered Philanthropists*, *An Optimistic Thrust* and *The Crimes of Vautrin*. Recently, he directed *Infidelities* at the Lyric Theatre, Hammersmith, and *The Way of the World* at the Theatre Royal, Haymarket.

William Gaunt

Actor and director. Artistic director of Liverpool Playhouse 1979–81, he worked with several Liverpool writers, including Willy Russell, with whom he produced *One for the Road* and at the Lyric Theatre, London, and *Educating Rita*. *Here's a Funny Thing* and *Skirmishes* were two other of his Liverpool productions from that period that were subsequently seen in London. Gaunt's production of *Judgement* by Barry Collins won a Fringe First at the Edinburgh Festival. Acting roles include: Arthur Crabtree in the popular BBC-TV series *No Place Like Home* among numerous other TV roles, and a starring role in *When Did You Last See Your Trousers?* at the Garrick Theatre.

Peter Gill

Theatre and TV director and writer. Born in Cardiff. Associate director of the Royal Court (1970–2) and directed many productions there in the 1960s and '70s, including: *A Collier's Friday Night* by D. H. Lawrence; *The Ruffian on the Stair* by Joe Orton; Chekhov's *A Provincial Life* (also adapted); *Crete and Sergeant Pepper* by John Antrobus. From 1976 to 1980, he was director of

the Riverside Studios, Hammersmith, where among his productions were: *Small Change* (which he also wrote); *The Changeling* by Myddleton & Rowley; *Julius Caesar*; *Scrape Off the Black* by Tunde Ikoli. Associate director at the National Theatre, 1980–4, where his productions included: Turgenev's *A Month in the Country*; Molière's *Don Juan*; Shaw's *Major Barbara*; *Fool for Love* by Sam Shepard; *Antigone* by Sophocles; and his own *Kick for Touch* and *Small Change*. In 1984, he became director of the National Theatre Studio, where he has directed the Festival of New Plays in 1985, his own *Mean Tears* in 1987 and *Mrs Klein* by Nicholas Wright in 1988. Television direction includes: *Grace* by James Joyce, *Girl* by James Robson, *A Matter of Taste* by Alex La Guma and *Fugitive* by Sean Walsh (all BBC-TV); *Hitting Town* by Stephen Poliakoff (1976; Thames). In addition to those already mentioned, he has written two plays – *Sleeper's Den* and *Over Gardens Out* – and also adapted *The Merry-go-round* and *Touch and Go* (from plays by D. H. Lawrence), *The Cherry Orchard* (a new version of the Chekhov play) and *As I Lay Dying* (from the novel by William Faulkner).

David Gilmore

Theatre director. Artistic director of the Nuffield Theatre, Southampton from 1979 to 1984, where he directed *Nuts* by Tom Topor, which transferred to the Whitehall Theatre; *Dead Men* by Mike Scott and *Working-class Hero*, a new play by Bob Mason, the latter two he had commissioned for the Nuffield Theatre. He directed the national tour of *An Ideal Husband*, several rock musicals and a production of Andrew

Lloyd Webber's *Song and Dance* in Australia. Recent West End productions include: *Daisy Pulls It Off* (Globe Theatre); *The Resistable Rise of Arturo Ui* (with Griff Rhys Jones as Ui, Queen's Theatre) and Jeffrey Archer's *Beyond Reasonable Doubt* (Queen's Theatre).

John Glen

Film director. Credits include: *Octopussy* (1983); *A View to a Kill* (1985); *The Living Daylights* (1987).

John Godber

Artistic director and writer, Hull Truck. Productions include: *Up 'n Under, Bouncers, Teechers, Shakers, Blood Sweat and Tears, Cramp, Happy Jack, September in the Rain, Salt of the Earth, On the Piste, The Ritz, The Continental.*

Jim Goddard

Film director. Credits include: *Reasonable Force; A Tale of Two Cities; Kennedy* (1984); *Bones* (1984); *Shanghai Surprise*.

Jack Gold

TV, film and theatre director. Started his career as a TV cameraman. Credits include: television: *Praying Mantis* (1982; Channel 4); *Red Monarch* (1983; Goldcrest); *Macbeth* (BBC-TV); *Murrow* (1985; HBO/TVS); *Escape from Sobibor* (CBS/Central); *Sakharov* (HBO/BBC);

films: *The Bofors Gun* (1968); *The Reckoning* (1969); *The Medusa Touch* (1978); *The Chain* (1986; Quintet/Rank); *Escape From Sobibor* (1987); *Ball Trap On The Cote Sauvage* (1989); *The Rose and the Jackal* (1990); *The War That Never Ends* (1991).

David Green

TV and film director. Credits include: *The Chinese Detective, East Lynne* and *The Golden Land* (3 films) (all BBC-TV); *Whicker Aboard the Orient Express* and *1914 All Out* (Yorkshire TV). Films: *Car Trouble* (1985); *Buster* (1988).

Peter Greenaway

Film director. Described by Derek Malcolm in the *Guardian* as 'a true original with an eccentric and bizarre sense of humour', Greenaway is an experimental film-maker whose *Draughtsman's Contract* (1983; BFI/Channel 4) broke through to a wider audience while retaining his enigmatic style. Other credits include: *A Walk Through H* (1978); *Vertical Features Remake* (1978); *The Falls* (1981); and, recently, *A Zed and Two Noughts, The Belly of an Architect* and *Drowning by Numbers*.

Justin Greene

Theatre director and writer. Has directed productions at Nottingham Playhouse, Leicester Haymarket Theatre, Derby Playhouse, Young Vic and for the touring company Paines Plough. Directed with Michael

Bogdanov at the National Theatre in 1982, collaborating on two workshop productions: *The Caucasian Chalk Circle* and *Macbeth*. In 1984, his production of David Pownall's *Master Class* with Timothy West as Stalin was seen at the Old Vic and at Wyndham's Theatre. As artistic director of the Nuffield Theatre in Southampton, his productions included: *Music to Murder By*; *Roll on Friday*; *Animal*; *The Assignment*. In the West End, he has directed *A Month of Sundays* with George Cole at the Duchess, *A Piece of My Mind* by Peter Nichols at the Apollo, and *Journey's End* by R. C. Sheriff at the Whitehall. He has written several stage and radio plays: *Ludwig and Bertie*, written with Steve Cook, was a very successful platform piece at the National Theatre, and *Totally Foxed*, also written with Cook, was performed at the Nuffield Theatre in 1986.

Andrew Grieve

Film and TV director; also commercials. Credits: *Storybook International* series (HTV); *Young Sherlock Holmes* (1985; EMI); *Suspicion* (1986; Hemisphere); *On the Black Hill* (1987; BFI/Channel 4); *Agatha Christie's Poirot* (1989); *Lorna Doone* (1990).

Mike Grigsby

TV and film director. Worked as a cameraman for Granada. In 1957, formed an independent film-making group, Unit Five Seven. Has made documentaries and drama/documentaries, using the people concerned and sometimes professional actors. Short films include: *Engineman* (1957; BFI);

Tomorrow's Saturday (1962; BFI). Television films include: *Unmarried Mothers* (1983), *Inside* (1965), *Deckie Learner* (1965), *The Pommies* (1966), *Death by Misadventure: SS Lusitania* (1967), *Deep South* (1969), *If the Village Dies* (1969), *I Was a Soldier* (1970), *Freshman* (1971), *Working the Land* (1972), *A Well-kept Secret* (1972), *A Life Apart* (1973), *A Life Underground* (1974), *The People's Land: The Eskimos of Pond Inlet* (1976), *Bag of Yeast* (1976; drama), *The Village that Would Not Die* (1978), *Living on the Edge* (1987) – all Granada TV; *Before the Monsoon* (1979; 3 episodes) and *For My Working Life* (1981) – both ATV; *Too Long a Sacrifice* (1985; Central). Subjects he has tackled include India, Northern Ireland, prisons, illiteracy, lives of deep-sea trawlermen, civil rights in the southern states of America. 'Mike Grigsby's remarkably consistent *oeuvre*, which has allowed the exploited, the forgotten, the taken-for-granted, the voiceless, to speak at some length and in their own words . . . *Living on the Edge* paints a terrifyingly bleak picture of contemporary Britain without really offering any solutions . . .' (Julian Petley). Of this last film, Grigsby said, 'The theme of so many of my films is betrayal of one kind or another, and this is a summation of that experience. It is about the betrayal of my own land' (*Monthly Film Bulletin*).

Val Guest

TV and film director and producer. In the 1930s, in the early days of his career, he worked as a writer on the screenplays of comedies for Will Hay, Arthur Askey and the Crazy Gang. Credits include: television: *Mark of the*

Devil, In Possession, Child's Play, Mistress of the Seas; film: *Boys in Blue; The Great Adventure; The Day The Earth Caught Fire.* He has since retired.

Tom Gutteridge

TV director and producer. Credits include: *A Kick Up the Eighties; Footlights; Molly Keane; The Hot Shoe Show; Song and Dance; Blue Suede Shoes;* Wayne Sleep's *Dash; Fire and Ice.*

Piers Haggard

TV, theatre and film director. Credits include: television: *Pennies from Heaven* (1978), *Mrs Reinhardt* (1981), *Knockback, Return to Treasure Island, Visitors, I'll Take Romance, Centrepoint.* Film: *A Summer Story, The Secret Plot of Dr Fu Manchu, Venom.* Theatre: *The Ticket-of-Leave Man* (1981; National Theatre).

Sir Peter Hall

Director of the National Theatre for 15 years; left on 1 September 1988 to set up his own company in the West End.

Prior to founding the Royal Shakespeare Company in 1960, which he ran until 1968, he directed the première of Samuel Beckett's *Waiting for Godot.* With the RSC, he directed 18 Shakespeare plays including *The Wars of the Roses* and *Hamlet* with (David Warner in the title role). In addition, he also directed the premières of *A Delicate Balance* and *All Over* by Edward Albee, *The Homecoming, Landscape, Silence, Old Times, No Man's Land, Betrayal* and *Other Places,* all by

Harold Pinter; as well as premières of plays by Anouilh, Peter Shaffer, John Mortimer and John Whiting.

In 1973, he became director of the National Theatre where he directed *John Gabriel Borkman, Happy Days, Hamlet, Judgement, Tamburlaine the Great, Bedroom Farce, Volpone, The Country Wife, The Cherry Orchard, Amadeus, Othello, The Oresteia, The Importance of Being Earnest, Animal Farm* (his own adaptation), *Coriolanus, Martine, Yonadab* and *Coming in to Land.* He has worked many times on Broadway, winning Tony awards for *The Homecoming* and *Amadeus.*

He is artistic director of Glyndebourne, where he has directed the operas *La Calisto, Il Ritorno D'Ulisse, The Marriage of Figaro, Don Giovanni, Cosi Fan Tutte, Fidelio, The Dream, Orfeo, L'Incoronazione di Poppaea, Carmen, Albert Herring,* and *Simon Boccanegra.* He has also directed opera at Covent Garden, New York, Bayreuth and Los Angeles.

He has directed *Carmen, The Oresteia, Albert Herring* and *L'Incoronazione di Poppaea* for TV and has made seven films, including *A Midsummer Night's Dream* (1968), *Three into Two Won't Go* (1969), *The Homecoming* (1973) and *Akenfield* (1974).

In his last two years at the National Theatre (1987–8), he directed *Antony and Cleopatra* with Judi Dench and Anthony Hopkins, *Entertaining Strangers* by David Edgar and the late Shakespeares: *The Winter's Tale, The Tempest* and *Cymbeline.* With his own company he has directed *Orpheus Descending, The Merchant Of Venice, The Wild Duck, The Homecoming, Twelfth Night,* and *The Rose Tattoo.*

In *Plays & Players* of June 1988, Michael Billington remarked how struck he was with 'how much Hall's own style as a director had changed over the years. When he started out he was a romantic. He confessed that his famous production of *Waiting for Godot* at the Arts in 1955 was probably far too cluttered and full of extraneous effects. His great years at the Royal Shakespeare Company from 1960 to 1968 marked a shift towards contemporary relevance: his production of *The Wars of the Roses* with John Barton coincided with a marked public cynicism about power, and his *Hamlet* with David Warner seemed all about youthful alienation in a morally bankrupt world. After the romantic and political Hall, we now have the classical Hall: a director obsessively concerned with divining the author's purpose. One actor who is in the current season of late plays said to me that it was almost like being directed by Shakespeare himself.'

Robert Hamlin

Director, Belgrade Theatre. Productions include: *Coventry Mystery Plays*, *Significant Others*, *Made In Bangkok*, *Guardian Angels*, *The Glass Menagerie*, *Tess of the D'Urbervilles*.

Terry Hands

Theatre and opera director. Founded the Liverpool Everyman Theatre in 1964 and was artistic director there for two years. In the late 1960s and in the 1970s, his work for the RSC included: Triana's *The Criminals*, *The Merry Wives of Windsor*, *Pericles*, *Women Beware Women*, *Richard III*, Jean Genet's *The Balcony*, Etherege's *Man of Mode*, *The Merchant of Venice*, T.S. Eliot's *Murder in the Cathedral*, *Romeo and Juliet* and

The Bewitched. In 1975, he directed all four productions in the centenary season at Stratford and the Aldwych: *Henry V*, *Henry IV Parts I & II* and *The Merry Wives of Windsor*. (*Henry V* was seen in New York as the official British Theatre offering to the US to celebrate their bi-centenary.) For his direction of the three parts of *Henry VI* in 1977, he was joint winner of the *Plays & Players* award for 'Best Production' and was also the Society of West End Theatres 'Director of the Year' for 1978.

He was awarded the Meilleur Spectacle de l'Année by the Paris drama critics for his production of *Richard III* for the Comédie Française in 1973. The following year, he was appointed consultant director of the Comédie Française, and Chevalier of Arts and Letters by the French government. His Paris production of *Twelfth Night* in 1976 won another Meilleur Spectacle de l'Année, and he has also directed the plays *Le Cid* and *Murder in the Cathedral* and the opera *Otello* in Paris. (The latter production was the official French operatic offering for the US bi-centennial celebrations.)

In 1979, he directed *Parsifal* at the Royal Opera House, and with productions of *Richard II* and *Richard III* in Stratford, he completed the whole of the Shakespeare history cycle, which he began in 1975. Among his other productions have been: *As You Like It*; *Troilus and Cressida*; *Much Ado about Nothing* (with Derek Jacobi & Sinead Cusack); *Arden of Faversham* (with Jenny Agutter); the musical *Poppy* by Peter Nichols and Monty Norman at the Barbican (winner of SWET award for 'Musical of the Year'). He also directed Derek Jacobi in a new production of Rostand's *Cyrano de Bergerac* at the Barbican, which collected nine awards including the SWET award for 'Best Director' and the Drama Awards'

'Best Director of a Classical Revival'. Recent credits include *Julius Caesar* (a production in which the crowd was notably absent), *The Winter's Tale* at the Barbican and Jean Genet's *The Balcony* at Stratford. Recent productions include *Love's Labours Lost* and *The Seagull*.

David Hare

Playwright and theatre, film and TV director. Plays he has written include: *Slag; The Great Exhibition; Brassneck* (co-wrote with Howard Brenton); *Knuckle; Fanshen* (with Joint Stock Theatre Group); *Teeth 'n' Smiles* (at Royal Court and Wyndham's – also directed); *Plenty* (National Theatre and Broadway; also directed; won the New York Critics' award Best Director); *A Map of the World* (National Theatre and Adelaide Festival; also directed); *Pravda* (National Theatre; co-wrote with Howard Brenton; also directed). Has directed many plays by his contemporaries, including Trevor Griffiths, Christopher Hampton and Howard Brenton. He co-founded Portable Theatre and Joint Stock Theatre Group, and has been resident dramatist at the Royal Court and at Nottingham Playhouse. For TV, he has written: *Licking Hitler* (1978) and *Dreams of Leaving* (1980; also directed) – both BBC *Play for Today; Saigon – Year of the Cat* (1983; Thames TV); *Paris by Night* (Zenith/Channel 4, also directed). He has written three screenplays: *Wetherby* (also directed; Golden Bear for 'Best Film' at Berlin Film Festival); *Plenty* (adaptation of his own play); *The Butter Mountain*.

Frank Hauser, CBE

Theatre director. Started his career as a BBC Radio producer, working with Alec Guinness, Peter Ustinov, Pamela Brown, John Gielgud and others. In this capacity, he engaged the then unknown Richard Burton to play Henry V. A few years later, Burton returned the favour by funding the Oxford Playhouse Company, which Frank Hauser ran for 17 years, and where many new plays were pioneered, including the stage version of *A Passage to India*, Aruzov's *The Promise*, Sartre's *Kean* and Molnar's *The Wolf* (the last two were translated by Hauser). He has also written the book, lyrics and music for three pantomimes, including *Cinderella*, which was mounted in London and gave Twiggy her stage debut as Cinders. In 1987, he became a Commander of the British Empire, and has since been freelancing. Work has included: *Captain Brassbound's Conversion* (with Penelope Keith); *A Village Wooing* (Judi Dench and Michael Williams); *The Assassin* (Edward Woodward); *Agnes of God* (Susannah York); *An Enemy of the People* (his own translation; with Roy Dotrice in New York). Recent credits include *Thursday's Ladies* at the Apollo, and *A Man for All Seasons* (with Charlton Heston) at the Savoy and on tour.

Brian Hewitt-Jones

Associate producer and director, E & B Productions (Paul Elliot). Productions include: *Children Of A Lesser God, Whose Life Is It Anyway?, Gaslight, Ross,*

Crown Matrimonial, Pride And Prejudice, The Fifteen Streets, The Pirates Of Penzance.

Mike Hodges

Film and TV director. Film credits include: *Get Carter* (1971); *Pulp* (1972); *The Terminal Man* (1973); *Flash Gordon* (1980); *Squaring the Circle* (1984); *Morons from Outer Space* (1984); *Buried Alive* (1985); *A Prayer for the Dying* (1987).

Jonathan Holloway

Theatre director. Founder Red Shift Theatre. Productions with Red Shift include: *The Duchess of Malfi, Romeo and Juliette, The Mill on the Floss, Le Misanthrope, In the Image of the Beast, Timon of Athens, Frida and Diego, Lulu, Fanny Hill, The Hammer.* At Lyric Belfast: *The Playboy of the Western World.* At NT: *Road.* At Central School: *Loot.* Television film drama: *Eclipsed.*

Andrew Holmes

Artistic director, Empty Space Theatre Company. Productions include: *Leaf Storm, The Rainbow, The Aspern Papers, Pilgrim's Progress, The Strange Case Of Dr Jekyll and Mr Hyde* (all with Empty Space); *A Taste Of Honey* (Colchester Mercury).

Christopher Honer

Director, Derby Playhouse. Productions include: *Land of Hope and Glory, A Midsummer Night's Dream, The Brewery Beano, Over The Bar, The Caucasian Chalk Circle, Charley's Aunt.*

Harry Hook

Film director. Credits include: *Art and Madness; Unknown Region; Sins of the Father; Snakes 'n' Ladders; Before I Die For Ever; The Kitchen Toto* (1987); *Lord of the Flies.*

Hugh Hudson

Film director. Credits include: *Fangio; Chariots of Fire* (1981; Academy Award for 'Best Picture'); *Greystoke: The Legend of Tarzan, Lord of the Apes* (1984); *Revolution* (1985); *Lost Angels* (1989).

Nicholas Hytner

Theatre and opera director. An associate director of the Royal Exchange Theatre in Manchester since 1985. Has directed at several repertory theatres, including Exeter and Leeds, and after impressing English National Opera director Colin Graham with one of his student productions at the Edinburgh Festival, he has worked as Jonathan Miller's assistant at the ENO and has directed several operas there including

Rienzi and *Xerxes*, which won the 1987 Laurence Olivier award for 'Best Opera Production'. Other operas he has directed include *King Priam*, *Turn of the Screw* and *Marriage of Figaro* for Kent Opera, and Handel's *Julius Caesar* in Paris. He has also directed the new opera, *The King Goes Forth to France* at Covent Garden. Theatre work has included: *Mumbo Jumbo*; *As You Like It*; *Jumpers* (with Julie Walters and Tom Courtenay); *Edward II* (Ian McDiarmid); *The Country Wife* (Cheryl Campbell); Schiller's *Don Carlos*; *The Scarlet Pimpernel* (Donald Sinden; at Chichester and in the West End). Recent credits include: *Measure for Measure* for the RSC in Stratford; *The Tempest* at Stratford; *The Magic Flute* for the ENO; *The Knot Garden* for the Royal Opera.

James Ivory

Film director. In partnership with producer Ismail Merchant and writer Ruth Prawer Jhabvala, he has made films touching on British colonial and expatriate experience, many of which are set in India. Credits include: *Savages* (1972); *Helen, Queen of the Nautch Girls* (1973); *Mahatma and the Mad Boy* (1974); *Autobiography of a Princess* (1975); *The Wild Party* (1975); *Roseland* (1977); *Hullabaloo over George and Bonnie's Pictures* (1978); *The Europeans* (1979); *Jane Austen in Manhattan* (1980); *Quartet* (1981); *Heat and Dust* (1983); *The Bostonians* (1984); and, recently, *A Room with a View* and *Maurice*.

Paul Jackson

TV director and producer. Credits include: *The Two Ronnies*; *Three of a Kind* (1981); *Carrott's Lib* (1982); *The Young Ones* (1983); *Happy Families* (1985); *Saturday Live* (1985); *Girls on Top* (1985); *Red Dwarf*; *Spitting Image* (1984).

Alby James

Productions include: *Romeo And Juliet*, *Porgy And Bess*, *Woza Albert*, *Scrape Off The Black*, *Live Like Pigs*, *Eden*, *Fences*, *Streetwise Momma Decemba*.

Derek Jarman

Film director. Worked as an art director for Ken Russell and has made promotional pop videos. Credits include: *Sebastiane* (1976); *Jubilee* (1978); *The Tempest* (1979); *Caravaggio* (1986); *The Last of England* (1987).

Roland Joffe

Film and TV director. In his early career, became the youngest director at the National Theatre, under Laurence Olivier, in 1973. Credits include: film: *The Killing Fields* (1984); *The Mission*; television: *The Spongers* (1978; BBC-TV *Play for Today*); *No, Mama, No*; *'Tis Pity She's a Whore* (1980; BBC-TV); *United Kingdom* (1981; BBC-TV).

Richard Jones

Opera and theatre director. Initially worked as a jazz musician, before being awarded an Arts Council trainee director's bursary in 1982 to work with Scottish Opera. Recent opera productions include: *The Love for Three Oranges* (Opera North/English National Opera); *The Plumber's Gift* (David Blake's new opera for English National Opera); *Rheingold and The Valkyrie* (Scottish Opera). Theatre credits include: *Too Clever by Half* by Ostrovsky, at the Old Vic for Jonathan Miller.

Terry Jones

Film director. Came to prominence as an actor with the TV series of *Monty Python's Flying Circus*. Film credits include: *Monty Python and the Holy Grail* (co-directed with Terry Gilliam); *Monty Python's Life of Brian*; *Monty Python's the Meaning of Life*; *Personal Services*; *Erik The Viking*.

Marek Kanievska

Film Director. Worked in television, where credits include: *Coronation Street* and *Muck and Brass* before directing the feature films: *Another Country* and *Horror Movie*.

Jude Kelly

Artistic director, West Yorkshire Playhouse. Productions include: *Guide To Sex* (National Theatre of Brent); *The Pink Briefcase* (Lyric Hammersmith); *Accidental Death Of An Anarchist* (Nuffield, Southampton); *Lynchville* (RSC); *Sarcophagus* (RSC); *Intimate Exchanges* (Bristol Old Vic); *The Tempest* (Roundabout Theatre, New York).

Nicolas Kent

Theatre and TV director. Has been an associate director at the Traverse Theatre in Edinburgh and the Oxford Playhouse. Currently artistic director of the Tricycle Theatre. Credits include: theatre: *Class Enemy* (1979; Young Vic), *Love of a Good Man* and *No End of Blame* by Howard Barker (1980 and 1981; Royal Court); *The Great White Hope* (Tricycle Theatre and RSC); *Factory Girls* (Tricycle). TV: *Oceans Apart* by Olwen Wymark, *The Prodigal Grandfather* by Donald Churchill, *Playboy of the West Indies*, *Pentecost* – all for BBC-TV.

Irvin Kershner

Film and TV director. Credits include: TV: *Amazing Stories* (1985; NBC/Universal), *Raid on Entebbe* (1977); film: *Robocop 2* (1990), *Never Say Never Again* (1983), *The Empire Strikes Back* (1980), *The Eyes of Laura Mars* (1978), *The Return of a Man Called Horse* (1976).

Jenny Killick

Theatre director. In 1986, when she was 25, she took over as artistic director of the Traverse Theatre in Edinburgh where she succeeded in maintaining the theatre's reputation as a powerhouse for new writing.

Financial constraints were met with an ambitious programme of visiting productions. New work included a 'Scottish Accents' season in 1988, comprising four plays by young Scottish writers. In an interview with Sarah Hemming in *Plays & Players* (February 1988), Killick said: 'I think if you don't want audience support you make a film or television. But you do theatre because you're a big show-off. You want the immediacy of response. But I think that's been forgotten. So I'm trying to stimulate that response again, to show that contemporary work can come from that very basic communicative root. A lot of new plays I've read have been terribly clever, but they have not moved me in the way that classical ones have. And I suppose the thing is to get contemporary work to aspire to those fundamental responses that are achieved by classical plays.' Jenny Killick left the Traverse Theatre in 1988, to be replaced by Ian Brown.

Christopher Lloyd King

TV director. Credits include: *Pulasky* (BBC-TV); episodes of *Boon* (Central); and *The Manageress* (Channel Four).

Alex Kirby

TV director. Credits include: *Maneaters of Kumaon* (BBC-TV) and episodes of *Boon* (Central), *Bergerac* (BBC); *The Voyage Of The Dawn Treader*; *The Chronicles Of Narnia*.

Robert Knights

TV director. Credits include: *The Glittering Prizes* (1976; BBC-TV; co-directed with Waris Husain); *The History Man* (1981; BBC-TV); *The Ebony Tower* (1984; Granada); *Tender is the Night*; *The Dawning* (1985; BBC-TV); *Porterhouse Blue* (1987; Channel Four).

Ian Knox

Film and TV director. Credits include: film: *The Stronger* (1980; National Film School), *The Privilege* (1982; HRP); TV: *Workhorses, Sweet Nothings, Shoot for the Sun, Down Where the Buffalo Go* – all BBC-TV; *Boon* (3 episodes; Central); *Saracen* (Central); *Valentine Falls* (Channel Four).

Bernard Krichefski

TV director and producer. Credits include: *Nanny* (from 1981); *Young Shoulders* (1984; *Play for Today*; producer), *Bird of Prey 2* (1984; producer), *Leaving Home* – all BBC-TV; *Family* and *Finding Sarah* (Channel Four).

Stanley Kubrick

Film director. Starting as a photographer on *Look* magazine, he made his first film – a short documentary called *Day of the Fight* – in 1950. Four years later, he set up his own production company to make *The Killing* with Sterling Hayden. He followed with *Paths of Glory* (1957), *Spartacus* (1960), *Lolita* (1962), *Dr Strangelove* (1964),

2001: A Space Odyssey (1968), *A Clockwork Orange* (1971), *Barry Lyndon* (1975), *The Shining* (1979), *Full Metal Jacket* (1987).

Barry Kyle

Theatre director. Currently associate director of the Royal Shakespeare Company. Gained a Thames TV director's bursary and went to Liverpool Playhouse where he became associate director to Antony Tuckey, and directed 21 productions including: *Saved, In Celebration, Hadrian VII, The Knack, St Joan* and *King Lear.* In 1972, he went to the Theatre Royal, York, as associate director, where *Forget-Me-Not Lane* and *The Investigation* were among his credits.

In 1973, he joined the RSC as assistant director, directing *Sylvia Plath* at The Place and co-directing *Cymbeline* and *King John* with John Barton. In 1974 he was director of The Place season in London, when he directed *Comrades* and co-directed several other productions. Work at The Other Place has included *The Churchill Play* by Howard Brenton, *The Maid's Tragedy* by Beaumont & Fletcher, *The Witch of Edmonton* (by Dekker, Ford & Rowley) and *Lear* by Edward Bond. Productions at the Warehouse have included *Sore Throats* and *Thirteenth Night* by Howard Brenton and *The Irish Play* by Ron Hutchinson. Other work for the RSC includes: *Measure for Measure; The White Guard* by Bulgakov; *The Taming of the Shrew; The Dillen* by Ron Hutchinson (adaptation of the book by Angela Hewins); Arthur Miller's *The Crucible; Golden Girls* by Louise Page; *Mary, After the Queen* (sequel to *The Dillen*); *Richard II; Two Noble Kinsmen.* In 1986, in Stratford, he directed *The Jew of Malta* and *Hyde Park,* both of which transferred to London for the 1988 season, when Kyle also directed *The Churchill Play* in the Barbican. Recent productions include *Moscow Gold; Dr Faustus;* and *All's Well That Ends Well.*

John Laing

Film director. Credits include: *Beyond Reasonable Doubt* (1980); *Other Halves* (1984).

Angela Langfield

Theatre director. Credits include: *Top Girls* (Leicester Haymarket); *Steaming* (Chester Gateway); *Blood Relations* (Derby Playhouse); *Season's Greetings* and *See How They Run* (Leeds Playhouse); *Billy Liar* and *Hobson's Choice* (Octagon Theatre, Bolton); *Kafka's Dick* (Leeds); *Hamlet* (Chester Gateway).

Simon Langton

TV and film director. Credits include: film: *The Whistle Blower* (with John Gielgud & Michael Caine); TV: *Smiley's People* (1982; BBC-TV), *I Remember Nelson* (1982; Central), *Thérèse Racquin; Rebecca* (1979; BBC-TV), *Anna Karenina* (CBS Ray Star), *Lost Honour of Katherine Beck* (CBS), *Mother Love* (BBC) and *Jeeves and Wooster.*

Mike Leigh

Playwright and theatre, TV and film director. Directed and designed the original production of *Little Malcolm and His Struggle Against the Eunuchs* at the Unity Theatre in 1965. Was associate director at the Midlands Arts Centre (1965–6) and assistant director at the Royal Shakespeare Company (1967–8). His first original piece for the stage was *The Box Play*, produced at the Midlands Arts Centre in 1966. All of his subsequent work, which he has scripted and directed, has evolved out of improvisation with actors. Theatre credits include: *Abigail's Party, Smelling A Rat; Greek Tragedy*. His recent film credits include *Life is Sweet* (1991).

David Leland

TV and film director and writer. Former actor. Wrote the screenplay for *Personal Services*, and for his directorial debut, delved further back into former madam Cynthia Payne's past with *Wish You Were Here*.

Leonard Lewis

TV, theatre and video director and producer. Credits include: *Softly Softly, When the Boat Comes In* (1975–7; producer), *The Prisoner of Zenda, Brat Farrar* and *Rockliffe's Babies, The Franchise Affair, Eastenders* – all BBC-TV; *Flambards* and *The Good Companions* (1980; producer) (Yorkshire TV); *Tales of the Unexpected* (Anglia).

Peter Lichtenfels

Theatre director. Began his career in summer stock theatre in Canada, then trained as a director at the Traverse Theatre in Edinburgh. Currently artistic director at the Haymarket Theatre, Leicester, where he has produced commercial hits as well as creating opportunities for new young directors, designers and writers. He also wants to develop a proper youth policy, to involve and educate the future young audience at the Haymarket.

Ken Loach

Film and TV director. Credits include: *Up the Junction* (1965; BBC *Wednesday Play*); *Cathy Come Home* (1966; BBC *Wednesday Play*); *Poor Cow* (1967); *Kes* (1969); *Family Life* (1971); *Days of Hope* (1976; BBC-TV).

Richard Loncraine

Film and TV director. Credits include: film: *Bellman and True* (1987), *Brimstone and Treacle* (1982), *The Missionary* (1983); TV: *Vanishing Army* (1978; BBC *Play for Today*), *Secret Orchards* (1979; Granada), *Blade on the Feather* (1980; LWT).

Mary Longford

Theatre director, often working with experimental material. Credits include: *A Bolt Out of the Blue* and *Looking for Something* (1985; Almeida); *Hilde's*

Opera (1980; The Venue); *Looking Through the Window* (1980; Drill Hall).

Vere Lorrimer

Theatre and TV director and TV producer. Directing credits include: theatre: *The Mousetrap* (1975, St Martin's); TV: *When the Boat Comes In.* As producer: *Blake's Seven* (from 1978); *Tenko* (1981–4); *Dark Side of the Sun; Maelstrom* (1985).

Robert Love

TV director and producer, currently controller of drama at Scottish TV. Credits include: *Van der Valk* (1972) and *Moody and Pegg* (1974) (Thames); *The House on the Hill* (1981; producer) and *Killer* (1983; producer) (STV); *Off-peak* (film); *The Marriage Contract* (opera); *Taggart* (STV); *Extras* (Channel 4 play); *Bookie* (STV).

Jonathan Lynn

Theatre and film director, actor and writer. Artistic director of the Cambridge Theatre Company (1977–81), directing 19 productions including *The Deep Blue Sea, Macbeth, The Relapse* and nine new plays and British premières. In London, has directed *The Plotters of Cabbage Patch Corner, The Glass Menagerie, The Gingerbread Man,* *The Unvarnished Truth, The Matchmaker, Arms and the Man, Pass the Butler, Loot* and *Songbook* (SWET award, 1979). For the Royal Shakespeare Company, he directed *Anna Christie,* and for the National Theatre, *A Little Hotel on the Side.* He has directed two short films – *Mick's People* and *The Case of the Shortsighted Boss* – and for Paramount, *Clue* (also wrote screenplay). In addition to many theatre and TV appearances as an actor, has written two series of *My Brother's Keeper* with George Layton and three series of *Yes Minister* (followed by *Yes Prime Minister*) with Anthony Jay. Recently, he has directed *Budgie,* the West End musical based on the early 1970s TV series. Recent work includes: *Three Men On A Horse* (Olivier Award Best Comedy); and *Nuns On The Run* (Handmade Films).

David McGillivray

Theatre director. Specializing in wacky comedy and alternative pantomime. Credits include: *The Farndale Avenue Housing Estate Townswomen's Guild Dramatic Society Production of Macbeth, The Haunted Through Lounge and Recessed Dining Nook at Farndale Castle, The Farndale . . . Murder Mystery, The Revenge of the Really Big Men, They Came from Mars . . .* (all with Entertainment Machine); *Living Skills* (King's Head).

John McGrath

Theatre and TV director and writer. Founded 7:84 Theatre Company in England in 1971 and in Scotland in 1973. Has written many stage plays, including: *Events while Guarding the Bofors Gun*; *The Cheviot, the Stag and the Black, Black Oil*; *Little Red Hen*; *Yobbo Nowt*; *Baby and the Bathwater*; *There Is a Happy Land*; *Bitter Apples* (musical); *Border Warfare*. Most of these were written for the 7:84 companies, and he directed many of them. He first came to prominence in TV in the 1960s, directing many of the early episodes of *Z Cars* (including the first one). At this time, he also wrote *The Diary of a Young Man* and *The Diary of a Nobody* (with Ken Russell). More recent TV productions he has written and directed include: *Come to Mecca* and *Dear Manju* (BBC-TV); *Sweetwater Memories* (1984; Channel 4); *Blood Red Roses* (1986; Channel 4); *There Is a Happy Land*. In film, he has worked with director Jack Gold on *The Bofors Gun* and *The Reckoning*, and wrote the film script for *The Virgin Soldiers*.

John Mackenzie

Film director. Credits include: *The Long Good Friday* (1980) and *The Fourth Protocol*.

Mary McMurray

TV, theatre and film director. Credits include: film: *The Assam Garden*; TV: *To Have and To Hold* (LWT), *Born in the RSA* (Channel 4), *Miss Marple* (1987; BBC-TV), *The Ruth Rendell Mysteries* (TVS); *Family* (Channel Four); *Spender* (BBC).

Terry Marcel

TV, film and theatre director. Credits include: theatre: *Dusa, Fish, Stas and Vi* (1985; Watermans Arts Centre); TV: *The Ferret* (1985); film: *Prisoners of the Lost Universe* (1982), *Hawk the Slayer* (1980); *There Goes the Bride* (1979); *Jane and the Lost City* (1987).

Nancy Meckler

Artistic director, Shared Experience. Productions include: *Abingdon Square, True West, Low Level Panic, The Bacchae, My Sister In This House, The Cherry Orchard, Who's Afraid Of Virginia Woolf?*

Peter Medak

Film and TV director. Film credits include: *A Day in the Death of Joe Egg* (1971), *Odd Job, Ghost in a Noonday's Sun* and *The Changeling* (1979 – all Columbia); *The Ruling Class* (1971; United Artists); *Zorro, the Gay Blade* (1981; Fox); *The Krays* (1989; Fugitive); *Negatives* (1968; Paramount). Also, over 100 hours of TV, including

Nabokov and *The Men's Club* for US public TV (PBS).

Nicholas Meyer

Film and TV director and writer. Credits include: film: *Time after Time* (1980; also screenplay), *Star Trek II: The Wrath of Khan* (1982); *The Deceivers* (1988; Merchant Ivory Films); TV: *The Day After* (1983; ABC). He has written several novels, including the bestseller *The Seven Per Cent Solution*, and the screenplay for the film adaptation. He has also written and re-written such screenplays as *Star Trek IV* and *Fatal Attraction*.

Roger Michell

Theatre director. Won the Buzz Goodbody prize in 1977 for his production of *Bingo* at the *Sunday Times* Student Drama Festival. Worked at the Royal Court for two years, where he assisted Beckett and Osborne and directed various plays in the Theatre Upstairs, including *The Key Tag* by Mike McGrath and *The Catch* by Nick Darke. Co-wrote and directed *The White Glove* with Richard Maher, which was performed at the Lyric, Hammersmith and in the West End. He then worked at Cambridge Theatre Company, Southampton, Hampstead, Brighton, Sheffield and at the Young Vic. Joining the Royal Shakespeare Company in 1984, he worked as assistant director and then directed the première of Nick Darke's *The Dead Monkey* for The Pit in 1986. He has directed two RSC/Nat West tour productions (*The Merchant of Venice* and *Hamlet*), the British première of Vaclav

Havel's *Temptation* for The Other Place and The Pit and, in 1988, *The Constant Couple*, *Restoration* and *Campesinos* for the Stratford season.

Robin Midgely

Freelance director. *One Flew Over The Cuckoo's Nest*, *Once In A Lifetime*, *The Fairy Queen*, *Someone Like You*, *Mrs Warren's Profession*, *The Taming Of The Shrew*, *Volpone*, *The Pilgrim*.

Gavin Millar

TV and film director. Credits include: film: *Dreamchild*; television: *Cream in My Coffee* (1980; LWT), *Intensive Care* (1982; BBC-TV), *The Weather in the Streets* (1984; BBC-TV), *The Russian Soldier* (1986), *Mr & Mrs Edgehill*; *Scoop*; *The Irons of Wrath*; *Tidy Endings*; *A Murder Of Quality*.

Jonathan Miller

Theatre and opera director and writer. Trained as a doctor of medicine, but sprang to prominence in the Cambridge Footlights in *Out of the Blue* in 1954. Co-wrote and appeared in *Beyond the Fringe* in 1960. More recent theatre credits as director include: *The Merchant of Venice* (National Theatre); *The Three Sisters*, *The Seagull* and *Long Day's Journey into Night* (London and Broadway); *The Emperor* (Royal Court); *The Taming of the Shrew* (Royal Shakespeare Company). He is currently artistic director of the Old Vic Theatre, where he has directed: *Andromache*; *One-Way Pendulum* (also

Royal Alexandra Theatre, Toronto); *Bussy D'Ambois*; *The Tempest*. Opera credits include: *Arabella*, *Otello*, *Rigoletto*, *Don Giovanni*, *The Magic Flute*, *Tosca*, *The Barber of Seville* and *The Mikado* for English National Opera, and productions for Scottish Opera (including *Candide*, with John Wells), Australian Opera, Los Angeles Opera and many others. Work for TV includes *The Body in Question*, *Cosi Fan Tutte* and 12 plays for the BBC Shakespeare series. He has written a number of books: *The Body in Question*; *States of Mind*; *The Human Body*; *Facts of Life*; *Subsequent Performances*.

Robert Ellis Miller

American film and TV director. Worked in TV before moving on to films. Film credits include: *The Buttercup Chain* (1970); *Hawks* (1988).

Christopher Morahan

Theatre, TV and film director. Studied at the Old Vic Theatre School under Michel St Denis and began directing at ATV, where his credits included *Emergency Ward 10*, *Probation Officer* and *John Gabriel Borkman* (1958). From 1961 to 1971 he worked as a freelance TV director on such productions as: *The Orwell Trilogy*; *Talking to a Stranger* (1966; BBC-TV); *The Ragged Trousered Philanthropists* (1967); *A Month in the Country*; *Uncle Vanya*; *The Gorge* (1968; BBC-TV); *Hearts and Flowers* (1970; BBC-TV); *Giants and Ogres*; *The Letter*; *The Chinese Prime Minister*. From 1972 to 1976, he was head of plays for BBC-TV, and directed *The Common* (1973; *Play of the Month*) and *Old Times*.

In 1982, he was co-director of *The Jewel in the Crown* for Granada, for which he received two British Academy Awards and an International Emmy.

After theatre work in the late 1960s and early '70s, which included *Little Murders*, *This Story of Yours*, *Flint* and *The Caretaker*, he joined the National Theatre and was deputy to the director (1979–80). His productions with the National have included *State of Revolution*, *Brand*, *Strife*, *The Philanderer*, *Richard III*, *Sisterly Feelings*, *Man and Superman* and, in 1984, *Wild Honey* with Ian McKellen, which won the Olivier, (London) *Evening Standard*, *Drama* and *Plays & Players* awards. Recently, he directed *In the Secret State* for the BBC, *Clockwise* for the cinema, Simon Gray's *After Pilkington* (a *Screen Two* success for the BBC), *Troubles* (Channel 4), *Old Flames*, *Can You Hear Me Thinking*, and *Paper Mask*.

Braham Murray

Theatre director and writer. Sprang to prominence while still at Oxford University when *Hang Down Your Head and Die*, which he co-wrote and directed, transferred to the West End and then to Broadway. Currently a resident artistic director of the Royal Exchange Company in Manchester, he had been artistic director of the Century Theatre and of the 69 Theatre Company in Manchester, directing, among other plays, *She Stoops to Conquer*, *Charley's Aunt*, *Mary Rose* and the musicals *'Erb* and *Catch My Soul*, all of which transferred to London. Other West End productions include *The Good Companions* (with John Mills and Judi Dench) and *The Black Mikado*. Among his many productions at the Royal Exchange are: *The Rivals*; *What*

the Butler Saw; Leaping Ginger; The
Dybbuk; Measure for Measure; Waiting
for Godot; Have You Anything to
Declare?; The Nerd (European première); Who's a Lucky Boy? (musical
conceived with Alan Price & Gerald
Scarfe); Riddley Walker (adaptation of
the cult novel by Russell Hoban). Most
recently, he has directed Court in the
Act, The Merchant of Venice and the
première of a new Woody Allen revue
The Bluebird of Unhappiness.

Neil Murray

Associate director, Dundee Repertory
Theatre, and freelance designer.
Productions he has directed include:
Equus, The Threepenny Opera, Phantom
of the Opera, Sweeney Todd, She Stoops to
Conquer, 'Tis Pity She's A Whore, David
Copperfield.

Ronald Neame

Film director. Credits include: The
Horse's Mouth (1958); Tunes of Glory
(1960); The Prime of Miss Jean Brodie
(1968); Scrooge (1970); The Poseidon
Adventure (1972); Hopscotch (1980); First
Monday in October (1982); Foreign Body
(1985).

Mike Newell

TV and film director. The Man in the
Iron Mask (1976; TV film); The
Awakening (1980); Dance with a Stranger

(1984); The Good Father (1986); Sour
Sweet (1987).

Adrian Noble

Theatre director. Artistic director of
the Royal Shakespeare Company
Worked for two years in Birmingham
in community and young people's
theatre and was accepted on the IBA
trainee director scheme. Went to
Bristol Old Vic where he became an
associate director; productions there
included: Ubu Rex; Man Is Man; A View
from the Bridge; Love for Love; Timon of
Athens; Comedians; The Recruiting
Officer. In 1979, he joined the RSC as
assistant director and worked on As
You Like It, Romeo and Juliet and Hamlet.
After a spell with the Royal Exchange
Theatre in Manchester (The Duchess of
Malfi with Helen Mirren and Dr
Faustus with Ben Kingsley), he re-
turned to Stratford to direct his first
RSC production, Ostrovsky's The
Forest, which transferred to London
and was named 'Best Revival' in the
1981 Drama awards. In 1982, he
directed King Lear (with Michael
Gambon and Anthony Sher) and
Antony and Cleopatra (with Michael
Gambon & Helen Mirren). Subsequent
productions for the RSC have in-
cluded: A New Way to Pay Old Debts by
Philip Massinger; The Comedy of Errors;
Measure for Measure; Henry V; The
Desert Air by Nicholas Wright; The
Winter's Tale; As You Like It; Mephisto
by Ariane Mnouchkine; Macbeth; The
Art of Success by Nick Dear; and for the
1988 season, Macbeth once again and
the Henry VI/Richard III cycle. Recent
work includes The Plantagenets;
Macbeth; The Master Builder.

Trevor Nunn

Director of theatre, opera, musicals and film. He won an ABC trainee director's scholarship to the Belgrade Theatre in Coventry and later became resident director there. In 1965, he became associate director of the Royal Shakespeare Company and, in 1968, artistic director. Work for the company in Stratford and London has included: *The Revenger's Tragedy*; *The Taming of the Shrew*; *The Relapse*; *King Lear*; *The Winter's Tale*; *Hamlet*; *Macbeth*; *Antony and Cleopatra*; *Hedda Gabler*; *Romeo and Juliet*; *The Comedy of Errors*; *As You Like It*; *The Alchemist*; *All's Well that Ends Well*; *Once in a Lifetime*; *Juno and the Paycock*; *The Life and Adventures of Nicholas Nickleby* (co-directed with John Caird) which made a successful transfer to Broadway and was shown on Channel 4. In 1982, he led the Royal Shakespeare Company into their new home in London at the Barbican, which opened with his production of *Henry IV Parts I & II*. This was followed by a Christmas production of *Peter Pan*. He has directed several highly successful musicals: *Chess*, *Starlight Express* and *Les Miserables* (which, with John Caird, his co-director, he also adapted from the Paris production). His Broadway production of *Cats* won a Tony award in 1983. Other recent credits include his first opera production at Glyndebourne, *Idomeneo* and the film, *Lady Jane*.

Mike Ockrent

Theatre director. From 1969 to 1973 was an ITV trainee director at the Perth Theatre, where he later became an associate director. He was artistic director of the Traverse Theatre (1973–6), where his productions included *To Damascus* and *Dream Play* by Strindberg and *Kasper* by Handke. In 1974, his production of Stanley Eveling's *Union Jack and Bonzo* played at the Hampstead Theatre, and *Schippel* (adapted by C. P. Taylor from Carl Sternheim's original) transferred to the Prince of Wales Theatre as *The Plumber's Progress* (with Harry Secombe). Other productions in the 1970s include: *The Merchant of Venice*; *Knickers* by Carl Sternheim; *Table Manners*; *The Admirable Crichton*; *Once a Catholic*; *See How They Run*; *A Respectable Wedding*; *One for the Road*; *A Nightingale Sang*. In 1980, he directed *Educating Rita* for the Royal Shakespeare Company, at the Warehouse, the Piccadilly Theatre and on tour. In 1982, he directed *Watch on the Rhine* by Lillian Hellman (starring Peggy Ashcroft) for the National Theatre, and Peter Nichol's *Passion Play* for the RSC and in Brussels. Other work includes: *Ducking Out* by Eduardo di Filippo at the Duke of York's Theatre; *Good* for the National Theatre of Belgium; *Short List* by Michael Rudman at the Hampstead Theatre; and *Inner Voices* by Eduardo di Filippo at the National Theatre. He has recently directed *Me and My Girl* at the Adelphi and *Follies* at the Shaftesbury.

Pat O'Connor

Film and TV director. Started with RTE in Ireland, making over 80 documentaries for them. Credits include: *Ballroom of Romance* (1982) and *One of Ourselves* (both BBC dramas), and the films *Cal* (1984), *A Month in the Country* (1987) and *Stars and Bars* (1988).

Horace Ové

Trinidadian-born film and TV director. Began his career as an independent film-maker in 1966 and, in 1986, won the BFI award for 'Independent Film and Television'. He has made the following short films: *The Art of the Needle* (1966); *Baldwin's Nigger* (1968); TV work includes: *Reggae* (1969; BBC documentary); *Coleherne Jazz and Keskidee Blues* (1972; BBC); *King Carnival* (1973; BBC *World About Us*); *Pressure* (1974); *Skateboard Kings* (1978; BBC *World About Us*); *Empire Road* (1978; BBC sit-com); *A Hole in Babylon* (1979; BBC); *The Latchkey Children* (1980; Thames); *The Professionals* (1981; LWT); *Shai Mala Khani/The Garland* (1981; BBC); *Music Fusion* (1982; Channel 4); *Good at Art* (1983; BBC); *Street Arts* (1983; Channel 4); *The Record* (1984, Channel 4); *Living Colour* (1985, Channel 4); *Moving Portraits* (1985, Channel 4); *Who Shall We Tell?* (1985; Channel 4 documentary about Bhopal); *Dabbawallahs* (1985; Channel 4); *Playing Away* (1987; *Film Four International*). Work in progress: feature film on the life of Charlie Parker and one on Phoolan Devi, the Bandit Queen of India, for Channel 4; also an adaptation of James Baldwin's novel *Giovanni's Room*.

'Here in England – all you are allowed to make is films about black people and their problems . . . that's why I made *Pressure* – I was tired of reading in the papers about young blacks hanging about on street corners, mugging old ladies. Nobody tried to find out why they were doing it . . . It was the same with *Hole in Babylon* (about the hold-up of the Spaghetti House restaurant by three young blacks and the resulting siege). The men in the siege were represented as a bunch of hooligans. Nobody looked at their backgrounds. They never went into the fact that they had a political motivation – that they wanted to set up a centre. One of them was a medical student, one was a poet and a writer and one of them had a background of mental illness . . .' Talking about *Giovanni's Room*: 'It will be the first time a black director has made a film just about white people. It will be fascinating to see the results' (Horace Ové talking to Sylvia Paskin).

Tony Palmer

Film and TV director. Credits include: *All My Loving* (1968; BBC-TV); *There Was a Time* (1980; LWT); *Once at a Border*; *Wagner* (1983; Channel 4); *At the Haunted End of the Day* (1981; LWT); *God Rot Tunbridge Wells*; *Richard Burton*, a film biography (1988; LWT); *Shostakovich*.

Alan Parker

Film director. Credits include: *Bugsy Malone* (1976); *Midnight Express* (1978); *Fame* (1980); *Shoot the Moon* (1981); *Pink Floyd: The Wall* (1982); *Birdy*; *Angel Heart* (1987); *Mississippi Burning* (1988); *Come See The Paradise* (1990).

Julia Pascal

Theatre director. Credits include: *Men Seldom Make Passes* (1978; National

Theatre); *The Caretaker* (1981; British Council tour); *James Joyce and the Israelites* (1982; Lyric Studio); *Mary's Men* (1984; Drill Hall); *Grombeen* (1985; Air Gallery); *Traitors* (Drill Hall); *The German Connection* (1986; Young Vic Studio); *Ghetto* (1987; Riverside Studios).

Raj Patel

Theatre, video and film director. Credits include: theatre: *Ahmed the Wonderful Oriental Gentleman*, *A Man I Never Knew*, *Anarkali* (all with British Asian Theatre, London); video: *Video Wicked*, *Caught in a Tangled Web* (also film; Star Productions).

Ron Peck

Film director. Credits include: *Nighthawks* (1979); *Empire State* (1987). *Empire State* is another film on the theme of docklands corruption, described by Mark Finch in the *Monthly Film Bulletin* as 'Not so much a side swipe at Thatcher's Britain as a last-gasp lunge at the throat.'

Harold Pinter

Playwright and theatre, film and TV director. Plays in chronological order are: *The Room*, *The Birthday Party*, *The Dumb Waiter*, *A Slight Ache*, *The Hothouse*, *A Night Out*, *The Caretaker*, *The Dwarfs*, *Night School*, *The Collection*, *The Lover*, *Tea Party*, *The Homecoming*, *The Basement*, *Landscape*, *Silence*, *Old Times*, *Monologue*, *No Man's Land*, *Betrayal*, *Family Voices*, *Victoria Station*, *A Kind of Alaska*, *One for the Road*. Screenplays: *The Servant* (1963); *The Pumpkin Eater* (1964); *The Quiller Memorandum* (1966); *Accident* (1967); *The Go-Between* (1970); *Langrishe Go Down*; *The Last Tycoon* (1976); *A la recherche du temps perdu*; *The French Lieutenant's Woman* (1981); *Turtle Diary*; and screenplays of his own plays: *The Caretaker* (1964); *The Birthday Party* (1968); *The Homecoming* (1973); *Betrayal* (1982). For the stage, he has directed: *The Collection* (co-directed with Peter Hall); *The Lover*; *The Birthday Party*; *The Hothouse*; Robert Shaw's *The Man in the Glass Booth*; James Joyce's *Exiles*; John Hopkin's *Next of Kin*; *Blithe Spirit*; William Archibald's *The Innocents* and six plays by Simon Gray (*Butley*, *Otherwise Engaged*, *The Rear Column*, *Close of Play*, *Quartermaine's Terms*, *The Common Pursuit*). Recent West End direction includes *Sweet Bird of Youth* by Tennessee Williams at the Theatre Royal, Haymarket (starring Lauren Bacall). For TV, he has directed *The Rear Column* and *Hothouse*, and film credits as a director include *Butley*. October 1988 saw the première at the National Theatre of *Mountain Language*, a 25-minute play which he also directed.

Stephen Poliakoff

Writer and TV and film director. Wrote his first play – *Day with My Sister* – while still at school; it was directed by David Halliwell at the Traverse Theatre, Edinburgh. Writer-in-residence at the National Theatre in 1976. As a TV scriptwriter, credits include: *Stronger than the Sun* (1977; BBC *Play for Today*); *City Sugar* (1978; STV); *Bloody Kids* (1980; ATV); *Caught on a Train* (1980; BBC); *Soft*

Targets (1982; BBC). Has directed some of the later productions. Film credits: *Strawberry Fields* (1986; Marten Teagen Films/Channel 4); *Runners* (screenplay, 1983).

Angela Pope

TV director and producer. Credits include: *Lol – A Bona Queen, The Treble* and *Shiftwork* for BBC-TV; *A Childhood* (series for Channel 4); *Sweet as You Are* with Liam Neeson and Miranda Richardson; *Dream Baby* (1989); *Children Crossing* (1990); *Mr Wakefield's Crusade* (1991).

Tristram Powell

TV director (drama and documentary). Credits include: *The Ghost Writer* by Philip Roth (1983; WGBH (Boston)/BBC); *My Dinner with Louis* (1983; BBC-TV); *Karen Blixen; Out of Africa* (1985; BBC/Danish TV); *The Journey Man: Norman Lewis, Travel Writer* (1985; BBC); *Alfred Hitchcock* (2-part documentary; 1986; BBC); *East of Ipswich* by Michael Palin (1987; BBC-TV); *The Temptation of Eileen Hughes, Soldiering On*.

Bill Pryde

Theatre director. Has worked at the Traverse Theatre, Edinburgh and was Scottish Arts Council trainee director at the Royal Lyceum, Edinburgh, associate director at the Young Lyceum and associate director of the Birmingham Repertory Theatre (main house and studio) for six years.

Productions there included: *All's Well that Ends Well; The Merchant of Venice; King Lear; Romeo and Juliet; She Stoops to Conquer; The Elder Statesman; Lady from the Sea; The Masterbuilder;* and Rogers and Hammerstein's *Cinderella*. Also directed the premières of Stephen Bill's *The Old Order* (John Whiting Award, 1980), Vince Foxall's *Gestures* (John Whiting Award, 1979) and *Strictly Entre Nous*, as well as Michael Hasting's *Midnite at the Starlite* and the British premières of *The Wicked Cooks*, Tremblay's *Hosanna* (Half Moon, London & Birmingham) and Vampilov's *Last Summer in Chulimsk*. Productions as artistic director of the Cambridge Theatre Company include: *George and Margaret; The Miser; Hayfever; The Vortex; Canaries Sometimes Sing*. In 1986, he directed the Birmingham Repertory and Leicester Haymarket production of *Pride and Prejudice* at the Old Vic. In 1988, he resigned as director of the Cambridge Theatre Company (*see* Touring companies). He subsequently directed *The Homecoming; The Way Of The World*.

Michael Radford

Film director and writer. Credits as director include: *Another Time, Another Place* (1983); *1984* (1984); *White Mischief* (1987).

John Reardon

Television producer and director. Credits include: *Two's Company* (1976–8; LWT); *Agony* (producer; 1979–81; LWT); *Whoops Apocalypse!* (1982; LWT); *We'll Meet Again* (1982; LWT);

Drummonds (1985; LWT); *Me and My Girl*; *London's Burning*.

John Retallack

Founded Actors Touring Company in 1978; awarded SWET award for *The Life And Death Of Don Quixote* and *The Provok'd Wide*; four years as Artistic Director of Oldham Coliseum and became Artistic Director of Oxford Stage Company in 1989.

Peter Richardson

Film and TV director and producer, writer and actor. Has been part of the Comic Strip team since 1979, devoting all his time to its productions. Credits include: *Five Go Mad in Dorset*, *A Fistful of Travellers Cheques*, *Gino* and, recently, *The Strike* (all seen on Channel 4); also *Supergrass* and *Eat the Rich*, which went on general release.

Bruce Robinson

Film director and writer. Has written 25 screenplays including *Withnail and I* (1986; Handmade Films) about life as a struggling actor in London at the end of the 1960s. Recently directed *How to Get Ahead in Advertising*.

Robert Robson

Artistic director, Dundee Repertory Theatre, since 1976. Most recent productions include: *The Cherry Orchard*, *When The Wind Blows*, *The Playboy Of*

The Western World, *A Man At Yir Back*, *The Turn Of The Screw*.

Nicolas Roeg

Film director. Began as a clapper boy and worked as a cinematographer before becoming a director in the 1970s. Credits include: *Performance* (co-directed with Donald Cammell; 1970); *Walkabout* (1971); *Don't Look Now* (1973); *The Man Who Fell to Earth* (1976); *Bad Timing* (1979); *Eureka* (1983); *Insignificance* (1984); *Castaway* and *Track 29* (1987).

Peter Rowe

Artistic director, Chester Gateway. Productions include: *The Elephant Man*, *Educating Rita*, *Ashes*, (all for Thorndike, Leatherhead); *Trafford Tanzi*, *School For Clowns*, *Stroll On*, (Solent People's Theatre); *Blood Brothers*, *A Midsummer Night's Dream*, *It's A Girl*, *The Cabaret Of Dr. Caligari*, *I Fought Yuppie Zombies From Hell* (London Bubble); *Cinderella And Her Rockin' Fella* (Liverpool Everyman); *Macbeth* (British Council Tour); *Our Day Out* (Chester Gateway).

Michael Rudman

Theatre director. He has directed at many regional theatres, among them Sheffield Playhouse; the Belgrade, Coventry; Theatre Royal, Bath; The Palace, Watford; the Citizens, Glasgow; and for the Royal Shakespeare Company Stratford and the Dublin

Festival. Assistant director at Nottingham Playhouse (1964–9), director of the Traverse Theatre, Edinburgh (1970–3), artistic director of Hampstead Theatre (1973–8) and director of the Lyttelton Theatre at the National from 1979 to 1982. West End productions have included: *Straight Up*; *Donkey's Years*; *Taking Steps*; *The Dragon's Tail*; *Camelot*. On Broadway, he has directed *The Changing Room*, *Death of a Salesman* and *Hamlet*. At the National Theatre (of which he is an associate director) his productions have included: *For Services Rendered*; *Death of a Salesman*; *Thee and Me*; *The Browning Version*; *Harlequinade*; *Measure for Measure*; *The Second Mrs Tanqueray*; *Brighton Beach Memoirs* by Neil Simon; *Ting Tang Mine* by Nick Darke (at the Cottesloe); *Waiting for Godot* (with Alec McCowen and John Alderton); *Six Characters in Search of an Author*; *Fathers and Sons* (a new adaptation of the Turgenev novel by Brian Friel).

Ken Russell

Film and TV director. Has worked as a ballet dancer and freelance photographer. Started working for BBC-TV as producer and director of arts programmes in the late 1950s, and gained fame by series of film biographies of leading composers. Once the *enfant terrible* of British cinema, his films are still often controversial. Credits include: *French Dressing* (1963); *Billion Dollar Brain* (1967); *Women in Love* (1969); *The Music Lovers* (1971); *The Devils* (1971); *The Boy Friend* (1972); *Savage Messiah* (1972); *Mahler* (1974); *Tommy* (1975); *Lisztomania* (1975); *Valentino* (1977); *Altered States* (1979); and, recently: *Salome's Last Dance*,

Gothic, *The Rainbow* and *The Lair of the White Worm*.

Jan Sargent

Theatre and TV director. Credits include: theatre: *Who's Afraid of Virginia Woolf?* (1982; Bristol Old Vic); TV: *Fire at Magilligan* (1984; BBC *Play for Today*), *Flowers Tomorrow* (BBC-TV), *The Cause of Liberty* (BBC-TV), *Without Prejudice*; *Winner Stays On*; *A Long Way Away*; *Juliet Bravo*; *Black Silk*; *Perfect Scoundrels*; *Big Deal*; *Truckers*.

Peter Sasdy

Film and TV director. Credits include: film: *The Lonely Lady* (1983); TV: Hammer House of Mystery and Suspense (3 films), *Lytton's Diary* (1985; Thames); *Secret Diary of Adrian Mole* (1985; Thames); *Blacke's Magic* (1986; NBC/MCA); *The Growing Pains of Adrian Mole*; *Imaginary Friends*; *It Had To Be You*; *Making News*; *Sherlock Holmes And The Leading Lady*.

John Schlesinger, CBE

Film director. Acted in student plays at Oxford and played character parts in the 1950s before joining the BBC as a director. In 1961, he won first prize at the Venice Film Festival for *Terminus*, a documentary about London's Waterloo Station. Credits include: *A Kind of Loving* (1962); *Billy Liar* (1963); *Darling* (1968); *Far from the Madding Crowd* (1967); *Midnight Cowboy* (1969; Academy Awards for 'Best Picture' & 'Best Director'); *Sunday*

Bloody Sunday (1971); *Marathon Man* (1976); *Yanks* (1979); *True West*; *Les Contes d'Hoffman*; *The Falcon and the Snowman*; *The Believers* and *Madame Sousatzka* (1988). For television: *An Englishman Abroad* (1983; BBC-TV); *Pacific Heights* (1990; Film).

Ridley Scott

Film director. A highly successful director of commercials, where he learned his craft. Film credits (mostly American) include: *The Duellists* (1977); *Alien* (1979); *Blade Runner* (1982); *Legend*; *Back to the Future* (1984); *Someone To Watch Over Me* (1987); *Black Rain* (1989).

Don Sharp

Film and TV director. Credits include: TV: *Woman of Substance*, *Hold the Dream*, *Tusitala*, *QED*; *Act Of Will*; *The Four Feathers* (1976; NBC); film: *Bear Island* (1979); *The 39 Steps* (1978); *Hennessy* (1975).

Bob Spiers

TV director. Long-time Comic Strip collaborator. Credits include: *Dad's Army*; *Fawlty Towers*; *Not the Nine O'Clock News*; and recently, for the Comic Strip: *Didn't You Kill My Brother?*

Max Stafford-Clark

Theatre director. Currently artistic director of the English Stage Company at the Royal Court Theatre in London. Has worked at the Traverse Theatre in Edinburgh and was a founder member of Joint Stock Theatre Group. Out of the Joint Stock adaptation of William Hinton's classic about the revolution in China, *Fanshen*, emerged the concept of a company that was run by all its constituents. Successful productions at the Royal Court have included Caryl Churchill's *Top Girls* and *Serious Money*. In 1988, after a row over the announcement, then cancellation, of Jim Allen's play *Perdition*, Stafford-Clark's contract as artistic director was not automatically renewed, but he applied for the job and, against strong opposition, won it back. He feels very much that: 'If you are involved with new work and new writing, which is where my career has been for 20 years in the theatre, then the Royal Court is the centre of the world, not just the staging post en route to the Himalayas of the South Bank' (from an interview with Jane Edwardes in *Time Out*). Recent credits include *The Recruiting Officer* and *Our Country's Good*.

Lou Stein

Theatre director. Currently artistic director at the Palace Theatre, Watford. Formerly director of the Chicago Chamber Theatre Ensemble and of the Gate Theatre Club at the Latchmere in London. Credits include: *Fear and Loathing in Las Vegas* (Gate Theatre and Fortune Theatre); *Down and Out in Paris and London* (Edinburgh Festival);

Spotted Dick; Madame Bovary; Are You Sitting Comfortably?; So Long on Lonely Street (British première). In an interview in *Plays & Players* (May 1987), he deplores the lack of funding: 'Despite the reputation of the theatre as a leading repertory company, the Palace Theatre is funded as a small repertory company. The pressure to do 100% business is great, since it is the only way we can maintain the high standard of work.' He hopes to attract younger and more minority audiences to the theatre, and this is reflected in his choice of casting – for instance, Claire Benedict, a young black actress, in *So Long on Lonely Street*.

Simon Stokes

Theatre director. Credits include: *Lone Star, Private Wars, The Miss Firecracker Contest, Topokana Martyrs Say, When I Was a Girl I Would Scream and Shout, California Dog Fight, Kiss of the Spiderwoman* and *The Garden Girls* – all at the Bush Theatre; and *When I Was a Girl . . .* at the Whitehall Theatre; *The Glass Menagerie* for Cambridge Theatre; *The Debutant Ball* for Hampstead.

Charles Sturridge

Film and TV director. Has worked on promotional pop videos. Credits include: television: *Brideshead Revisited* (1981); film: *Runners* (1983); *A Handful of Dust* (1988).

Jeremy Summers

TV and video director, also commercials. Credits include: *Tenko* (1982 and 1984), *Strangers & Brothers* (1984) and *Big Deal* (1984–5) (all BBC-TV); *Coronation Street* (6 episodes; Granada); *Search for Tomorrow* (TV video productions; NBC); *Truckers* for BBC-TV; *All Creatures Great And Small* (BBC-TV); *The Bill* (Thames); *Howard's Way* (BBC-TV).

Jeff Teare

Freelance director. Theatre Royal, Stratford East: *The Fighting Kite, Twelfth Night, Dick Whittington, World Storytime, Revolting Peasants*.

David Thacker

Theatre director. Began work as a stage manager at York Theatre Royal, where he became assistant director in 1975. In 1976 he was awarded an Arts Council assistant director's bursary and went to the Chester Gateway Theatre. In 1978, he set up Rolling Stock Theatre Company in Crewe, which specialized in young people's and community theatre. In 1979, he became Arts Council assistant director at the Duke's Playhouse in Lancaster, in 1980 becoming director there. Appointed director of the Young Vic in 1984, and has since directed: *Othello; The Jail Diary of Albie Sachs; Stags and Hens; Macbeth; Hamlet; Measure for Measure; The Enemies Within; The Crucible; Romeo and Juliet; A Midsummer Night's Dream; Some Kind of Hero; Julius*

Caesar; Ghosts (with Vanessa Redgrave); *A Touch of the Poet* (with Timothy Dalton and Vanessa Redgrave); *An Enemy of the People; Pericles; Two Gentlemen Of Verona.*

Gerald Thomas

Film and light entertainment director. Credits include: film: *Time Lock* (1957), *Vicious Circle* (1957), *Please Turn Over* (1959), *Twice Round the Daffodils* (1962), and all *Carry On* films; TV: *Carry On* series (Thames and BBC); *Just for Laughs* (Thames).

Ralph Thomas

Film director. Credits include: *Doctor in the House* (1954); *Tale of Two Cities* (1962); *No Love for Johnnie* (1966); *The Wind Cannot Read* (1969); *The Biggest Bank Robbery* (1980); *Pop Pirates* (1984).

Bob Tomson

Artistic director, Queen's Theatre, Hornchurch. Has worked at Liverpool Everyman, Avon Touring, Cleveland, Coventry, Belfast, The Shaw, The Cockpit, and Theatr Powys. Productions include: *Having A Ball, Funny Peculiar, Jesus Christ Superstar, Oliver!, James And The Giant Peach, West Side Story, One Careful Owner, Hair, Grease* and currently at the Albery, *Blood Brothers.*

Wendy Toye

Theatre, opera, musicals director and producer. Credits include: *Madwoman of Chaillot* (Shaw Festival Theatre, Canada); *Kiss Me, Kate* (Copenhagen); *Once Upon a Mattress* (director & choreographer, Watermill Theatre); *Laburnham Grove* (1987; Palace Theatre, Watford); *Miranda* (1987; Chichester Festival); *Moll Flanders;* (Watermill, Bangor); *Heavens Up* (Playhouse Theatre).

Di Trevis

Theatre director. The first woman director of a company at the National Theatre. Started her career as an actor with Glasgow Citizens, Sheffield Crucible and at the National Theatre. However, a frustration with the passivity of the actor's role and a need to explore 'the whole experience' rather than one aspect of it led her into directing. Productions at the National have included: *The Taming of the Shrew; Miss Julie; Happy End; The Mother; School for Wives; Yerma.* She has also directed *The Revenger's Tragedy* for the Royal Shakespeare Company. She has directed a large proportion of classic scripts and revivals, and in an interview with Naseem Khan in *Plays & Players* (March 1987) said: '. . . It's a political decision. I realized quite early on that women were beginning to emerge into the fringe. And I felt there was really a place for women to work in the classical field because that history belongs to us too, even though it's being brought to us by men.'

Robert Tronson

TV and theatre director. Credits include: *Murder of a Moderate Man* (episode of *Sharing Time* series; 1984) and *Bergerac* for BBC-TV; *Boon* (Central); *Chelworth* and *Campion* (BBC-TV); *The Darling Buds Of May*.

Michael Tuchner

TV and film director. Credits include: TV: *Barmitzvah Boy* (1976; BBC); *The One and Only Phyllis Dixey* (1978; Thames); *Summer of My German Soldier* (1979; NBC); *The Hunchback of Notre Dame* (1982; CBS); *Adam* (1983; NBC); *Haywire* (1980); *Not My Kid* (1985); *Amos* (1985); *Trapped in Silence*; *At Mother's Request* (all CBS); *Wilt* (1989; Rank).

Colin Tucker

TV director and producer. Credits include: *The Waterfall, Fair Stood the Wind for France* (1981) and *The Gathering Seed* (producer; 1983) – all BBC-TV; *Drummonds* (producer; 1985; LWT).

David Tucker

TV and film director. Credits include: *Honeymoon* (1985; BBC *Play for Today*); *The Holy Experiment* (1985; BBC *Play of the Month*); *A Very Peculiar Practice* (1987–8; BBC-TV); *Miss Marple: Nemesis* (1986; BBC-TV); *It's in the Can* (sponsored film for Video Arts); *Ticket to Ride* (1988); *The Gravy Train* (1989; Channel Four); *Coasting* (1990); *Stanley And The Women* (1991).

Jonnie Turpie

Video director. Credits include: *Out of Order* (Birmingham Film and Video Workshop, in association with British Film Institute and Channel 4). The latest in a line of remarkable collaborations between Birmingham Film & Video Workshop and Dead Honest Soul Searchers Group (DHSS) in Telford, who make videos which 'are not products of television professionals' notions of what young people are supposed to want; rather, they represent a pioneering form of direct communication between the young, using their own distinct verbal and visual language' (Julian Petley, *Monthly Film Bulletin*, August 1988).

Charles Vance

Theatre director and producing manager. Began his career as an actor at the Gaiety Theatre, Dublin, and subsequently played leading roles in numerous national tours of the UK. Directed his first production – *The Glass Menagerie* – at The Arts Theatre, Cambridge in 1960. Recent credits include: *The Mating Game; Bubbling Brown Sugar* (Germany); *Jack and the Beanstalk; Dick Whittington; Sleeping Beauty; Cinderella; A Taste of Honey; Policy for Murder* by Tony Clayton; *Verdict* by Agatha Christie; *Jane Eyre; Wuthering Heights; Spider's Web; The Other Day In Rome*.

Mike Vardy

TV, video and theatre director. Credits include: *Let's Run Away to Africa* (Yorkshire TV); *Heart Attack Hotel* (1983); *Time and the Conways*, *A Still Small Shout*, *Thunder Rock*, *Bon Voyage*, *Claws* (all BBC-TV); *Capital City* (1989; Euston); *The Bill* (Thames).

Clare Venables

Theatre director. Artistic director of the Crucible Theatre, Sheffield. Recent credits include: *The Importance of Being Earnest*, *The Park* and *The Cherry Orchard* (with Steve Pimlott). 'The whirlpool of a writer meeting an audience via an actor creates energy which may, in the long term, raise us out of the depression under which we're living to remind us that it is only developed, imaginative individuals working as a group that can effect change that is worth making . . . The Crucible has the perfect name for the activity – a place where high-quality ingredients are melted together to be transformed into something greater than the sum of its parts . . . The reality is meetings, worries, arguments, computers, order forms, too-short rehearsals, too-small workshops . . .' (from an article by Clare Venables in *Plays & Players*, August 1987).

Jatinder Verma

Artistic director, Tara Arts. Wrote or adapted and directed over forty stage productions for Tara Arts, which he established in 1976. Productions range from those exploring contemporary Asian issues in Britain (*Chilli In Your Eyes*, and *Yes, Memsahib*); to European and Indian classics including *The Broken Thigh*, *The Little Clay Cart*, *The Government Inspector*, *Danton's Death*, *The Proposal*. In 1990 became the first director from among Britain's ethnic communities to be invited to direct at the Royal National Theatre, where he produced his own adaptation of *Tartuffe*.

Voytek

Theatre and TV director and designer. Credits include: TV: *Four People*, *Pilgrim's Progress*, *Frankenstein*, *Office Party*, *Callan*, *Joke* and *Sean* (4 episodes of adaptation of Sean O'Casey's autobiography); theatre: *Desire under the Elms*.

Glen Walford

Theatre director. Artistic director (until spring 1989) of the Everyman Theatre in Liverpool, where her credits include: *Tosca*; *Hamlet* and *The Winter's Tale*. Artistic director of Chung-Ying Company, Hong Kong (1979–82). Previous theatre work includes: *Return to the Forbidden Planet* (Tricycle Theatre, London); *Archangels Don't Play Pinball* (Theatre Royal, Bristol); *Much Ado about Nothing* (Rhyming Theatre Company, Tokyo); *Animal Farm* (tour of Malaysia). Recently: *Comedy of Errors* for the English Shakespeare Company.

Robert Walker

Theatre and TV director. Previously director of the Half Moon Theatre, London, where productions included: *Can't Pay? Won't Pay!* (also West End); *Alfredo Guarez – Twelve Shifts of Gear* by Juan Vera; *Guys and Dolls*; *Woyzeck*; *Mahagonny – The Songspiel* by Brecht and Weill; *Hamlet*; *Mayakovsky* by Stefan Schutz. Other credits include: theatre: *Pal Joey* (Albery Theatre and Half Moon); *Yakety Yak!* (West End); TV: *Night Kids* and *Angels in the Annexe* (BBC *Plays for Today*); *Deasey Desperate* (BBC film); *Dead Ahead* (BBC 4-part series by Howard Brenton); *Way to Go* (R. Walker Productions/Channel 4).

Deborah Warner

Theatre director. Currently resident director at the Royal Shakespeare Company. Trained as a stage manager at Central School of Speech and Drama, and worked at the Orange Tree and New End theatres and as an administrator for Steven Berkoff's London Theatre Group. In 1980, she decided to form her own theatre company to see if she could direct, and called it 'Kick' to symbolize energy. Kick quickly earned an international reputation for its highly innovative Shakespearean productions – *The Tempest*, *Measure for Measure*, *Hamlet*, *King Lear* and *Coriolanus* – many of which toured worldwide and three of which won Fringe Firsts at the Edinburgh Festival. Other productions with Kick were: *The Good Person of Setzuan* and *Woyzeck*. In 1986, she received the *Time Out* award for 'Director of the Year', and the next year was invited to Bangladesh to

direct Bengali actors in a new version of *The Tempest*. In 1987, the Royal Shakespeare Company asked her to direct *Titus Andronicus* at the Swan Theatre in Stratford, which was a resounding critical success and transferred to The Pit. In 1988, she became a resident director at the RSC, and has directed *King John* at The Other Place and Sophocles' *Electra* at The Pit.

Keith Washington

Theatre and TV director. Credits include: theatre: *Gimme Shelter* and *An Empty Desk* (both Royal Court); TV: *Angels*, *Brookside*, *Gems*, *Collectors*, *Howard's Way*, *Rockcliffe's Babies*, *Casualty*, *The Bill*.

Les Waters

Theatre director. Credits include: *Fen* and *A Mouthful of Birds* (Joint Stock Theatre Group); *Fen* and *Rum and Coke* (Public Theatre, New York); *Abel's Sister* and *The Overgrown Path* (Royal Court); *The Seagull* (Liverpool Playhouse); *Fanshen* (National Theatre); *School For Scandal* (Bristol Old Vic); *Ice Cream/Hot Fudge* (Public Theatre, New York).

Tony Wharmby

The two police series, *Dempsey and Makepeace* and *The Gentle Touch*, were created and directed by Tony Wharmby. He also directed: episodes of *Lillie*, the biography of Lillie Langtry, actress and mistress of the Prince of Wales; *We'll Meet Again*;

Bouquet of Barbed Wire (also adapted by him from Andrea Newman's novel); *Enemy at the Door; Love for Lydia; Helen, A Woman of Today.* As an executive producer, he has been responsible for the action adventure series *The Professionals; Eighteen Months to Balcombe Street,* a docu-drama about the IRA, nominated for the BAFTA award for Best Docu-Drama; and TV films by Dennis Potter and Alan Bennett. He has won many awards in Britain and the US.

Clifford Williams

Theatre director. Was made an associate director of the Royal Shakespeare Company in 1963 and has directed over 30 productions there, including plays by Shakespeare, Marlowe, Webster, Shaw, Durrenmatt, Rudkin, Hochhuth and Solzhenitsyn. He has also directed for the national theatres of Great Britain, Yugoslavia, Finland, Bulgaria, Mexico and Spain, as well as in Japan, France, Denmark, the US, Sweden, Canada and West Germany. West End credits include: *The Old Country* by Alan Bennett; *Born in the Gardens* by Peter Nichols; *What Every Woman Knows* by J. M. Barrie; *Too Good to Be True* by G. B. Shaw; *Wild Oats* by John O'Keefe; *Sleuth* by Anthony Shaffer; Pirandello's *Henry IV; Overheard* by Peter Ustinov; Lonsdale's *Aren't We All?*; Whitemore's *Stevie, Pack of Lies* and *Breaking the Code* (with Derek Jacobi) at the Theatre Royal, Haymarket and on Broadway. He has recently directed Jacobi in *Richard II* and *Richard III.*

Terence Williams

TV director and producer. Credits include: *Juliet Bravo* (producer); *The Chinese Detective* (producer, 1981); *Give Us a Break; Big Deal* (producer; 1984–5) and *Truckers* (8-part film series) – all for BBC-TV.

Ronald Wilson

TV director. Credits include: *To Serve Them All My Days* (1980); *Frost in May* (1982); *Strangers and Brothers* (1984) – all BBC-TV; *Sam Hughes's War* (CBC); *Drummonds* (1985; LWT); *The Black Tower* (Anglia); *The Bretts* (Central); *The London Embassy* (1987; Thames); *Ghost Story* (1990; BBC).

Michael Winner

Film director. Began making films for the BBC in the mid-1950s. Often works in Hollywood, where he has been responsible for several Charles Bronson blockbusters. Credits include: *Play It Cool* (1962); *I'll Never Forget What's 'is Name* (1967); *The Games* (1970); *Lawman* (1971); *Scorpio* (1972); *The Mechanic* (1972); *Death Wish* (1974); *Death Wish II* (1981); *The Wicked Lady* (1982); *Scream for Help* (1983); *Death Wish III* (1985); *Appointment with Death* (1987); *A Chorus Of Disapproval* (1988); *Bullseye* (1989).

Peter Wood

Theatre, opera, film and TV director. In the West End, he has directed *The*

Bald Prima Donna/The New Tennant; No Laughing Matter; The Wit to Woo; The Iceman Cometh; The Birthday Party; Who's Your Father?; Mary Stuart; Five Finger Exercise; The Private Ear and the Public Eye; Loot; Incident at Vichy; The Prime of Miss Jean Brodie; White Liars/Black Comedy; Dear Love; Night and Day; Windy City; The Real Thing; Wildfire. For the Royal Shakespeare Company, he has directed *The Devils, Hamlet, The Beggar's Opera* and *Travesties.* Wood is an associate director of the National Theatre; productions there include: *The Master Builder; Love for Love; Jumpers* (1972 and 1976); *The Guardsman; The Double Dealer; Undiscovered Country; The Provok'd Wife; On the Razzle; The Rivals; Rough Crossing; Dalliance; Threepenny Opera; The American Clock.* Opera credits include *Don Giovanni* at the Royal Opera House, and *Macbeth* and *Otello* at the Vienna State Opera. Recent work includes Tom Stoppard's *Hapgood* at the Aldwych Theatre.

Peter Yates

Film and theatre director. Trained at RADA, and worked as an actor and stage manager before directing his first plays – *An American Dream* by Edward Albee and *The Death of Bessie Smith* at the Royal Court. In New York, he directed Steve Tesich's *Passing Games* at the American Palace Theatre. For TV, he directed episodes for *Danger Man, The Saint* and other series. He has directed 16 feature films, including *Summer Holiday* (1963), *One-Way Pendulum* (1964), *Bullitt* (1968), *The Friends of Eddie Coyle* (1973), and *Breaking Away* by Steve Tesich and *The Dresser* by Ronald Harwood, for both of which he received Academy Award nominations as director and producer. Recent films include *Eleni,* starring Kate Nelligan and John Malkovich, and *The House on Carroll Street* (1988).

Robert William Young

TV director; also commercials. Credits include: *The Mad Death* (1983) and *Bergerac* (film dramas) for BBC-TV; *Minder* for Euston Films; *Fairly Secret Army* (1984) for Video Arts/Channel 4; *Robin of Sherwood* for HTV/Showtime; *The Worst Witch* for HBO/Central; and *Three Wishes for Jamie* for Columbia/HTV; *Harry's Kingdom* (1987; BBC); *Jeeves And Wooster* (1989); *GBH* (1990; Channel Four).

Part 4 Organisations, Associations and Societies

20 *Equity*

Equity guide to membership

Equity provides the following guidelines for potential members.

Membership of Equity is open to anyone currently exercising professional skills in the entertainment industry.

To be eligible to apply, it is essential that you furnish proof of a current Equity contract (and details of previous engagements, if any). Upon receipt of acceptable evidence, an application form will be sent to you to complete and return, together with the specified entrance fee and annual subscription. Your completed application form will then be placed before the Equity Council who shall, in such matters, be the final arbiter.

In most areas of work, casting agreements have been made with employers which stipulate that only artists with previous professional experience, proof of which is membership of Equity, or an agreed quota of newcomers (who subsequently become members) are eligible to be considered for work.

In normal circumstances, it will not be possible for you to obtain your first job and Equity membership in the West End theatre, the National Theatre, television, commercials, films or radio.

Membership can be obtained through engagements in the following areas of work:

Theatre

- As a performer or assistant stage manager (ASM) in a subsidized repertory or Theatre-in-Education or young people's theatre company, under the quota of newcomer places that we have agreed with the Theatrical Management Association (TMA).*

  *In the above areas, the newcomer quota does not apply to 'registered graduates' (i.e. students who have registered with us on completing acting or stage management courses accredited by the National Council for Drama Training), who are eligible for membership on obtaining an engagement.

- As a performer or ASM in a provincial commercial sessional work company (usually children's theatre) or non-subsidized repertory company, under the quota of newcomer places agreed with the TMA.

343

- As a performer in a provincial commercial summer season, pantomime or tour, under the quota of newcomer places agreed with the TMA.
- As an ASM with no obligation to act or understudy, in a provincial commercial theatre summer season, pantomime or tour.
- As a performer or ASM in a small-scale ('fringe') company which has a quota of newcomer places that we have agreed with the Independent Theatre Council (ITC).
- As a performer with the Royal Shakespeare Company at Stratford-upon-Avon, or with Chichester Festival Theatre, under the agreed quota of newcomers.

Opera and ballet
- As a singer engaged by an opera company on the Opera Singers' or Guest Artists' Contract.
- As a dancer with a ballet or dance company on the Ballet Contract.
- As an ASM with an opera or ballet company on the Stage Management Contract.

Directors, designers & choreographers
- As a director, designer or choreographer engaged on the appropriate theatre contract.

Variety or circus
- As a variety or circus artist, when you will need to be able to prove that you have been employed on a number of separate occasions (not less than eight) on a professional basis. The application will first be considered by the Variety Branch nearest to your permanent address.

- As a dancer with an overseas dance troupe, engaged on the approved Overseas Contract.

Other categories
- As a professional broadcaster in television or radio.
- As a concert or session singer, when you will need to be able to prove you have been employed on a number of separate occasions on a professional basis in these categories.

Work overseas
If you have worked professionally overseas and provide proof of your employment, together with the details of membership of the relevant union in that country, you may be granted exemption from the casting agreements. This will mean that, depending on the length of your previous employment, you will be entitled to seek work in the UK as though you were an existing Equity member. This arrangement, which is only available to UK or EEC citizens, or people from abroad who do not require work permits to work in this country, will not entitle you to Equity membership, but it will make it easier for you to obtain your first job in this country.

Equity's Guide to Membership issued August 1988 is available from Equity's offices. Please enclose SAE.

British Actors Equity Association (incorporating Variety Artistes Federation)

8 Harley Street, London W1N 2AB
Tel (071) 636 6367/637 9311
General Secretary Peter Plouviez

Scotland
65 Bath Street, Glasgow G2 2BX
Tel (041) 332 1669
Scottish secretary/Secretary to Northern Ireland National Committee
Jim Service, Mary Picken

North
Conavon Court, 12 Blackfriars Street, Salford M3 5BQ
Tel (061) 832 3183
Northern area organizer Bill Tankard

Wales & South West
Transport House, 1 Cathedral Road, Cardiff CF1 9SD
Tel (0222) 397971
Secretary to the Welsh National Committee Christopher Ryde

Founded 1930. Membership open to actors, club and circus performers, stage management, theatre designers and directors, choreographers, dancers, singers and many others in the entertainment industry. Deputies elected in each theatre company, TV production and film unit, etc. collect subscriptions and maintain contact between members and the Equity office.

Equity's principal functions are 'to secure the best possible terms and conditions for its members through collective bargaining, and to make representations to government and other bodies on matters of policy relating to the performing arts.' Standard contracts laying down minimum terms and conditions have been negotiated in virtually every section of entertainment (*see below*). Free legal advice is available for any case of dispute in connection with professional engagements, and advice can be given on National Insurance, income tax and VAT. *Equity Journal* is issued free to members.

A number of registers are maintained for the benefit of members and are circulated or made available to employers. The list includes: Afro-Asian artists, disabled artists, foreign language speakers, ITV announcers, ITV stage managers, puppeteers, theatre choreographers, twins/triplets, walk-ons, Welsh speakers.

Subscription rates

ANNUAL GROSS EARNINGS	SUBSCRIPTION
Less than £4000	£32.00
£4001–5000	£42.00
£5001–6000	£52.00
£6001–7000	£62.00
£7001–8000	£72.00
£8001–9000	£82.00
£9001–10,000	£92.00
More than £10,000	1% of gross earnings to a maximum of £1000 p.a.

Any member whose earnings do not exceed £3000 p.a. may pay a subscription of £20.00, subject to enclosing with the subscription a signed statement declaring those earnings.

Selected extracts from Equity agreements

Television

ITV Agreement
(dated 1 July 1989)

Six transmission areas
A. London: Thames TV, LWT
B. Midlands: Central TV
C. Lancashire: Granada TV
D. Yorkshire: Yorkshire TV
E. Rest of the country: remaining independent companies
F. Channel 4: any or all of the above areas serviced by Channel 4

Payment of a negotiated programme fee entitles a company to transmit in *one area only* (except Channel 4). Each additional area transmission must be on payment of 100% of the programme fee. Payment for four areas shall include the right to transmission in the fifth area without extra payment.

Minimum rehearsal day fee: £25.00
Minimum production day fee: £35.00
Minimum programme fee: £62.50

Minimum Guaranteed rate (per week of network engagement)

When an actor is engaged in a network production, the total earnings are calculated and then the total divided by the total number of weeks of the engagement to give an average weekly earnings figure. If this average is less than the minimum weekly rate, then the difference for the number of weeks is paid. Total earnings include production day, rehearsal day payments, programme fee, overtime, payment

for location work and a gap of up to six weeks. One week consists of five out of seven consecutive days.

There must be one day of rehearsal for each six minutes of programme length.

- 90-minute programmes must have at least 15 days of rehearsal and three full days in the studio (of which one need only be an afternoon or evening run-through on the set).
- 60-minute programmes: 10 days rehearsal + 2 studio days.
- 30-minute programmes: 5 days rehearsal + 1 studio day.

The script must be sent to the actor at least three days before first rehearsal day.

Normal maximum number of production days should be:
- for programmes exceeding 60 minutes: 5 days
- for programmes exceeding 30 minutes: 4 days
- for programmes under 30 minutes: 3 days

Different guidelines exist for series and serials.

A production day in the *studio* consists of up to nine hours, during which time rehearsal and/or recording can take place and two meal breaks of one hour each. Overtime is paid for each full or part hour at £22.50; make-up and costuming at £22.50 per hour.

A production day on *location* consists of up to ten hours, including one hour break and up to one hour travelling. Overtime is paid for each full or part hour at £22.50 per hour.

Night work is work in the studio or on location scheduled to extend beyond midnight or to commence between midnight and 7 am. Payment is $1\frac{1}{2}$ times the production day payment, with overtime at $1\frac{1}{2}$ times the daily overtime rate.

Repeats

Programmes may not be transmitted more than twice in any one area within three years from date of first transmission in the UK without the prior consent of Equity. A repeat within two years will result in the payment of 100% of the programme fee for each area, and a repeat between two and three years from the date of first transmission in the UK will result in the payment of 150% of the programme fee for each area. Four years = 175%, with an increase of 25% for each subsequent year from date of first transmission.

BBC-TV Agreement
(dated 31 October 1989)

Minimum fees
Category 1 – £304
Entitles the BBC to five rehearsal days and one performance day within seven days for programmes up to and including 30 minutes' transmission time.

Category 2 – £608
Entitles the BBC to eight rehearsal days and one performance day within 14 days for programmes between 40 and 60 minutes' inclusive transmission time.

Category 2a – £456
The use of this category is restricted to serials with a guaranteed repeat within one week. Entitlement as Category 2.

Category 3 – £912
Entitles the BBC to 14 rehearsal days and one performance day with 21 days for programmes between 61 and 90 minutes' transmission time.

Category 4 – £1216

Entitles the BBC to 20 rehearsal days and one performance day within 28 days for programmes over 90 minutes' transmission time.

All these fees are negotiable by the actor or his agent, and the BBC have the right to offer 'special high' or 'special low' fees appropriate to the actor's contribution to the programme.

Knock-on fees
The amount by which a category rate is increased each year (approximately 5%).

Hours of work
Studio: an aggregate of up to 10 hours work in an overall period of 12 hours.
Location: a continuous period of nine hours, including up to eight hours' work and not less than one hour's meal break but excluding an aggregate of one hour's travelling time.
Overtime: studio: £21.75 for each 15 minutes or part thereof; location: £19.50 for each hour or part thereof.
Serials that are rehearsed and performed within seven days are subject to special rates.

Expenses
When the actor is required to travel from his own region (where he lives or normally works), the BBC pay travel and subsistence.

Repeat fees (UK)
The BBC can transmit two repeats within two years from the date of the original transmission on both BBC1 and BBC2. 80% of the aggregate fee is paid, but if the programme is shown later than two years from the original transmission (but not more than $2^{1}/_{2}$ years), the amount is 90% of the aggregate fee.*

*The aggregate fee is the sum total of the engagement fee and additional rehearsal day fees. The aggregate fee for weekly serials is calculated by dividing the total fees by the number of episodes the actor appears in that week.

Negotiation of payment takes into account the weight of the actor's contribution to the programme, an overall spread of time involved (particularly on longer individual programmes), the number of pre-rehearsal and pre-recording days involved, the actor's professional status, his earning power in other fields and his value to broadcasting.

Payment of fees entitles the BBC to transmit or permit the transmission of the artist's performance in the relevant programme once only from every transmitter of the relevant BBC-TV channel, either simultaneously or at different times in different regions.

Radio

BBC Radio Agreement
(dated 1 September 1990)

Minimum fee: £81 with a rehearsal day fee of £51.

Radio Drama Company & the Schools Rep Company: minimum weekly salary of £244 with a maximum of £340.

Television commercials

Television commercials agreement
(dated 13 January 1988)
between Equity and the Advertising Film and Videotape Producers Association, and the Institute of Practitioners in Advertising

Auditions

1. For a first call, there is no payment, nor for videotapes and/or photographs taken.
2. For a recall, expenses are paid by the producer or advertiser for travel and out-of-pocket expenses (not less than £16.00). This also applies if the recall is on the same day as the first call.
3. For videotape at recall, the actor is paid not less than £24.00 to cover reasonable travel and out-of-pocket expenses (not in addition to No. 2 above).
4. If a script is sent to the actor prior to the first call, that call counts as a recall and the above expenses can be claimed.
5. If, for audition purposes, a voice-over artist is called in to record a script, not less than £16.00 must be paid to the artist. This is in addition to travel and out-of-pocket expenses claimed above.

Wig/wardrobe fittings
If the actor is required to attend a wig/wardrobe fitting outside the period of engagement, a payment of £27.00 is paid for a half day (up to $4^1/_2$ hours) and £50.00 for a full day (up to 10 hours including an hour break).

Studio or session fees
The basic studio fee (BSF) is the fee for each working day. Minimum rate: £95.00. Repeat/use fees are based on the BSF. The life of a commercial is three years from the date of the first studio/location day.

Rehearsal call
A half-day rehearsal (up to $4^1/_2$ hours) entitles the actor to 50% of his BSF. For a call of more than $4^1/_2$ hours, he receives his full BSF.

Additional voice work

If the actor is required on a day other than the visual recording day(s) to do additional voice work (e.g. post synching), the actor must receive 50% of his BSF for each two-hour session.

Working hours

A working day or night is normally no more than nine hours, excluding an hour's meal break. (Time spent in make-up, hairdressing and wardrobe is included in working hours.) Day calls commence between 7.30 am and 12 noon. Dawn calls are for services rendered between 4.00 am and 7.30 am. For these calls, overtime at the rate of one-fifth of the BSF for each hour or part hour up to 7.30 am is paid in addition to the BSF. Night calls are those scheduled to extend beyond midnight or to commence between midnight and 4.00 am. A fee of 50% of the BSF is paid in addition to the BSF in respect of each session of night work. This night fee does not qualify for use fees.

Overtime

One-fifth of the BSF is paid for each hour or part hour (but a produer may use the actor for up to 15 minutes over the normal day to complete a take). Overtime (other than a night call) after midnight is paid at one-third of the BSF for each hour or part hour. No overtime payment qualifies for use fees.

Breaks between calls

Not less than 12 hours between the end of any one period of work and the time of the next call must be allowed. Additional payments are made if, for unavoidable reasons, this break is reduced.

Sundays and public holidays

Not less than 50% of the BSF (in addition to the BSF) is paid for work on these days. (This does not qualify for use fees.)

Travelling time

Where transport is not provided, time spent in travelling to and from a studio or location within a 20-mile radius of Charing Cross, London is not included in working hours. If more than 20 miles, it is included in the working hours, excluding 30 minutes each way.

Where transport is provided from a central London rendezvous, the working hours are calculated from 30 minutes after the time of call to the rendezvous until 30 minutes before the time the actor is returned to the rendezvous.

Where transport is provided from the performer's home, and when he is required to travel to and from a studio or location more than 30 miles from Charing Cross, travelling time is included in the working hours, excluding 30 minutes each way.

Meal and rest breaks

The performer is not required to work for more than five consecutive hours without a break (of not less than one hour) for rest and refreshment. If, for any reason, a main meal break is curtailed or delayed for more than 30 minutes, the actor is paid one-fifth of the BSF in compensation.

Use fees

A commercial may be shown once in each area on either ITV, Channel 4 or TV-AM without payment to the performer. Thereafter, the payments are made in a sliding scale of areas and times shown. They may be shown in blocks of ten or on a single transmission basis. There is also a different rate for a short commercial of ten seconds in length or under.

Ancillary use

The use of a commercial is limited to TV transmission in the UK. Any extension to other media in the UK or elsewhere, such as cinema, radio or press advertising or inclusion in a film or television documentary, shall be subject to agreed terms between the performer and the producer/advertiser.

Stills

The producer/advertiser has no right to use still photographs of the actor without his consent. This consent will be subject to agreement and payment of a negotiated fee.

Overseas use

Subject to the consent of the performer.

Payment

Remuneration is due not later than the end of the same month when worksheets/invoices are received by the 15th, or not later than the 15th of the month following when worksheets/invoices have been received between the 15th and end of the month. (It seems to be common practice for the majority of advertisers not to pay before a month has elapsed.)

The advertising agency is responsible for having Performer's Work Record forms at the shoot. These should be completed and signed in duplicate at the end of the day's shoot.

West End Theatres

West End Agreement
(dated 11 January 1990)
between Equity and the Society of West End Theatres (SWET)

Wages

Minimum weekly: £199.26 (once nightly) and £232.39 (twice nightly/daily).

Artists under the age of 16 years: minimum salaries are one-half of the amounts stated above.

Holiday pay

Subject to at least 24 weeks (26 weeks for musicals) having elapsed since the first rehearsal of the production, and to the artist's engagement having subsisted for at least ten weeks, he is entitled to one-half day's holiday for each week (maximum annual entitlement of 18 days).

Hours of work

Not less than three weeks' rehearsal (four weeks for musicals) for every new production. In the event of 75% of more of the cast being replaced at any one time, there shall be an adequate rehearsal period of not less than two weeks. A rehearsal period shall not exceed six weeks for straight plays (eight for musicals) without Equity's consent.

Rehearsal salary shall not be paid for more than the initial 5 weeks of rehearsal (7 in the case of musicians).

Rehearsals

The working week consists of 45 hours, Monday to Saturday. Overtime is paid for any time in excess of these 45 hours.

Performance time

Defined as beginning 35 minutes (50 for full body make-up) before rise of curtain and running continuously until 15 minutes after curtain down (30 for heavy or full body make-up).

Performances

Maximum of eight performances (Monday to Saturday) per week (once nightly) or 12 per week (twice nightly-/daily) and a maximum of two performances on any one day. Any performances additional to these attract an additional payment of one-eighth of the artist's salary. If, after the production has opened, the manager wishes to give occasional additional performances, the cast shall be given not less than two weeks' prior notice, and such performances will be included in the weekly hours of work.

Photo calls

The manager shall use his best endeavours to ensure that photographs of the artist shall not be published for any purpose other than publicity for or advertisement of the play. Photographs involving any element of nudity taken by a photographer employed by the manager shall not be used for purposes other than publicizing the play.

If the manager wishes the artist to pose for photographs involving any element of nudity, the manager must obtain the artist's prior consent, and his written consent for the release of any nude photographs must also be obtained. No publication or display of these photographs shall be allowed until copies of the released photographs signed by the artist are lodged with Equity.

Understudies

Management are obliged to provide adequate and suitable understudy cover for every character in the production except for one-person shows.

No walking understudy shall be required to cover more than one leading role or two non-leading roles for the minimum salary.

Minimum performance salary for each performance as an understudy is £15.70 for a leading role and £9.49 in up to two non-leading roles.

Responsibility payment is £18.32 per week for each leading role, £13.74 for two non-leading roles.

Costumes, etc.

The management is responsible for supplying costumes and wig/hairpieces, and for keeping them clean and repaired. When a performance is so strenuous that the actor needs to change his T-shirt or underwear either betwen performances or in order to go home after the performance, the management shall where appropriate provide the T-shirt(s) and underwear necessary for such change(s).

Programme notes

The artist has the right of approving all biographical material to be included in the programme. If there are any errors in the programme, it shall be slipped as soon as reasonably practical and the programme must be corrected at the next reprint.

Insurance

Where the performer is required to undertake business of a hazardous nature, including any fight sequence, management shall arrange personal accident insurance for the artist.

Medical treatment

If management refers the artist to a physician, dentist or osteopath for treatment (other than in cases where the artist's negligence has occasioned his incapacity), the management shall pay the cost of treatment and of any repeat treatment prescribed by such physician, etc.

Flying

Unless specially engaged for the purpose, the artist has the right to refuse to be lifted for flying.

Stage management

A team of not less than one stage manager (SM) or company & stage manager (CSM), one deputy stage manager (DSM) (none of whom shall act or understudy) and one assistant stage manager (ASM; who shall not act in any production or understudy in musicals with casts of more than six artists) shall be employed.

Wages

ASM: £199.26 (once nightly) & £232.39 (twice nightly)
DSM: £249.07 (once nightly) & £290.49 (twice nightly)
SM: £278.96 (once nightly) & £325.25 (twice nightly)
CSM: £298.89 (once nightly) & £348.58 (twice nightly)

Provincial Theatres

Provincial Theatres Agreement
(dated 4 April 1988)
between Equity and the Theatrical Management Association (TMA)

This agreement covers most provincial theatres not covered by the subsidized rep agreement (*see below*) – i.e. non-subsidized rep and tours.

Wages

Two tier system of payments – a higher minimum of £159.00 (once nightly) and £174.00 (twice nightly) and a lower minimum of £137.50 (once nightly) and £145.58 (twice nightly).

The higher minimum weekly wage generally applies unless most of the following conditions apply:
1. None of the actors is a West End or national name.
2. The production is not advertised as pre- or post-West End.
3. The production is non-subsidized rep or uses the sessional contract.
4. The number in the cast is less than 12.
5. The theatre seating capacity is generally under 650.
6. The population within a 25-mile radius is not more than one million.

Subsistence

£35 per week for the first 12 weeks if the actor's home address is 25 miles or more from the place of employment.

Touring allowance

£18.60 per day (daily rate) and £74.95 (weekly rate). These figures are increased in line with the retail price index (RPI) every 13 weeks.

Failure to produce

If the management abandons the production, payment due to the actor is as follows:
● four or more weeks' notice given – two weeks' salary.
● less than four weeks' notice – three weeks' salary.
● All monies owing until the date of notice must also be paid.

Performances per week

Eight once nightly; 12 twice nightly.

Exclusive services

Written permission is needed from the manager to perform elsewhere.

Hours of work

A week of six days (Monday to Saturday inclusive) consisting of 48 hours (including costume fittings) and not more than eight hours out of ten in any one day between 8.30 am and 11.00 pm. No actor is required to work in excess of 12 hours a day. After the first performance, rehearsals are normally limited to nine hours a week.

Holiday pay
Half a day's holiday pay per week.

Understudying
The actor may be required to cover up to two major or three minor roles. No actor can be expected to cover an 'unreasonable number of roles'.

Stage management
Minimum staff of not less than one senior stage manager (SM) – or company & stage manager (CSM) – one deputy stage manager (DSM), one assistant stage manager (ASM).

Wages
Two-tier system as for actors:
CSM: once nightly = £206.25 (lower), £238.50 (higher); twice nightly = £218.25 (lower), £261.00 (higher)
SM: once nightly = £192.50 (lower), £222.60 (higher); twice nightly = £203.70 (lower), £243.60 (higher)
DSM: once nightly = £171.87 (lower), £198.75 (higher); twice nightly = £181.87 (lower), £217.50 (higher)
ASM: once nightly = £137.50 (lower), £159.00 (higher); twice nightly = £145.50 (lower), £174.00 (higher)

Subsidized Rep

Subsidized Rep Agreement
(dated 4 April 1988
rates up-dated 1990)
between Equity and the Theatrical Management Association (TMA)

Wages
Each theatre has a 'middle-range salary level' (MRSL). This is worked out by dividing the 'total basic salaries' paid by the total number of 'actor weeks' in the year. There are four levels, the minimums of which are:
1. £191.00
2. £167.00
3. £154.00
4. £143.00
Negotiation of salaries in rep is generally fairly restricted.

Subsistence
Payable for the first 12 weeks of a contract to an actor whose home address is 25 miles or more from the theatre or place of rehearsal. This currently stands at £41.00 per week.

Touring allowance
£17.75 per day (daily rate) and £88.50 (weekly rate); out-of-pocket expenses: £5.90. These figures are increased in line with the retail price index (RPI) every 13 weeks.

Hours
48 hours per week, 16 sessions of no more than four hours in a session (except dress rehearsals and performances of a production running longer than four hours, including the 'half' and 15 minutes at the end of the performance for make-up removal and/or changing).

Travel
Second-class rail fare or the equivalent is paid to and from the actor's home address at the beginning and end of the engagement.

Holiday pay
Two days' holiday pay for every four weeks worked and pro rata.

Performances per week
Eight (not more than two on any one day).

Stage management
Minimum staffing: Repertory: not less than one stage manager (SM), one deputy stage manager (DSM) and one assistant stage manager (ASM) – none of whom shall act or understudy. Repertoire: not less than two teams of: 1 SM, 1 DSM, 1 ASM (none of whom shall act or understudy).

Wages
Minimum: ASM = £135.00; DSM = £156.06; SM = £172.80 (£191.00 in MRSL Grade 1 theatres).

Small-scale Tours

Small-scale Touring Companies Agreement
(dated 4 April 1989 –
rates updated April 1990)
between Independent Theatre Council (ITC) & Equity

This contract generally applies to those that are not TMA, subsidized rep, West End or a No. 1 tour.

Wages
Minimum of £168.50 per week.

Hours
Six days – 45 hours per week.

Travelling time on performance days
Six hours maximum.

Free days
At least one in every six.

Performances
No more than twice a day. If it is a full-length play, there can be seven per week, and eight if the company is in one venue for the whole week. For a short play (one hour ten minutes), ten performances per week.

Overtime
Paid for anything over the 45 hours per week.

Subsistence
Paid for the first 16 weeks if the member is working 25 miles or more from his home address: £32.80 (out of London) and £37.45 (in London). This is linked to the retail price index (RPI) and changes quarterly. *NB* Subsistence is not paid if the actor is in receipt of a touring allowance that covers accommodation.

Travel
Second-class rail fare or the equivalent is paid from and to the actor's home address at the beginning and end of the contract.

Holiday pay
One-half day's pay for each week of the engagement.

Exclusive engagement
Written permission from the management must be obtained for work outside of the engagement.

Broken weeks
Count as full weeks for the purposes of wages.

21 *Associations and Societies*

Actors' Benevolent Fund

13 Short's Gardens, London
WC2H 9AT
Tel (071) 836 6378
President Penelope Keith OBE
General Secretary Mrs Rosemary
Stevens
Minimum subscription £1.00 p.a.

Founded 1882. The foremost representative charity of the theatrical profession in the UK. The objects of the Fund are to help, by allowances, grants and loans, elderly or distressed actors and actresses, managers, stage managers, business managers and their wives; also choristers whose efforts are entirely devoted to theatrical work. Those connected with the theatrical profession, coming within the Fund's scope, can become members on payment of the minimum subscription; they then will be entitled to participate in all matters affecting the welfare of the Fund.

The Actors' Centre

4 Chenies Street, London WC1E 7EP
Tel (071) 631 3599 (membership &
bookings)
Tel (071) 631 3619 (administration)
Membership £28.75 p.a.

Founded 1980, by a group of established performers for the benefit of the acting profession. As well as enabling members to develop their professional skills and acquire fresh ones, it offers the opportunity for the exploration of new ideas and methods of work away from commercial pressures. The Centre's extensive premises provide excellent club facilities: a green room, licensed servery, pay telephones, notice boards, trade journals and information on current theatrical events; three studios (two with piano) and two meeting/audition rooms for the wide range of classes and workshops programmed for Equity members. The Centre does not employ permanent teaching staff. Classes and workshops are taken by directors and tutors, all of whom are actively working in the industry. In addition to Equity membership, there is also an Associate membership to cater for those wanting more dialogue and closer cooperation between performers and those working in production. Schedules detailing times, tutors and directors, etc. are mailed six times a year, plus a newsletter. Schedules cover: acting, audition, text, verse, writing dialect, voice, singing, TV, radio, fencing, movement, musicals. All classes and workshops are at subsidized prices.

The Actors' Centre (Birmingham)

MAC, Cannon Hill Park, Birmingham B12 9QH
Tel (021) 475 1921
Administrator Karen Benjamin
Membership £3.50 per season

Founded 1988. Working under the umbrella of The Actors' Centres of London and Manchester, offers classes and workshops on TV, text, radio, auditions, etc. (plus projects with the Theatre Writers' Union sponsored by BBC-TV Pebble Mill) for Equity members living in and working from the Midlands. Spring and summer seasons for 1991 planned. Membership includes membership of the London and Manchester centres. Classes and workshops: £5.00–£20.00. Sponsored by BBC-TV, Birmingham City Council and the Actors' Centre.

The Actors' Centre (Manchester)

The Old School, Little John Street, Manchester M3 4PQ
Tel (061) 832 3430
Administrator Joanna Blatchley
Membership £23.00 p.a.

Founded 1986. The second Actors' Centre to be set up offers a wide range of classes and workshops for Equity members. Three studios, green room

with restaurant, pay telephones, information notice boards and trade journals available. A schedule of classes is sent out to members six times a year. All classes and workshops are offered at subsidized prices.

Actors' Charitable Trust and Denville Hall

19–20 Euston Centre, London NW1 3JH
Tel (071) 380 6212
General Secretary Althea Stewart

Formerly the Actors' Orphanage Fund. Assists the children of actors and actresses during family crises with financial grants. The object is to help children while keeping them in their own homes with their parents. The Trust also administers Denville Hall, a residential care home for members of the theatrical professions in Northwood, Middx (the original house was donated by Alfred Denville, the actor-manager).

Actors' Church Union

St Paul's Church, Bedford Street, London WC2E 9ED
Tel (071) 836 5221
Minimum subscription £5.00 p.a.

'The Church in action in the world of entertainment, aiming to make personal contact with all artists, technicians and other staff of any or no denomination at all wherever they may be at work. The whole purpose is to bring the Church's ministrations more easily within the reach of the theatrical profession.' Run on a voluntary basis with funding coming from members' and associates' subscriptions, and from gifts, legacies and Church collections.

The Actors' Institute

137 Goswell Road, London EC1V 7ET
Tel (071) 251 8178

A centre for the fostering of creativity in theatre and the arts generally. Activities include acting classes for all levels from beginners to professional, including a ten-week foundation course, with tuition by experienced professional actors, directors and writers. Also runs a series of workshops dealing with the issue of creativity in the context of performance – including 'The Mastery', 'Leadership and Creativity', 'Mastery of Excellence' – and a ten-week early-morning career course, 'Samurai'.

Association of Cinematograph, Television & Allied Technicians (ACTT)

111 Wardour Street, London W1V 4AY
Tel (071) 437 8506
General Secretary Alan Sapper
Subscription 1% of annual income

Founded 1935. Film and television technicians' union, covering the whole of the film and broadcasting industry. Approximately 27,000 members.

Alliance of North American Artists (ANAA)

36 York Way, London N1 9AB
Tel (01) 837 7402/4
Membership £50.00 p.a. or £35.00 covenant

The longest-running organization promoting North American arts in Great Britain. Its aims are to encourage and develop works with North American perspectives, and to create opportunities for members to meet and to develop and explore their work. It also has a funding operation with grants occasionally available to member organizations, usually for project-based schemes.

The Arts Club

40 Dover Street, London W1X 3RB
Tel (071) 499 8581
Membership secretary Mrs Ridgway
Subscription Assessed individually: town £345.

Founded 1863. Some connection with the arts necessary for membership, which is only available by application with two sponsors.

Association of Independent Producers

17 Great Pulteney Street, London W1R 3DG
Tel (071) 434 0181
Contact Matthew Crampton
Subscription £75.00 p.a.

Founded 1976. Membership is open. Benefits include: an information service, a regular magazine, information packs on various aspects of production and a free copy of *The Independent Production Handbook*. Offers information about production, how to get in touch with producers, etc. The general aims of the association are to encourage film and TV production and to broaden the base of finance and exhibition.

BAFTA (British Academy of Film & Television Arts)

195 Piccadilly, London W1V 9LG
Tel (071) 734 0022
Director A. J. Byrne
Ordinary subscription £80.00 p.a.

Founded 1947. Membership limited to 'those who have contributed creatively to the industry'. Provide facilities for screenings and discussions; encourage research and experimentation; lobby Parliament; make annual awards.

BETA

See **Broadcasting & Entertainment Trades Alliance.**

British American Arts Association

116 Commercial Street, London
E1 6NF
Tel (071) 247 5385
Fax (071) 247 5256
Director Jennifer Williams

Organization addressing the problems of transatlantic cultural exchange. Offers advice and counselling in all arts disciplines, runs a conference programme and takes on special projects. Emphasis is on the non-profit sector. BAAA is not a grant-giving organization.

British Arts Festival Association

P.O. Box 925, London N6 5XX
Coordinator Gwyn Rhydderch

Issues a free annual brochure giving advance information on more than forty leading professional arts festivals that are members of the Association,

including Aldeburgh, Cheltenham, Buxton, Salisbury, etc.

The British Council

11 Portland Place, London W1N 4EJ
Tel (071) 636 6888
Fax (071) 389 3199/3057
Telex 8952201 BRICON G
Director General R.T.L. Francis
Director of drama & dance Christine Bradwell

Founded 1934. The British Council exists to promote a wider knowledge of Britain and the English language abroad and to develop closer cultural relations between Britain and other countries. It maintains staff in 92 countries, and from 13 offices in Britain advises and assists visitors and students from overseas. The Council organizes tours overseas by British theatre, dance and opera companies and individual recitalists and by orchestras and individual musicians, enabling them to perform in most parts of the world, including Africa, the Indian sub-continent and the Far East, where opportunities for British artists would otherwise be rare.

British Film Institute

21 Stephen Street, London W1P 1PL
Tel (071) 255 1444
Telex 27624 BFI LDNG
Membership £28.95 (includes *Monthly Film Bulletin*) or £15.75
Associateship £13.50 (plus concessions)

Founded 1933. Committed to the development of the art and appreciation of film and TV. Runs the National Film Theatre and the National Film Archive in London and funds film theatres in the regions, as well as supporting the making of new films, video and TV programmes largely through the Regional Arts Associations, but also through direct grants. 1988 saw the opening of MOMI – the Institute's Museum of Moving Image on the South Bank: open Tuesday–Saturday (10 am to 8 pm) and Sunday (10 am to 6 pm); admission £3.95 and concessions.

British Library National Sound Archive

29 Exhibition Road, London SW7 2AS
Tel (071) 589 6603
Fax (071) 823 8970

An archive of over 800,000 discs and over 60,000 hours of tape recordings including all types of music, oral history, drama, wildlife, selected BBC broadcasts and BBC Sound Archive material. Open 10.00 am to 5.00 pm Monday to Friday; late opening Thursday to 9.00 pm. Listening service (by appointment: 10.00 am to 5.00 pm Monday to Friday; late opening Thursday to 9.00 pm).

Northern Listening Service at British Library Document Supply Centre, Boston Spa, W. Yorks. Tel: (0937) 843434. Open 9.15 am to 4.30 pm Monday to Friday.

British Music Hall Society

Honorary membership secretary
Wendy Lunn
74 Turnpike Drive, Luton, Beds.
LU3 3RF

Founded 1963. An influential, world-wide group of British music hall and variety enthusiasts, including many professionals from the world of entertainment – artistes, agents and managers. The central aims of the Society are 'to preserve the history of British Music Hall and Variety, to recall the artistes who created it, and to encourage and support the entertainers of the present era – including new talent.' The Society holds regular show meetings on the first Tuesday of each month (in January 1987, they presented the first traditional variety bill at the re-opened Hackney Empire). Publish a quarterly journal, *The Call Boy*, giving news, views and information on all aspects of music hall and variety, which is issued free to members. Contributes to theatrical and hospital charities out of the proceeds of its variety shows and exhibitions. Membership application forms available from the membership secretary.

British Screen Finance

37–39 Oxford Street, London
W1R 1RE
Tel (071) 434 0291
Fax (071) 434 9933
Telex 888694 BRISCR G

A private company aided by government grant, which took over from the National Film Finance Council (NFFC) in 1986; backed by consortium including Rank, Channel 4, Granada and Cannon. Has two functions: National Film Development Fund, for script development (contact Tessa Ross); and production investment (contact Simon Perry). Develop around 12 projects per year, and have invested in 56 British films in the last five years.

Broadcasting & Entertainment Trades Alliance (BETA)

181–185 Wardour Street, London
W1V 3AA
Tel (071) 439 7585
Fax (071) 434 3974
General Secretary D. A. Hearn

Founded 1984, by the amalgamation of the National Association of Theatrical Television and Kine Employees (NATTKE) and the Association of Broadcasting Staff (ABS). Expected to amalgamate by end 1990 with the Association of Cinematograph Television and Allied Technicians (ACTT). TUC-affiliated trade union covering all areas of non-performing categories in theatre, broadcasting, film and other sectors of the media and entertainment industries. Negotiates minimum rates and conditions with West End (SWET) theatre management, regional (TMA) theatre management, and individual theatre employers. All theatre staff, both full- and part-time, are eligible for membership.

Central Entertainment Agents Council

64 Port Street, Evesham, Worcs.
WR11 6AP
Tel (0386) 2819/3456
General Secretary Derek Wells

Founded 1978. 'An active trade organization open to all licensed entertainment agents, the Council has gained recognition as a consultancy for the industry, instituting branches throughout the UK. Benefits include: standard contracts for all situations, effective promotion to increase business, help for members in dispute, advice plus legal aid, regular trade

showcases and a monthly news-sheet.' All applicants for enrolment are required to serve a probationary period. Further details available from the General Secretary.

Directors' Guild of Great Britain

125 Tottenham Court Road, London
W1P 9HN
Tel (071) 387 7131
Administrator Suzan Dormer

The Guild speaks for directors and their craft in all areas of the media – film, TV (where producers are included), commercials, radio, opera and dance. Covers freelance and staff directors in the UK and abroad. Campaigns for directors' copyright (in 1986, made extensive submissions to the government which should finally result in legal recognition of rights); recently published *A Directors' Guide to Copyright and Contract*. Annually publishes *The Directors' Guild Directory*, which lists all members and their principal credits, and *Direct*, the Guild magazine which is published eight times a year. Membership application forms available from the above address.

Educational Television Association

King's Manor, Exhibition Square, York
YO1 2EP
Tel (0904) 433929
Administrator Mrs Josie Key

An umbrella organization for individuals and organizations using TV for education and training. Annual Award Scheme; Schools Video Competition; Annual Conference. New members welcome, contact administrator for details.

Entertainment Express

P.O. Box 1, St Albans, Herts.
Tel (0727) 41175
Membership £10.00 p.a. (Equity members only)

Provides a comprehensive national and international travel and accommodation service for the entertainment industry with discounts for individuals and companies.

Film Artistes' Association

61 Marloes Road, London W8 6LF
Tel (071) 937 4567

The Film Artistes' Association has over 2000 members, and provides doubles, stand-ins and background artistes for feature films that are shot in the London area and at the recognized studios; also for all filming within a 40-mile radius of London.

Independent Programme Producers Association

50–51 Berwick Street, London
W1V 4RD
Tel (071) 439 7034
Fax (071) 494 2700
Deputy director Fred Hasson
Membership Officer Tommy Welensky
Subscription Corporate: £350 + VAT; individual: £100 + VAT

The Independent Programme Producers' Association (IPPA) is the trade association for British independent television producers. Founded in 1981 by producers making programmes for the newly-established Channel 4,

IPPA currently represents over 700 organisations throughout the UK. Services to members include an industrial relations unit, model contracts, a seminar programme on current business issues, business affairs and sponsorship advice services, the publication of a regular journal, an international directory and a number of specialist guidebooks, a European producers' network, plus links with Commonwealth countries, and advice on all matters relating to independent production for television and satellite.

IPPA led the successful compaign, now being legislated into UK law, for 25% of all new British TV programmes to be made by independent producers. In the wake of the Government's commitment to the 25% figure, IPPA has negotiated with the BBC and ITV to establish a code of practice and trading guidelines similar to those previously agreed by the Association with Channel 4. IPPA continues to liaise with all UK broadcasters to influence decisions that may affect independent producers and maintains an active lobby to ensure that the needs of the UK independent sector are properly heard and understood by government in Britain and Europe.

Independent Theatre Council (ITC)

Old Loom House, Backchurch Lane, London E1 1LU
Tel (071) 488 1229
Administrator Philip Bernays

The ITC is both the representative body of and the managers' association for small- to middle-scale professional theatre companies: national and regional touring companies; producing venues; Theatre-in-Education teams; community, children's and young people's theatres; mime, dance and puppet companies; cabaret, revue and street performers; also individual and associate members.

ITC campaigns for increased recognition and funding for these theatres and initiates support or opposition to any legislation or action which may affect the interests of the membership. It negotiates and administers standard contracts of employment with Equity, MSF (Manufacturing, Science, Finance – formerly ASTMS) and the writers' unions, and operates joint procedures for consultation and settling disputes. Provides an information and advice service for members on employment and other matters related to theatre management. Offers a training programme of one- and two-day courses on various aspects of running a theatre company. Regular membership mailings provide news, information and a noticeboard service. ITC produces an information pack (price £4), which contains: information sheets and application forms for ITC membership and 'approved manager status'; a reference sheet on sources of information and legal requirements for starting a theatre company; and copies of ITC's standard contracts.

International Theatre Institute

British centre: 4 St George's House, 15 Hanover Square, London W1R 9AJ Tel (071) 486 6363 Fax (071) 408 1388
Director Neville Shulman OBE
Administrator Elaine Kidd

Founded 1948 under the auspices of UNESCO to 'promote international exchange of knowledge and practice of the performing arts, to stimulate creation and increase cooperation between theatre practitioners.' The Institute has over 70 centres throughout the world. In 1962 ITI established a World Theatre Day, 27 March, celebrated worldwide, and the British Centre celebrates with a reception and its presentation of two Awards, Excellence in International Theatre and Excellence in International Dance. The winners in 1990 were Peter James, Artistic Director of the Lyric Theatre, Hammersmith and Val Bourne, Director of Dance Umbrella. A Biennial Congress is held, 1987 Cuba, 1989 Finland, 1991 Turkey. Membership is open to all those with an interest in theatre and the performing arts. The British Centre issues a regular bulletin of international and relevant national information and news.

London & Provincial Theatre Councils (LTC & PTC)

Bedford Chambers, The Piazza, Covent Garden, London WC2E 8HQ Tel (071) 836 0971

The Councils, which are composed of equal numbers of representatives from Equity and from management, serve as a forum for the discussion of matters in dispute between managements and artists. The Councils aim to secure the organization and cooperation of managers and artists by approving standard term contracts for use by approved managers – including all members of the Society of West End Theatre (SWET) and the Theatrical Management Association (TMA) – when employing Equity members. Managers who are not members of SWET or TMA are required to register productions with the appropriate Council and place a deposit. The

Councils also provide an arbitration service for Equity members and managers in dispute, which can be convened rapidly if necessary.

Musicians' Union

National Office: 60–62 Clapham Road, London SW9 0JJ
Tel (071) 582 5566
General Secretary Dennis Scard
Subscription rates
Weekly earnings from music up to £100: £46.60 pa + £1 entrance fee; weekly earnings over £100 but less than £270: £88.40 pa + £1 entrance fee; weekly earnings over £270: £125.84 + £1 entrance fee.

The Musicians' Union caters for all who make their living, or part of their living, from performing music; bands, groups, orchestral musicians, chamber musicians, folk and jazz. The Union negotiates basic rates of pay, recovers unpaid fees, gives advice on contracts, and provides legal assistance and aid.

National Campaign For The Arts

Francis House, Francis Street, London SW1P 1DE
Tel (071) 828 4448
Fax (071) 828 5504

The NCA is an independent lobby for the arts. Its is committed to changing public and political attitudes to the arts and to making the arts a higher priority for opinion-formers and decision-makers. The Campaign specialises in research, information services, parliamentary lobbying and public campaigning and publishes a series of publications including NCA News, a quarterly magazine on the Arts and Politics. 'A Manifesto for the Arts' was published in December 1990 and outlines the Campaign's objectives. The Campaign is funded entirely by membership – £15 and £10 for individuals and £30 to £500 for organisations depending upon turnover. It currently has over 1500 members with the bulk of its funding coming from Equity, TMA, SWET, BETA, MU and ABO.

National Council for Drama Training

5 Tavistock Place, London WC1H 9SS
Tel (071) 387 3650
Chairman David Forder
Secretary Miss E.M. Kay

The National Council for Drama Training was established in 1976 following the report of the Committee of Inquiry set up by the Calouste Gulbenkian Foundation into professional training for drama.

The Council (NCDT) is composed of representatives from the three main sections of the theatrical profession: the British Actors Equity Association (the union), the Conference of Drama Schools (training establishments) and the Theatrical Management Association, the Society of West End Theatre and the British Broadcasting Corporation (employers/management).

It is an independent body, registered as a charity and is funded by the participating organisations mentioned above and by grants from The Television Fund and Channel Four Television.

The purpose of the Council is the encouragement of the highest possible standards of vocational education and training for the theatre and the provision of a forum within which the different sides of the profession can discuss matters of common interest in relation to training. It is particularly concerned to promote the closest possible links between those engaged in training and those working in the profession.

Since its establishment, the Council has perceived the accreditation of courses in drama schools as its first priority. The reasons are fourfold: first there is the contribution that accreditation makes in helping to raise the standard of drama training generally; secondly, there is the guidance that the list of courses accredited by the NCDT gives to local education authorities in determing awards to students; thirdly, the involvement of all sides of the profession in the accreditation process helps to promote closer links between the profession and the training sector; and fourthly, it is intended that accreditation will help to make entry into the profession a smoother process for those graduating from accredited courses than has sometimes been the case hitherto.

There are two Accreditation Boards with responsibility for the accreditation of courses. The Accreditation Board for Acting Courses has as its Chairman Ronald Mason, former Head of Drama, Radio at the BBC. The Chairman of the Accreditation Board for Stage Management Courses is Alice Lidderdale, a stage manager of long experience.

New Playwrights' Trust

Whitechapel Library, 77 Whitechapel High Street, London E1 7QX
Tel (071) 377 5429
Contact Polly Thomas/Ben Payne
Subscription £15.00 waged;
£9.00 part-waged; £6.00 unwaged;
also group rates

Organizes projects (including joint ones) such as rehearsed readings, workshops and discussions. Runs script reading service, bulletin and library service. There is also a 'link service' between writers and theatre companies. Monthly newsletter. Membership open to would- be actors, playwrights and directors. Recent projects include ongoing workshops, Script Forum, One Person Play Festival at the Etcetera Theatre Camden, and publication of Black Playwrights Directory.

Performing Right Society

29–33 Berners Street, London
W1P 4AA
Tel (071) 580 5544
Fax (071) 631 4138
Telex 892678 PRSLON G

Collects and distributes royalties arising from performances and broadcasts of its members' copyright music.

Personal Managers' Association Ltd (PMA)

Rivercroft, One Summer Road, East Molesley, Surrey KT8 9LX
Liaison secretary Angela Adler

An association of artists' and dramatists' agents (membership not open to individuals). Monthly meetings for exchange of information, discussion; acts as a lobby when necessary. Applicants screened; code of conduct maintained.

Provincial Theatre Council

See **London & Provincial Theatre Councils**

The Playwrights' Co-operative

103 Waterloo Road, London SE1
Tel (071) 633 9811

Founded in 1978, the Playwrights' Co-operative has evolved a regular process for developing playscripts. This is a flexible sequence of readings, discussions, and workshops aimed at helping the writers make their plays as good as possible. By developing the individual works, this programme develops the writers as well, through story conferences, rehearsed readings, workshops and professional advisors.

Pub Theatre Network (PTN)

118 Finborough Road, London
SW10 9ED
Tel (071) 835 1853
Contact Jessica Dromgoole
Membership Associate (for small theatres): £25.00 per quarter; friendship: £10.00 p.a.

Founded 1986. PTN, now with a membership of 26, is the most active representative body for small theatre venues in and around London, the majority of which are pub theatres. It is a pioneering arts charity with a systematic programme to raise the profile of small theatre and increase public awareness of this field of work. PTN seeks to promote, protect and develop the small theatre venue.

It is able to offer advice to actors interested in working on the small theatre circuit, with practical details on the facilities and size of venues, and availability for those wishing to mount a production. It provides a sustained publicity programme of up-to-date information on all member theatres and productions through printing tourist brochures and a fortnightly listings, and distributes all publicity material to PTN racks round London. It also maintains a clear channel of communication between theatres and companies, and issues the fortnightly *PTN Newsletter*. Associate membership gives access to all PTN information and involvement in and benefit from all PTN activities. Friendship of PTN includes, if desired, a subscription to the listings information or newsletter.

Royal Television Society

Tavistock House East, Tavistock Square, London WC1H 9HR
Tel (071) 387 1970/1332
Subscription £25.00 (full UK membership)

Founded 1927. Covers all disciplines involved in the TV industry. Provides a forum for debate and conferences on technical, social and cultural aspects of the medium. Presents journalism and programme awards, and runs a wide range of training courses.

Royal Theatrical Fund

11 Garrick Street, London WC2E 9AR
Tel (071) 836 3322
President Donald Sinden
Hon. Secretary John Berkeley

Founded 1839, by Charles Dickens and his friends to provide pensions for actors. The Fund was granted its royal charter by Queen Victoria in 1853. In 1974, it became a general charity for people in the profession, giving such help as contributions to a shortfall in nursing home fees for elderly actors or cash grants for people who are ill or convalescing. It is not a fund-raising charity – money comes from 'good house-keeping and investment'. Currently in the process of publishing a history of the Fund.

Scottish Society of Playwrights

Tron Theatre, 38 Parnie Street, Glasgow G1 5HB
Tel (041) 553 1425
Secretary Donneil Kennedy
Membership £20.00 p.a.

Founded 1973, by a group of playwrights. The Society acts as a pressure group for playwrights and negotiates contracts with managements. Full membership is open to anyone who has had a play professionally produced on stage, TV or radio.

Society of British Fight Directors

87 Redington Road, London
NW3 7RR
Tel (071) 435 2281
or (071) 624 1837 (Convenor)
Secretary Penelope Lemont
Membership £5.00 p.a. (Friend of the Society)

Founded 1969. Professional organization of fight directors, the aims of which are to raise the standard of stage and screen fighting in this country and the status of the fight directors. It acts as a clearing house for information on fight directing in all its aspects, including historical information on weaponry and methods used. It provides names of individual fight directors. Two of its major concerns are the welfare and safety of actors who perform combat on stage, and the training of the young actor in drama school. The Society conducts a proficiency test for drama students

who, if they are successful, may obtain a certificate of their safety and effectiveness as performers of stage combat. British Actors' Equity now has a Fight Directors' Committee and a Fight Directors' Register; to become a fight director and be accepted on to the Register, it is necessary to undertake a training programme run by the Society. Issue a tri-annual magazine, *The Fight Director*.

Society for Theatre Research

c/o The Theatre Museum, 1e Tavistock Street, London WC2E 7PA
Contact Hon. Secretary

Founded 1948, to 'foster research into historical and current theatre practice'. The Society provides a meeting-point for all those interested in the history and technique of British theatre – scholars, research workers, stage artists and other practitioners in theatre, as well as theatre-goers. Annual awards, ranging from £100 to £1000, are made to offset the cost of research concerned with the history and practice of the British theatre. The Society administers the William Poel Memorial Festival, an annual event at which prizes for good stage speech are awarded to two students from an accredited theatre school; candidates present a duologue from Elizabethan or Jacobean drama. Annual publications include *Theatre Notebook*, which is published three times a year and sent free to members. Lectures and events are held regularly in London. A prospectus and details of current subscription rates are available from the

Hon. Secretary. All communications must be made by post.

Society of West End Theatre (SWET)

Bedford Chambers, The Piazza,
Covent Garden, London WC2E 8HQ
Tel (071) 836 0971
Fax (071) 479 2543

The Society comprises managers and proprietors of theatres and producers of shows in the West End of London, with both the commercial and the subsidized sectors represented. The Society serves to facilitate concerted action in the interest of theatre managers in cooperation with the TMA (Theatrical Management Association) and the TNC (Theatres National Committee), but concentrates its efforts on those issues of direct concern to the West End. There is a marketing office that promotes ticket sales for West End productions, sells West End Theatre Gift Tokens, provides an information service based on The London Theatre Guide, and conducts audience research.

The Society also negotiates minimum rates of pay and conditions of employment with the theatrical unions: Equity (performers, stage management, directors and designers), the Broadcasting & Entertainment Trades Alliance (BETA: theatre staff) and the Musicians' Union (MU). An arbitration and conciliation service is provided for disputes between managers and artists through the Society's partnership with Equity in the London Theatre Council (LTC).

Since 1976, the Society has presented its own annual awards – now known as the Olivier Awards – to the profession to recognize talent in West End performances. The Laurence Olivier Bursary, set up in 1987 to mark Lord Olivier's 80th birthday, is awarded to a financially deprived second-year drama student to complete his/her studies. 1990 joint winners: Michael Sheen (21) at RADA and Anna Farnworth (23) at LAMDA.

Stage Management Association (SMA)

Southbank House, Black Prince Road,
London SE1 7SJ
Tel (071) 240 7831

Representative organization for all professional stage management staff. Recently announced an annual award, 'For Services to the British Theatre in the field of Stage Management' – members and non-members of the SMA are eligible.

The Theatre Museum

1e Tavistock Street, London
WC2E 7PA
Tel (071) 836 7891
Open Tuesday to Sunday 11.00 to 19.00: closed Monday
Admission £2.50, concessions £1.50

The Theatre Museum is Britain's National Museum of the Performing Arts and a branch of the Victoria and Albert Museum. Housed in Covent Garden's old Flower Market, the Museum has the largest and most important collection of theatrical artifacts in the world. Its permanent displays tell the story of the British stage and cover most forms of live entertainment from theatre, ballet and opera to circus, magic and rock and pop. There are two large galleries devoted to special exhibitions while the Museum's Studio Theatre is used for a varied and popular programme of live theatre and educational events. The Museum also has a shop, a box-office selling tickets for West End shows, and an attractive cafe.

Theatres National Committee (TNC)

Bedford Chambers, The Piazza,
Covent Garden, London WC2E 8HQ
Tel (071) 836 0971

The Committee – composed of SWET, TMA and the Independent Theatre Council (ITC) – is the collective voice and representative of theatrical management on broad political, economic and social issues to the extent that they affect live theatre – e.g. safety, licensing, taxation, copyright, overseas tours. The Committee negotiates with the unions industry agreements which have national significance – for example, Nudity on Stage.

The Theatres Trust

10 St Martin's Court, St Martin's Lane,
London WC2N 4AJ
Tel (071) 836 8591
Life chairman The Lord Goodman CH
Chairman Sir David Crouch
Director John Earl
Membership £7.00 p.a.; life
membership: £100.00

Founded 1976. A statutory body set up 'to promote the better protection of theatres for the benefit of the nation'. The Trust must be consulted by all planning authorities before they issue a decision on any planning application affecting a theatre (used or disused). In all its work, the Trust's principal objective is not simply to see buildings preserved but to safeguard their live theatre use – or potential for such use. Membership as a 'Friend' of the Theatres Trust gives you reduced prices or other benefits at some London and provincial theatres; reduced prices at events organized by the Trust; regular reports on the work of the Trust.

The associated *Theatres Trust Charitable Fund* exists to provide small grants to theatres towards both new building and refurbishment. Its income is derived from donations and subscriptions to the Friends of the Theatres Trust.

Theatrical Management Association (TMA)

Bedford Chambers, The Piazza,
Covent Garden, London WC2E 8HQ
Tel (071) 836 0971
Fax (071) 497 2543

The Association represents those concerned with theatrical production in the provinces, both in the commercial and the subsidized sectors. Members may either be managers of theatres (or other venues) or producers of shows that are presented at such theatres. The Association negotiates minimum terms and conditions with the theatrical unions. However, the Association also promotes the interests of its members in other areas, both in cooperation with the Society of West End Theatre (SWET) and the Theatres National Committee (TNC) and individually, and provides an arbitration service for inter-management disputes and a conciliation service through its partnership with Equity in the Provincial Theatre Council.

Writers' Guild of Great Britain

430 Edgware Road, London W2 1EH
Tel (071) 723 8074
General Secretary Walter J. Jeffrey
Annual subscription 1% of that part
of the author's income earned in the
areas in which the Guild operates, with
a minimum of £50 and a maximum of
£480.

Founded in 1959, the Writers' Guild is
the writers' trade union, affiliated to
the TUC, and representing writers in
film, radio, television, theatre and
publishing. The Guild advises on all
aspects of writers' agreements and
leads the way in campaigns for minimum terms for writers working in
film, radio and theatre. In 1979 the
Guild, with the Theatre Writers'
Union, negotiated the first ever industrial agreement for theatre writers.
Since then an agreement with
Regional Theatre has been achieved.
In 1991 it hopes for a new agreement
with Fringe Theatres and Theatre In
Education – after some twelve years of
negotiation. Along with the Society of
Authors, the Guild has played a major
role in advancing the Minimum Terms
Agreement for authors. Membership
is by a points system. One major piece
of work (a full-length book, an hour-
long television or radio play, a feature
film, etc) entitles the author to full
membership; lesser work helps to
accumulate enough points for full
membership, while temporary membership may be enjoyed in the mean-
time. Temporary members can pay a
minimum subscription of £30 in their
first year.

22 *Arts Councils and Regional Arts Associations*

Impending reorganization of the Regional Arts Associations may result in some of the associations listed below vanishing or being merged with others.

Arts Councils

Arts Council of Great Britain

14 Great Peter Street, London
SW1P 8NQ
Tel (071) 333 0100
Chairman Peter Palumbo
Secretary General Anthony Everitt
Information officer Rod Fisher

The 1988/89 grant dispensed by the Arts Council stands at £150 million. From it, the Arts Council supports arts organizations, artists, performers and others; grants can also be made for particular productions, exhibitions and projects. The total amount set aside for drama in 1988/9 is £27,477,525.
Drama director Ian Brown
Deputy drama director
Jean Bullwinkle
The Drama Department assesses fund-ing of 56 professional theatre companies divided into two main categories: 23 touring and 33 theatre-based. It also looks at applications for separate new projects, often by emergent new companies. The Department also administers a number of training schemes designed to offer advanced in-service and further training to professional designers, directors, performers, technicians, stage managers and adminstrators, as well as to those working in children's theatre and puppetry. A number of bursaries are awarded to individuals to undertake short practical working attachments or specific training projects or courses. Applications are assessed on individual merit throughout the year and while funds are available. The Council's Touring Department funds a number of projects which are suitable for presentation in large- and middle-scale mixed programme theatres.

However these generally originate from established companies. Further information available from the free Arts Council leaflet *Awards & Schemes*.

Arts Council of Northern Ireland

181a Stranmillis Road, Belfast
BT9 5DU
Tel (0232) 381591
Drama & Dance director Denis Smith

Provides funding for the Lyric Players' Theatre, Belfast Civic Arts Theatre, Theatre Ulster, Charabanc, and Field Day Theatre Company. Supports the youth drama scheme. Individual awards are made to performers, directors and choreographers on assessment by a panel. Details and applications can be obtained from the drama & dance director.

Scottish Arts Council

12 Manor Place, Edinburgh EH3 7DD
Tel (031) 226 6051
Drama & dance director Anna Stapleton
Contact Charles Bell (drama officer)

The Council's bursaries scheme for theatre practitioners (actors, directors, technicians, administrators, etc.) is aimed at providing career refreshment and reinforcement by enabling candidates to extend their expertise in specific areas of work. Bursaries are generally provided to enable attendance at short-term or part-time training or to undertake a period of study or a special research project. Applicants should have a minimum of three years' professional experience in Scotland.

Welsh Arts Council

Museum Place, Cardiff CF1 3NX
Tel (0222) 394711
Drama director Roger Tomlinson

Funding is 'tight', and as a result, most of the work of the drama department is concerned with theatres and touring companies including Theatr Clwyd, the Made-in-Wales Stage Company and Moving Being. In 1988, after much public debate, the Council approved a strategy of increased funding to Welsh-language theatre, and with additional funding from the Welsh Office and local authorities, Theatre-in-Education companies are now able to present projects in Welsh as well as English. In 1987/88, the drama department received partnership funding from Sianel Pedwar Cymru, enabling them to embark on a series of training initiatives with emphasis on assisting theatre practitioners working in Welsh, including a summer school for directors, a director's training awards scheme and the start of a series of international exchanges.

Regional Arts Associations

Council of Regional Arts Associations

Litton Lodge, 13a Clifton Road, Winchester, Hants SO22 5BP
Tel (0962) 51063
Drama secretary Liz Wright (at Lincolnshire and Humberside Arts; *see below*)

CORAA is a service organization for the corporate needs of the 13 regional arts associations of England. (Scotland, Wales and Northern Ireland have their own arts councils and are not regionally split in this way.)

The Regional Arts Associations (RAAs) are one part of a system which sustains, promotes and develops the arts. RAAs are concerned with all the arts – community arts, dance, mime, drama, literature, music, opera, the visual arts, crafts, film, video, photography and performance arts, etc. RAAs are independent and autonomous; they are neither regional branches of the Arts Council, nor are they local authority associations, but they receive funding from both. The RAAs vary in age from 14 to 30 years, with budgets varying from £1.1 million to £9.0 million. They provide financial support for professional theatre companies, dance and mime companies, music ensembles; some assistance is also given to support amateur work.

RAAs offer a number of opportunities for individual artists; many of these are aimed at helping them to reach a new and wider audience. A variety of commissions, bursaries, fellowships and residencies are available to writers, artists, craftsmen, composers, photographers, etc. Information for specific schemes offered are available on request from the RAAs.

Buckinghamshire Arts Association

55 High Street, Aylesbury, Bucks. HP20 1SA
Tel (0296) 434704

'The Association does not offer grant-aid to actors, although its extensive programme of support for professional theatre performances is of obvious indirect benefit. Grant-aid is provided to the Limelight Theatre, Aylesbury and the Milton Keynes Theatre Consortium, both of which organize year-round programmes of small-scale theatre and dance; to Theatre of Fact, the county's professional Theatre-in-Education company; and to companies from outside the county that wish to tour to schools or to areas of the county away from Aylesbury and Milton Keynes. In addition, schools, colleges, amateur companies and other groups may engage professionals for workshops, residencies or, perhaps, to direct. In these cases, the Association can contribute up to 50% of the costs.'

East Midlands Arts

Mountfields House, Forest Road, Loughborough, Leics. LE11 3HU
Tel (0509) 218292
Senior Arts officer, Drama and Dance Helen Flach
Dance and Mime officer Rachel Gibson

Covers Leicestershire, Nottinghamshire, Derbyshire (excluding the High Peak District) and Northamptonshire. 'Out of the total allocation to drama, nearly 90% is spent on resident companies and artists.' The Drama budget is split into three categories:

1. Regional Theatre
The bulk goes to three companies, Derby Playhouse, Northampton Repertory Players and New Perspectives Theatre Company. Two further allocations under this heading are grants to building-based companies to tour small communities, and grants to independent companies.

2. Visiting companies
Grants to promoters of visiting companies; grants to companies to tour the

region; grants to promoters of residencies including workshops and performances; grants to companies that have developed a relationship with the region and offer work that cannot be provided by resident companies.

3. Projects

Out of this fund is supported the drama education work, notably the 'Artists at Your Service' scheme, training, new writing projects in the community, local documentaries, commissions and some workshops that do not meet the criteria of the 'Artists at Your Service' scheme.

Eastern Arts Association

Cherry Hinton Hall, Cambridge
CB1 4DW
Tel (0223) 215355
Drama officer Alan Orme
Drama assistant Vivien Peters

Covers Bedfordshire, Cambridgeshire, Essex, Hertfordshire, Norfolk and Suffolk. Over the past year, the Association has been reconsidering the way in which support is being given to theatres, small-scale venues, regional companies and touring throughout the area. In future, the drama budget will primarily be used to support work in these areas.

Lincolnshire & Humberside Arts

St Hugh's, Newport, Lincoln LN1 3DN
Tel (0522) 533555
Principal officer (drama & dance)
Liz Wright

Lincolnshire & Humberside Arts does not operate a specific scheme related to training for the professional actor. Applications for financial support to assist qualified and experienced actors in further developing their professional skills by attendance at appropriate and recognized courses may be considered. Applications from technicians, designers and other professional theatre workers may also be considered on a similar basis. Financial support is not available to assist with full-time vocational training.

Merseyside Arts

Bluecoat Chambers, School Lane,
Liverpool L1 3BX
Tel (051) 709 0671
Acting development officer (drama/literature) Theresa Griffin

Merseyside Arts is the regional arts association for Liverpool, Knowsley, Sefton, Wirral, St Helens, Ellesmere Port and Neston, and W. Lancashire. Companies resident in Merseyside may apply to the Performing Arts Investment Fund (PAIF) if they display the potential to develop as professional companies. Individuals may apply to the Merseyside Arts' training budget for assistance with short courses.

Northern Arts

9–10 Osborne Terrace, Jesmond,
Newcastle upon Tyne NE2 1NZ
Tel (091) 281 6334
Drama officer Sheila Harborth

Northern Arts covers Cleveland, Cumbria, Durham, Northumberland and Tyne & Wear, and was the first regional arts association in the country to be set up by local authorities. It provides funding through the promoters for small-scale touring companies able to set up a complete programme of work, such as a tour of youth clubs in the region. Priority areas for support are black and Asian communities, young people and people with disabilities. Lists of promoters are available from Northern Arts with a rough indication of promoters' interests.

North West Arts

4th floor, 12 Harter Street, Manchester
M1 6HY
Tel (061) 228 3062
Drama officer Ivor Davies

Covers Cheshire, Greater Manchester, Lancashire (except W. Lancashire) and the High Peak of Derbyshire.

The Drama Panel offers small awards and advice to emerging theatre companies. It also has a strong commitment to theatre and drama activity in education, in the community, and in theatre buildings. We aim to provide an up-to-date information resource to people across the region.

N.B. – Due to be merged with Merseyside Arts into Arts Board: North West, sometime during 1991/92.

Southern Arts

19 Southgate Street, Winchester,
Hants SO23 9DQ
Tel (0962) 55099
Drama officer Fiona Ellis

Southern Arts is the arts development agency for central southern England, covering Berkshire, Hampshire, E. Dorset, Isle of Wight, Oxfordshire, and Wiltshire – a region of 4 million people and 80 arts centres, theatres and concert halls. Its support for theatre is concentrated in funding a wide range of companies, developing

audiences and supporting small- and middle-scale touring.

South East Arts

10 Mount Ephraim, Tunbridge Wells,
Kent TN4 8AS
Tel (0892) 515210
Drama officer Robert Henry

South East Arts covers the counties of Kent, Surrey and Sussex. The Drama Panel works towards the consolidation of existing theatre and drama and the nurturing of new initiatives from venues and companies. It assists innovative and experimental projects involving young people, and encourages the development of training opportunities for people active in drama. The Association revenue funds two major regional theatres and helps in the organization of regional touring. The Association is currently developing new links with northern France.

South West Arts

Bradninch Place, Gandy Street,
Exeter, Devon EC4 3LS
Tel (0392) 218188 Fax (0392) 413554
Drama officer Hilary Garnham

South West Arts covers Avon, Cornwall, Devon, much of Dorset, Gloucestershire and Somerset. 'The central theme running through the Association's constitution is development . . . increasing, improving, encouraging, advancing and coordinating.' SW Arts financially supports the Everyman Theatre in Cheltenham and gives grants to professional companies working in the fields of Theatre-in-Education (TIE), children's theatre, small-scale touring and puppetry both based in and touring into the regions. Support is also given for the development of new writing and training at an advanced level. 'We are always prepared to consider applications from any source for activities that break new ground within our overall policies.'

West Midlands Arts

82 Granville Street, Birmingham
B1 2LH
Tel (021) 631 3121
Fax (021) 643 7239
Drama officer Mike Kay

Covers Herefordshire, Worcestershire, Shropshire, Staffordshire and Warwickshire. Open to applications for training grants only by individuals within a company existing in the West Midlands region. Priority given to developing Asian/Afro-Caribbean companies, and audience areas of special need such as people with disabilities or young people. Operate a 'Community Projects' scheme that focuses on community groups – play groups, old people's homes and day centres – giving them the chance to work with professional workers.

Yorkshire Arts

Glyde House, Bradford BD5 0BQ
Tel (0274) 723051
Drama officer Shea Connolly

Yorkshire Arts offers advice, contact and support to theatre and drama projects through its performing arts department. The department includes a drama officer, dance & mime officer, music officer and two officers working across all these areas. New companies can get advice about setting up tours, making contacts, establishing good working practices, Equal Opportunities policies and financial systems. Support can be given for fees to guest practitioners or rehearsal costs, but it cannot be given towards fees for full-time study. The first point of contact is through one of the officers who can develop a plan of action with you.

23 *Awards, Bursaries and Fellowships*

Arts Council of Great Britain

Award a number of bursaries for short practical working attachments or specific training projects/courses (*see* Arts Councils & Regional Arts Associations).

Arts Council of Northern Ireland

Awards to individuals (*see* Arts Councils and Regional Arts Associations).

BAC Young Directors Award

Battersea Arts Centre, Old Town Hall, Lavender Hill, London SW11 5TF
Tel (071) 223 2223
Administrator Judith Hibberd

Annual Award for Young Directors under the age of 35. Entry is by written application to the above address in response to advertisements in the national press. A list of applicant directors is narrowed down to a finalist by way of a two day directing workshop watched and judged by leading theatre critics, directors, and other professionals. The Award Winner goes on to direct a professional production at BAC, receiving an ACGB Bursary to allow them to train in a regional British theatre later that year.

East Midlands Arts

Some funding for training. (*See* Arts Councils and Regional Arts Associations).

Merseyside Arts

Occasionally fund actors/technicians for training courses (*see* Arts Councils and Regional Arts Associations).

Scottish Arts Council

Bursaries for short-term or part-time training (*see* Arts Councils and Regional Arts Associations).

Society of West End Theatres (SWET)

Olivier Awards annually, and Olivier Bursary for second-year drama student at accredited drama school (*see* Associations and Societies).

Stage Management Association (SMA)

Annual award 'For Services to the British Theatre in the field of Stage Management' (*see* Associations and Societies).

West Midlands Arts

Open to applications for training grants only by individuals within a company in the West Midland region. (*See* Arts Councils and Regional Arts Associations).

Winston Churchill Travelling Fellowship

The Winston Churchill Memorial Trust, 15 Queen's Gate, London SW7 5PR. Awarded for overseas trips in connection with specific drama-related projects. Details and application forms from the above address.

The William Poel Memorial Festival

The Society for Theatre Research, c/o The Theatre Museum, 1e Tavistock Street, London WC2E 7PA

Founded 1952. A prize for good stage speech created from the proceeds of a matinee organized at the Old Vic Theatre to celebrate the centenary of the birth of William Poel, and further donations from Dame Edith Evans. The fund has subsequently been augmented by donations from members of the Society for Theatre Research. The Festival is usually held on an afternoon in May at the National Theatre and is open to the public. Candidates from all the theatre schools in the country which offer courses accredited by the National Council for Drama Training may participate. Two students, chosen by each of the schools represented at the Festival, present a duologue from Elizabethan or Jacobean drama.

24 Publications

Amateur Stage
83 George Street, London W1H 5PL
Tel (071) 486 1732

Monthly. Review of amateur drama, with reviews of the latest productions and practical techniques.

Film Log
Subscribers: P.O. Box 100, Broadstairs, Kent and *Editorial*: P.O. Box 11, London SW15 6AY
Tel (0843) 860885 (subscribers) (081) 789 0408 (editorial)
Subscription £9.00 (3 months); £18.00 (6 months); £30.00 (12 months)

Monthly. Listing of UK-based films in pre-production and future pre-productions, giving details of production managers and casting directors.

Plays International
33a Lurline Gardens, London SW11 4DD
Tel (071) 720 1950
Owner Chancery Publications
Editor Peter Roberts

Monthly. *Plays International* is a mixture of interviews, reviews and a complete play text every month.

Plays & Players
248 High Street, Croydon, Surrey CR0 1NF
Tel (081) 681 7817 Fax (081) 688 9573

Monthly. Focuses on the British theatre. For professionals and the general public.

Professional Casting Report (PCR)
Subscribers: P.O. Box 100, Broadstairs, Kent and
Editorial: P.O. Box 11, London SW15 6AY
Tel (0843) 860885 (subscribers)
Tel (081) 789 0408 (editorial)
Subscription £17.00 (5 weeks); £34.00 (10 weeks); £85.00 (26 weeks).

Weekly. For Equity/ACTT members only. Gives details of imminent TV, film and theatre casting.
 Who's Where, an A-to-Z of contacts within the industry (film, TV and theatre) issued annually with addenda from time to time. Available only to subscribers of the above at £4.00 p.a.

Repertory Report
Subscribers: P.O. Box 100, Broadstairs, Kent and
Editorial: P.O. Box 11, London SW15 6AY

Tel (0843) 860885 (subscribers)
(081) 789 0408 (editorial)
Subscription £9.00 (3 months); £18.00
(6 months); £30.00 (12 months)

Monthly. Listing of provincial theatres
and their production schedules.

Script Breakdown Service (SBS)
SBS Ltd, Suite 1, 16 Sidmouth Road,
London NW2 5JX
Tel (081) 459 2781/451 2852

Weekly. Available only to agents. A
list of casting requirements for film,
TV, theatre, light entertainment, commercials, videos and documentaries.

Sight & Sound
21 Stephen Street, London W1P 1PL
Tel (071) 255 1444
Fax (071) 436 7950

British Film Institute monthly. Covers
all aspects of the cinema for professionals in the industry.

The Spotlight
7 Leicester Place, London WC2H 7BP
Tel (071) 437 7631
Rates $^1/_2$ page £83.10; $^1/_4$ page £45.30.
Annual. A photographic casting directory used throughout the business by
agents, casting directors and directors.

Essential for all actors. *Actresses* published in October; final date for entries
1 April. *Actors* published in April; final
date for entries 22 October. *New Actors
and Actresses* published in February,
through the Conference of Drama
Schools.

The Spotlight maintains computer-
ized records for over 40,000 members
of the profession, which are continuously up-dated and are referred to at
the rate of around 500 telephone calls a
day. An advisory service is available to
everyone who advertises in or sub-
scribes to *The Spotlight*.

The Stage & Television Today
Stage House, 47 Bermondsey Street,
London SE1 3XT
Tel (071) 403 1818
Fax (071) 430 1418

Weekly. A newspaper for professionals in the entertainment
industry, with new openings, jobs and
reviews.

Who's Where
See **Professional Casting Report
(PCR).**

Acknowledgements

Many people were consulted in compiling this book. Particular thanks are due to Paul Barnard, Katy Birrell, Carol Ann Crawford, Kim Dambaek, Sue Daniels, Rob Edwards, Gill Hambleton, Tyrone Huggins, Ace McCarron, Jeremy Raison, and Tracy Jane White. Special thanks also to Tracey Smith and all in the basement at Bloomsbury.

Part 5 *Index*

Index